D1460759

COLLINS SHORTER GUIDE TO THE

Pests, Diseases and Disorders

OF GARDEN PLANTS

COLLINS
SHORTER GUIDE TO THE

Pests, Diseases and Disorders

OF GARDEN PLANTS

Stefan T. Buczacki
and
Keith M. Harris

Illustrated by
Brian Hargreaves

COLLINS
Grafton Street, London

William Collins Sons & Co Ltd
London · Glasgow · Sydney · Auckland
Toronto · Johannesburg

First published 1983

ISBN 0 00 219074 5
Filmset by Ace Filmsetting Ltd, Frome
Colour reproduction by Adroit Photo-Litho Ltd, Birmingham
Made and printed in Great Britain by
William Collins Sons and Co Ltd, Glasgow

Contents

Colour Plates

Acknowledgements

Although we are personally familiar with almost every condition that we describe in this book, we would not claim to be authorities on more than a few of them. Because of this, and because much of the factual information we have required is inaccessible or unpublished, we have had to depend on the advice and opinions of numerous friends and professional colleagues. It is impossible to mention individually all those who have read portions of our script, discussed specific items with us, directed us to obscure literature, provided raw material for the illustrations or helped in other ways. We therefore thank collectively the employees of the Agricultural Research Council, Natural Environment Research Council, British Museum (Natural History), Ministry of Agriculture, Commonwealth Institute of Entomology, Commonwealth Mycological Institute, Royal Horticultural Society, Forestry Commission and of many universities, colleges and agrochemical manufacturers for their time, trouble and patience with our enquiries. While we have welcomed their assistance however, we dissociate them from any errors of fact or advice that may remain and which are entirely our responsibility. We have also relied heavily on the official publications of the above organisations and many of these are mentioned in the bibliography.

We owe a very special debt of gratitude to our artist Brian Hargreaves who has brought his impressive talents to bear upon an astonishing variety of subject matter presented to him in an equally astonishing variety of ways. We hope that his plates will not only aid significantly in identifying problems but also demonstrate the singular aesthetic appeal that can be shown by such ostensibly morbid subjects. To our wives Beverley and Elizabeth and to our families we are of course especially indebted for their unfailing patience and support and for their tolerance not only in finding their lives shared with dead and dying plants but also in making time to tend the gardens that we have neglected!

Preface

This book is a practical guide to the pests, diseases and disorders that commonly affect fruit, vegetable and ornamental plants growing in gardens in Britain and northern Europe. At first sight it may seem a depressingly morbid catalogue of plant failures but we believe that a good understanding of the many different causes of such failures provides the best basis for successfully avoiding them or minimising their effects in the future. Our main aim therefore is to improve plant health and ensure that gardeners derive maximum enjoyment from the plants that they cultivate. It is inevitable that all gardeners will encounter some pests, diseases and disorders sooner or later but we hope that no single gardener will ever have the misfortune of seeing all the afflictions recorded here!

This is a guide book rather than an encyclopaedia, since the subject matter is too vast to be dealt with fully in the space available. A more extensive treatment of the subject is given in the earlier edition of this book which was published in 1981. Although it is intended primarily for gardeners, it may therefore also be of use to professional horticulturists and to teachers, students and naturalists. Most of the information on pests, diseases and disorders that is readily available to gardeners consists of either a few pages at the end of general gardening books and articles or brief notes in the promotional literature of manufacturers and suppliers of gardening chemicals. Information in the former is often imprecise and in the latter tends to be biased towards the use of chemicals in general and towards a restricted range of active ingredients. We have tried to give accurate and concise information on the symptoms, biology and control of a balanced selection of pests, diseases and disorders. In making this selection we have used published and unpublished records and the advice of many colleagues but we have also been greatly influenced by our own professional experience in Britain. British gardens are therefore our main concern but most of the included pests, diseases and disorders occur throughout northern Europe. We have not attempted to cover southern Europe since the warmer climate there produces quite different conditions, favouring other pests and diseases that are beyond the scope of this book.

How to Use this Book

This book has been specially planned so that gardeners with little or no technical knowledge can quickly identify and treat the pests, diseases and disorders that commonly affect their plants. Problems are therefore approached from the point of view of a gardener dealing with a particular plant or group of plants.

IDENTIFICATION

Correct identification of the cause of trouble is the first and most important step. Careful consideration of the symptoms and circumstances will usually result in a positive diagnosis and, since different plants are affected by different ranges of pests, diseases and disorders, the quickest way of achieving this is to use the plant as a starting point. The first main section of the book (p. 19) therefore consists of an alphabetical listing (A–Z) of the main garden plants that are commonly affected. Under each of these plant entries we indicate the most likely causes of trouble and the reader is then referred from them to the detailed entries in the sections on pests, diseases and disorders, where descriptions of the symptoms can be used to confirm or reject the preliminary diagnosis. Once this diagnosis has been confirmed, information on biology and treatment can be used to determine the best course of action. For example, if rolled leaves are seen on roses, look in the A–Z under **Rose** (p. 72). The entry there will refer to **Rosa** (p. 71), which is the botanical name for the genus to which roses belong, and there you will find that the entry against 'Leaves with leaflets tightly rolled along their length and drooping' leads to 'Leaf-rolling Rose Sawfly' on p. 157. A description of the symptoms is given there, followed by details of the biology of this pest and recommendations for chemical and non-chemical treatment. Similarly, if large, irregular, solid swellings are found on the roots of brassicas, look under **Brassicas** in the A–Z and the entry against 'Roots with irregular swellings not containing caterpillars or holes' will lead to 'Clubroot' on p. 223, where a detailed account of the symptoms, biology and treatment of this disease is given. There are separate entries in the A–Z for 280 different plants or groups of plants. Fruits and vegetables are listed under their common names (apples, pears, parsnips, turnips, etc.) and ornamental plants are listed under the correct botanical name for the genus (*Dahlia*, *Euonymus*, *Rhododendron*, etc.) with cross-references from non-botanical common names, when necessary (e.g., Busy Lizzie – see *Impatiens*; Rubber Plant – see *Ficus*, etc.). It is obviously impracticable to list all garden plants in the A–Z but if a plant is not listed by name, relevant information may be found under one of the group entries (Alpine and Rock Garden Plants; Aquatic Plants; Bedding Plants; Bulbs, Corms, Rhizomes and Tubers; Cacti and Succulents; Climbing Plants; Conifers; Ferns; Glasshouse and House Plants; Hedges; Lawns; Perennials; Seedlings; Shrubs; Trees). Diagnosis of most common conditions will usually be relatively easy but atypical symptoms sometimes develop and symptoms of different troubles are occasionally confusingly similar. Incorrect diagnosis will result in wrong treatment and doubtful cases should therefore be referred to experts for advice (see p. 304).

INFORMATION

Detailed information about each condition is given in the three main sections on Pests (p. 83), Diseases (p. 189) and Disorders (p. 283), which bring together similar groups of problems, so avoiding unnecessary duplication. Within the Pests section these groupings are of closely related organisms (eelworms, slugs and snails, aphids, beetles, flies, mites, birds, mammals, etc.). This arrangement works well for pests, since related species generally damage plants in similar ways, but it does not work so well for fungi, bacteria and other disease organisms, since unrelated species may cause very similar symptoms. The Diseases section is therefore organised more on the basis of symptoms (cankers, rots, etc.) than on close relationships of causative organisms, except for a few types of fungi and for viruses, which are sufficiently distinct to be treated as separate groups. Disorders are simply grouped under the main factors causing them (physiological, mechanical, climatic, nutritional, etc.).

A brief introduction to each of the main sections and to each of the subsidiary groups summarises general information on structure, size, symptoms, biology and, where appropriate, general methods of treatment and these introductions are followed by detailed accounts of individual pests, diseases and disorders. The common English name is given for each pest or disease and is followed by the currently correct scientific name. General distribution, frequency of occurrence and approximate size is indicated, where appropriate, and for the more important entries information is then summarised under sub-headings covering Symptoms, Biology and Treatment. Disorders are dealt with in a similar fashion but they do not have scientific names since they are not caused by living organisms. The arrangement of entries within the main sections varies a little. In the Pests section the pests of fruit and vegetables are dealt with first and then the pests of ornamental plants. There is of course some overlap, since some pest species may affect fruits, vegetables and ornamentals. In the accounts of the major groups of pests (aphids, caterpillars, flies, beetles and mites) the most important species are usually dealt with first and are followed by the less important species. In the Diseases and Disorders sections the arrangement is different and the entries are presented in alphabetical order of their common names.

Additional information and advice, especially on non-chemical and chemical methods of treatment, is given in the General Introduction (p. 13), which should be read before making detailed use of the rest of the book.

Sources of information in other books and pamphlets are summarised in the Bibliography (p. 302), which also includes details of general and specialist journals and magazines that help to keep gardeners informed of changes such as the appearance of new pests and diseases or the development of new methods of treatment.

Technical terms have been used sparingly and those that have had to be used are defined in the Glossary (p. 305), which is followed by a comprehensive Index (p. 309).

Note:

The advice contained in this book is given in good faith but so many factors affect local conditions that the authors cannot guarantee the success of all of their recommendations, nor can they accept liability for any consequence of their use. They stress that the manufacturer's instructions for all proprietary products should be strictly observed and that expert advice should be sought if any doubt arises.

General Introduction

Pests are those animals that damage cultivated plants; diseases result from infections of plants by certain bacteria, fungi, viruses or mycoplasmas (collectively termed pathogens), while disorders are malfunctions caused by factors such as nutrient deficiencies, drought, water-logging, weather or pollutants that are not living organisms. The many different pests, diseases and disorders that affect cultivated plants are of course only a very small part of the extremely complex system of interactions between all living organisms and their environments and it should be realised that most of the organisms that live on or in plants do no harm and are not pests or pathogens. Indeed many are positively beneficial, good examples being the predaceous and parasitic insects that feed on pests or the root-nodule bacteria and mycorrhizal fungi associated with the roots of some plants.

Deciding whether a pest or disease organism should be classed as important may be very much a matter of opinion, especially in the garden situation. In commercial horticulture and agriculture it is often possible to assess the financial losses caused by a particular pest, disease or disorder and so determine whether it is sufficiently important to justify the expenditure of time and money on investigation and treatment. In gardens it is not so easy, since most gardeners grow plants for their beauty and interest rather than for financial gain. The relative importance attached to a particular pest, disease or disorder must therefore be finally determined by individual gardeners in the light of their own experience and circumstances.

We have selected the pests, diseases and disorders that we consider to be of general importance in Britain and northern Europe. There will not be complete agreement about this selection, even among experts, but we have based it on our own experiences in advising gardeners during the past fifteen years and we have tried to include all conditions that we know are common causes of concern even if they do not always cause appreciable damage. Many uncommon conditions have been left out in order to keep the book to acceptable limits and we stress that it is a guide, not an encyclopaedia. If additional information is needed, it should be sought in the many references listed in the bibliography.

Many (but by no means all) of the problems that arise when plants are cultivated result from disturbances of the natural relationships between the plants and their normal environments. In natural circumstances plants have evolved gradually over millions of years and have therefore become well adapted to soil, seasons, weather and other local environmental factors. During the last 10,000 years increasing numbers of plants have been cultivated in the unnatural circumstances of agriculture, forestry and horticulture but, despite this, most are remarkably healthy.

SYMPTOMS

Many pests, diseases and disorders produce characteristic symptoms that make it possible to diagnose the causes of trouble with a fair degree of certainty. These symptoms are described in detail later in the book and the most important or the most typical of each type are illustrated in the colour plates. In all cases we have described the symptoms that are most likely to be noticed by gardeners and we have tried to describe the most typical symptoms. There is obviously bound to be considerable variation in the manifestation of symptoms on different plants, in different seasons and places and on different cultivars, so that the relatively brief descriptions given should not be taken to be absolutely exact for all circumstances. Although many diagnoses are simple and certain, there are also many cases where diagnosis is difficult. If in doubt, seek expert advice, since wrong diagnosis and wrong treatment will waste time and money.

Symptoms are often conspicuous and may give a clear indication of the severity of damage. Good examples of this category are the sudden wilting and collapse of whole plants caused by cabbage root fly on recently transplanted brassicas, by wilt diseases on tomatoes, or by severe frost on potato plants in spring and autumn. In other cases, such as eelworm attacks, virus infections or nutrient deficiencies, symptoms may be less obvious and must be looked for carefully. In all cases it is important to look out for the first signs of symptoms developing since early diagnosis and treatment may make it possible to prevent or minimise damage. Different pests, diseases and disorders affect different parts of plants and symptoms may therefore appear on roots, bulbs, tubers, corms, rhizomes, stems, buds, leaves, flowers, fruits or seeds. In the detailed descriptions reference is made to the main parts affected and, where appropriate, to the time of year when symptoms normally appear. Where pests are involved, brief descriptions of adult and immature stages are given if they are likely to be easily seen on damaged plants but detailed descriptions are not given for those stages, such as adult moths or flies, that are unlikely to be seen. Descriptions of diseases similarly emphasise the gross symptoms produced and do not describe microscopic details of the causative organisms. Sizes of organisms or symptoms, where relevant, are indicated by approximate measurements but these give only a rough guide, since there can be considerable variation, even within species.

BIOLOGY

Relevant information about the biology of pests and diseases and about the biological basis of disorders explains how and why plants are damaged and is also most useful in deciding what methods can be used to prevent or limit this damage. Much information has been published about most major pests, diseases and disorders and from the scientific literature we have prepared summaries of the essential facts about overwintering stages and sites, development during the growing season, methods of reproduction and dispersal, host ranges and geographical distribution, and many other topics. There are considerable differences in the general biology of the major groups of pests (eelworms, mites, insects, birds, mammals) and of disease organisms (fungi, bacteria, viruses and mycoplasmas) and these are summarised at the beginning of each relevant part of the book. Similar summaries are also given for important groups of insects (aphids, caterpillars, flies, sawflies, beetles), and for certain groups of fungi (rusts, smuts, downy mildews, powdery mildews).

This arrangement takes advantage of the fact that closely related groups of organisms tend to live, feed and breed in similar ways and it is relatively easy to write about them in general terms. Even so, there is much variation within these restricted groups and most generalisations are subject to some exceptions.

TREATMENT

Specific recommendations for treatment are given in the detailed entries in the pest, disease and disorder sections but there are some general principles that are best summarised here. Our aim in making recommendations for treatment has been to select methods that are safe, practicable and effective when used in gardens. Commercial situations are usually quite distinct, since different criteria apply, and we have not tried to cover them. Firstly, we emphasise that choice of treatment must be personal. Only the individual gardener can decide what monetary, aesthetic or sentimental value is to be placed on his/her plants; what levels of perfection he/she wishes to achieve, and what methods are feasible in his/her circumstances. Some gardeners will prefer to rely entirely on natural controls; others will use varying degrees of non-chemical and chemical control. We have tried to indicate the range of possible effective treatments that are available and have also tried to provide sufficient biological information to indicate when and why treatment may be necessary and how it can best be achieved. Many recommendations made elsewhere in the gardening literature will not be found here and in most cases they will have been omitted because we are not convinced that they are effective and/or safe.

Secondly, we urge the use of non-chemical methods whenever possible. Chemicals are generally a poor substitute for good gardening, are expensive, and may also have harmful side-effects. There are, however, many cases where chemicals offer the only possibility of prevention and cure and the gardener's choice must then be between the use of chemicals or the risk of serious damage and possible loss of plants. In such cases we recommend chemicals that have been cleared by the Ministry of Agriculture.

Non-chemical Treatments. These usually aim at preventing trouble rather than curing it and in many instances the best way to do this is to ensure that plants are well-grown in situations and circumstances that suit them. Plants growing in unfavourable conditions are less likely to thrive, although they may also respond to special care. In addition, good garden hygiene, regular cultivation, adequate rotations of crops and the use of resistant or tolerant cultivars may help to reduce the effects of pests, diseases and disorders. Other non-chemical techniques that are described in relevant sections of the main text include the use of netting, fencing and scaring devices against birds and mammals, the use of traps against small mammals and various insects and the use of various specialised techniques, such as the biological control of glasshouse pests and the hot water treatment of bulbs to control eelworms.

Chemical Treatments. The regular use of chemicals to control pests and diseases dates from the second half of the nineteenth century and some of the chemicals used then, Bordeaux mixture and nicotine for example, are still in use today. At first the range of materials was restricted but since the 1940s, a vast array of synthetic chemicals has been developed, primarily for agriculture, horticulture and forestry, and some of these have been made available to gardeners.

In 1982, about 55 different chemical pesticides were on sale for garden use, including about 30 different insecticides and about 20 different fungicides, the remainder being various rodenticides, molluscicides and acaricides. We refer to these chemicals by their common chemical names (bromophos, dimethoate, malathion, benomyl, etc.), so avoiding the use of complex chemical names and formulae. They are sold under about 200 different trade names, with widely used active ingredients, such as malathion, marketed under at least a dozen different trade names. It is difficult to keep up to date with these names, which tend to change frequently, and we have not used them, but current lists of them can be obtained from the British Agrochemicals Association, the Royal Horticultural Society (members only), gardening journals or individual manufacturers. In addition, it is usually possible to find the names of active ingredients on pack labels, though they may be in very small print.

Excellent guidance on the selection and safe use of these pesticides is given by the Ministry of Agriculture, especially through the Pesticides Safety Precautions Scheme and through their advisory literature. We have relied heavily on these sources of information when making detailed recommendations in the main text.

Modes of action. Pesticides may act in a number of different ways and these different modes of action affect their possible uses. Most insecticides act by direct external contact with the target organisms, either immediately on application or within a few days. Some insecticides, especially those that kill biting and chewing insects, leave a persistent residue on treated plants, and others are used as persistent poisons in baits (e.g. ant baits) which attract pests to them. Fungicides may act in an eradicant fashion and kill pathogens already existing on the plant or as protectants on healthy tissues when they form a barrier that prevents fungal development and penetration. A few insecticides and fungicides act as fumigants and many of the most recently developed insecticides and fungicides are absorbed into the sap of treated plants and have a systemic action, which is particularly effective against pests that feed on sap or against fungi that permeate plant tissues. Such systemic materials have the added advantages that usually they are required in much smaller quantities, do not suffer from washing off by rain as the externally acting pesticides do and, because they are absorbed into the plant's tissues and moved within, do not require such accuracy in application. Most pesticides can act in more than one way, so that differences in mode of action are not always clear-cut. For example, nicotine has contact and fumigant action; dimethoate has contact and systemic action; HCH has contact, fumigant and slight systemic action, and benomyl has protectant, eradicant and systemic action.

Formulations. Pesticides are formulated in various different ways, mainly to make application easier but also to enhance their efficiency. Most are formulated as spray concentrates that are diluted with water before application by sprayer or watering-can but some are specially formulated as granules, dusts, aerosols, fumigant smoke-cones, baits, seed-dressings or ultra-low-volume sprays.

Resistance to pesticides. Frequent or continuous exposure of a pest or pathogen to a particular pesticide can result in the selection of new strains that are resistant to that pesticide, and possibly to related pesticides. This is a case of artificial selection and is similar to the system of selection that has produced many of our modern cultivars of garden plants. The pesticide kills all susceptible individuals but in any population there are likely to be at least some individuals that are less susceptible and are therefore not killed. If there is an inheritable genetic basis for this lack of susceptibility, such as slight differences in structure, behaviour or physiology (e.g. detoxifying mechanisms), it will be passed on to the next generation when the survivors breed. If selection for tolerance continues, through continuing use of the same pesticide, the new strain of the pest or disease may eventually be quite resistant to the pesticide. Resistance to insecticides and acaricides tends to develop most readily in prolific species, such as red spider mites or aphids, which pass through successive generations quickly, so that the whole process of selection is speeded up, and in such cases resistance can appear within a few years of using a new chemical.

The only really important cases at present involve glasshouse red spider mites, glasshouse whitefly, peach-potato aphid and some other aphids, and some flies, especially carrot fly, cabbage root fly and bean seed fly. A similar situation exists with some pathogens that have developed tolerance to fungicides, the most important instance in Britain being the tolerance shown by strains of the grey mould fungus, *Botrytis cinerea* to the widely used fungicide benomyl and similar materials. Where resistance is known to occur, the choice of pesticides will have to be varied and recommendations are given under the entries for the main pests and diseases concerned.

Phytotoxicity. Pesticides are not only toxic to animals; they may also affect some plants and the injury that results is attributed to the phytotoxicity of the pesticide. The most phytotoxic chemicals are eliminated during the early stages of development of new pesticides since there is no point in achieving good control of a pest or disease if the chemical also kills the plants. Information about both phytotoxicity and taint is usually included in the label instructions on pesticide packs and additional guidance may sometimes be obtained from manufacturers.

Safety precautions

No garden is ever entirely free from pests and diseases but some will suffer more than others and some plants will be more susceptible than others. If circumstances indicate that chemical control is the only feasible solution, then select and use the correct pesticide with care and follow these basic rules:

Only use chemicals when you really must.

Select suitable materials carefully, preferably well in advance, and ensure that they will be both effective and safe. Check possible phytotoxic effects and observe safe minimum intervals for pre-harvest applications to fruits and vegetables.

Read the pack label carefully before using a pesticide and then apply it at the correct concentration, at the right time, and as thoroughly as possible. Inefficient and late application does more harm than good. Whenever possible, apply pesticides during cool, dry, cloudy, windless weather. During hot, sunny periods, apply pesticides in the late evening, when temperatures and wind speeds are lower.

Do not apply insecticides to flowers that are being visited by hive bees, bumble bees or other pollinating insects. Wait until the flowering period is over or apply insecticides before the flowering period starts.

Store all gardening chemicals safely, well away from children and pets, preferably on a high shelf in a locked shed and always in a shaded position away from direct sunlight and free from frost.

Clean out spraying and other equipment immediately after use and wash out empty containers before putting them in a rubbish bin. Surplus spray and water used to wash sprayers and containers should go into an outside drain, sump or deep hole. Do not contaminate ponds, streams or rivers with insecticides, many of which are highly toxic to fish and other aquatic animals.

Never transfer chemical concentrates or dilute spray solutions into milk bottles, soft drink bottles or other unlabelled containers. Children may be tempted to drink from them and could be poisoned.

Do not apply pesticides with sprayers or other equipment that has been used to apply weed killers. There is always a possibility that traces of weed killer may persist and damage plants.

A–Z Key

Abies (Firs). Also see **Conifers** and **Trees**

Leaves shed prematurely	See discussion under Needle Casts p. 210
Leaves, buds and stems with tufts of white woolly wax; growth distorted and sometimes dying	Silver Fir Adelgids p. 122
Stems with cankers and/or dying back of branches or crown	Cankers and Diebacks p. 214

Abutilon. Also see **Glasshouse and House Plants**

Leaves with fine angular yellow/green variegation	Viruses p. 277

Acacia. See **Glasshouse and House Plants** and for False Acacia see **Robinia**

Acer (Sycamore and Maples). Also see **Trees**

Leaves with powdery white coating	Powdery Mildew p. 204
Leaves with black or less commonly other coloured spots	Tar Spot p. 260
Leaves infested by small insects, especially on undersides; foliage sticky and sooty	Aphids p. 104
Leaves of sycamores and field maples with rashes of small red pimples	Sycamore Gall Mite p. 179
Bark deeply grooved; esp. on hedgerow maples	Winged Cork p. 298
Branches and trunks with brown scales and tufts of white woolly wax	Horse Chestnut Scale p. 125

Achimenes. See **Glasshouse and House Plants**

Acidanthera. Also see **Bulbs etc.**

Corms with sunken lesions; leaves spotted or browning rapidly	Corm Rot p. 231

Aconite. For **Winter Aconite** see **Eranthis**

Acorus (Flag). See **Bulbs etc.**

Adiantum (Maidenhair). See **Ferns**

Aesculus (Horse Chestnut). Also see **Trees**

Leaves with irregular brown blotches	Leaf Blotch p. 271
Leaves yellowed or with irregular patterns	Viruses p. 277
Branches and trunks with brown scales and tufts of white woolly wax	Horse Chestnut Scale p. 125

African Marigold. See **Tagetes**

Alder. See **Alnus**

Allium. For ornamental species see **Onion**

Almond. Also see **Apricot, Nectarine and Peach** and **Trees**

Flowers and/or leaves scorched, shrivelled or killed in spring	Frost p. 292
Leaves with brown or black pustules beneath; small yellow spots above	Plum Rust p. 198
Leaves and/or other parts with powdery white coating	Powdery Mildew p. 204
Leaves with irregular yellowish patterns	Viruses p. 277
Leaves with silvery sheen; branches may die back	Silver Leaf p. 221
Leaves blistered, crumpled and reddish in early summer	Peach Leaf Curl p. 225
Leaves with more or less regular holes	Peach Shot Hole p. 268
Fruit with soft brown rot; terminal shoot may wither	Brown Rot p. 235
Root and stem base decayed; toadstools and bootlace-like strands may be present and branches die back	Honey Fungus p. 249

Alnus (Alder) Also see **Trees**

Leaves blistered and curled; may be yellow coating	Leaf Curls p. 222
Leaves with irregular holes and pieces eaten away	Caterpillars p. 132
Branches and stems with larger brown scales and white wax egg sacs	Woolly Currant Scale p. 125

Aloe. See **Cacti and Succulents** and **Glasshouse and House Plants**

Alpine and Rock Garden Plants. Also see **Glasshouse and House Plants** and **Cacti and Succulents**

Pests, diseases and disorders seldom cause serious trouble on plants growing in alpine houses and in rock gardens. This is partly due to the general hardiness of this group of plants and to the fact that many of them grow most actively and flower early in the season when temperatures are low and pest and disease organisms are therefore less prevalent. Some pests and diseases are listed under those plant genera that are especially susceptible and the following key can be used to identify general troubles on other plants:

Flowers and leaves torn; plants sometimes uprooted	Birds p. 179
Flowers, leaves and young shoots with irregular holes and pieces eaten away; slime trails on or near plants	Slugs and Snails p. 90
Plants unthrifty, small white insects on roots	Root Mealybugs p. 128 Root Aphids p. 120
Flowers, leaves and young shoots with irregular holes and pieces eaten away, sometimes with silk webbing over damaged parts; no slime trails	Caterpillars p. 132
Leaves, buds and shoots infested by small green, yellow, brown or black wingless and winged insects; foliage sticky, sometimes sooty	Aphids p. 104
Leaves and/or other parts with powdery white coating	Powdery Mildew p. 204
Plants generally unthrifty; roots blackened and/or decayed	Root and Foot Rots p. 242

Plant / Symptom	Cause
Alstroemeria	
Leaves, stems and young shoots with irregular holes; slime trails present on or near plants	Slugs and Snails p. 90
Roots eaten by white caterpillars in soil	Swift Moths p. 137
Althaea (Hollyhocks)	
Leaves with small, ragged holes, mainly on younger leaves	Capsid Bugs p. 97
Leaves, buds and flowers with larger holes	Caterpillars p. 132
Leaves yellowing and drying, numerous small mites on undersides, sometimes with silk webbing	Glasshouse Red Spider Mites p. 173
Leaves and stem with raised orange-brown pustules	Rust p. 191
Stem and/or root with large irregular swelling	Crown Gall p. 224
Alyssum	
Leaves of young seedlings with numerous small round holes and pits	Flea Beetles p. 165
Leaves and/or other parts with powdery white coating	Powdery Mildew p. 204
Roots with irregular nodular swellings	Clubroot p. 223
Amaryllis	
Leaves red-brown and becoming shrivelled from tip downwards	Narcissus Leaf Scorch p. 267
Leaves mottled	Viruses p. 277
For indoor Amaryllis (Hippeastrum) see **Glasshouse and House Plants**	
Amelanchier. Also see **Trees**	
Flowers and/or leaves shrivelled; shoots may exude slime and die back	Fireblight p. 217
Androsace. See **Alpine and Rock Garden Plants**	
Anemone	
Flowers and/or buds with fluffy grey mould growth	Grey Mould p. 232
Leaves and/or other parts with powdery white coating	Powdery Mildew p. 204
Leaves with small, cup-like bodies on undersides	Plum Rust p. 198
Leaves of young seedlings with numerous small round holes and pits	Flea Beetles p. 165
Leaves, stems, flowers and buds with irregular large holes	Caterpillars p. 132
Leaves with irregular pieces eaten away; slime trails present	Slugs and Snails p. 90
Leaves, stems, flowers and buds sticky, sometimes sooty; small insects present	Aphids p. 104
Roots eaten by white caterpillars in soil	Swift Moths p. 137
Roots eaten by dirty grey-brown caterpillars in soil	Cutworms p. 136
Annuals. See **Bedding Plants**	
Anthurium. See **Glasshouse and House Plants**	
Antirrhinum (Snapdragons)	
Flowers and shoot tips distorted, buds sometimes killed	Strawberry Mite p. 177
Flowers, leaves, stems and buds sticky, sometimes sooty, small insects present	Aphids p. 104

Symptom	Cause
Leaves (undersides) and/or stem with chocolate brown pustules	Rust p. 191
Leaves with dark spots	Leaf Spot p. 258
Leaves and/or other parts with powdery white coating	Powdery Mildew p. 204

Aphelandra. See **Glasshouse and House Plants**

Apple. Also see **Trees**

During their long period of growth apple trees may be affected by many different pests, diseases and disorders. Only the most important of these are noted here. For more detailed information consult specialist publications (see Bibliography p. 302).

The following key to symptoms has been divided into sections for easier reference and, since the fruit is the end-product of cultivation, damage to mature fruit is dealt with first.

FRUIT

Symptom	Cause
Fruit in store with large pieces eaten away, often with small tooth marks showing	Mice p. 185
Fruit with rotten cores tunnelled by caterpillars, often with holes to exterior	Codling Moth p. 134
Fruit with superficial galleries in flesh, often under leaves attached to surface of fruit by silk webbing	Fruit Tortrix Moths p. 135
Fruit with small pieces pecked away	Birds p. 179
Fruit misshapen and with curved, discoloured scars in skin; fruitlets with rotten cores, mostly falling prematurely	Apple Sawfly p. 154
Fruitlets irregularly misshapen after earlier infestation by aphids	Rosy Apple Aphid p. 106
Fruit misshapen, with superficial bumps and discoloured patches on skin	Capsid Bugs p. 97
Fruit with soft brown rot and usually off-white cottony pustules; associated twigs may die back	Brown Rot p. 235
Fruit with round, dark, saucer-like depressions; usually only in store	Bitter Rot p. 234
Fruit leathery and cracked; often on windfalls and low hanging fruit	Leathery Rots p. 237
Fruit rotted and with grey powdery mould growth; usually in store	Grey Mould Rot p. 236
Fruit otherwise rotted; especially in store	Minor Rots p. 238
Fruit split or hollow	Splitting p. 298
Fruit scorched following very hot weather	High Temperature Injury p. 294
Fruit with corky patches both on and within flesh	Boron Deficiency p. 289
Fruit with dark spots or pits both on and within flesh	Calcium Deficiency p. 286
Fruit with very dark green more or less rounded corky patches on surface only	Scab p. 228
Fruit with dark green mouldy patches on surface; easily wiped off	Sooty Blotch p. 271
Fruit abnormally small and red	Nitrogen Deficiency p. 284

FLOWERS

Symptom	Cause
Flowers fail to open and petals turn brown, small insect larvae sometimes present inside closed flowers	Apple Blossom Weevil p. 168
Flowers and flower buds discoloured, failing to develop normally, often sticky and with small flattened insects present	Apple Sucker p. 100
Flowers and flower buds with holes; small looper-type caterpillars often present	Winter Moths p. 133
Flowers and then spur leaves wilt	Brown Rot Blossom Wilt p. 235
Flowers and/or buds die suddenly	Frost p. 292

LEAVES

Symptom	Cause
Leaves with small, irregular, tattered holes, especially at tips of shoots	Capsid Bugs p. 97
Leaves with larger, irregular holes and pieces eaten away	Caterpillars p. 132 Leaf Weevils p. 169 Chafers p. 163
Leaves, shoots and buds infested by small insects; foliage sticky and sooty and sometimes discoloured and distorted	Apple Aphids p. 106
Leaves bronzing and drying in summer, numerous small mites on undersides	Fruit Tree Red Spider Mite p. 175
Leaves with fine light flecking, moult skins of insects sometimes on undersides	Leafhoppers p. 98
Leaves and young shoots with frothy masses of spit-like substance	Froghoppers p. 98
Leaves with irregular yellowish streaks and patterns in early summer	Virus p. 277
Leaves scorched at margins in spring	Frost p. 292
Leaves and/or other parts with powdery white coating	Powdery Mildew p. 204
Leaves and/or other parts with sticky black coating	Sooty Mould p. 209
Leaves with silvery sheen; branches may die back	Silver Leaf p. 221
Leaves with irregular dark green blotches	Scab p. 228
Leaves more or less bleached; veins remain dark green	Iron Deficiency p. 288
Leaves with irregular marbling; may drop prematurely	Magnesium Deficiency p. 287

BUDS

Symptom	Cause
Buds pecked in winter and spring, causing lack of blossom and leaves	Birds p. 179

BRANCHES, TWIGS AND SHOOTS

Symptom	Cause
Branches and twigs with tufts of white woolly wax, often associated with hard, irregular woody swellings	Woolly Aphid p. 108
Branches tunnelled by large caterpillars, causing wilting of shoots and leaves	Leopard Moth p. 136

Symptom	Cause
Branches die back in absence of stem lesions; leaves silvery	Silver Leaf p. 221
Branches die back; stem base and roots decayed; toadstools and bootlace-like strands may be present	Honey Fungus p. 249
Branches with canker lesions; may die back beyond lesions	Canker p. 214
Branches die back; masses of small, usually pink pustules present	Coral Spot p. 216
Branches with parasitic leathery plant growing from them	Mistletoe p. 276
Branches and/or stem with hard irregular swelling	Crown Gall p. 224
Branches (esp. of cv. 'Lord Lambourne') pliable and rubbery	Mycoplasma p. 278
Shoots exude slime and die back; flowers and/or leaves shrivelled	Fireblight p. 217

TRUNKS AND STEMS

Symptom	Cause
Trunks and stems of young trees with bark stripped near and just above ground level	Rabbits p. 183 Voles p. 186 Hares p. 184

ROOTS

Symptom	Cause
Roots and stem base decayed; toadstools and bootlace-like strands may be present and branches die back	Honey Fungus p. 249

GENERAL DEBILITY

Symptom	Cause
Trees generally unthrifty	Latent Viruses p. 277 Deficiencies of Nitrogen p. 284 Phosphorus p. 285 and Potassium p. 285

Apricot, Nectarine and Peach. Also see **Trees**

Symptom	Cause
Fruits with holes eaten in ripening flesh	Birds p. 179 Wasps p. 161
Fruit with soft brown rot and usually off-white cottony pustules; associated twigs may die back	Brown Rot p. 235
Fruit otherwise rotted; especially in store	Minor Rots p. 238
Flowers and/or buds die suddenly	Frost p. 292
Flowers and then spur leaves wilt	Brown Rot Blossom Wilt p. 235
Leaves with irregular yellowish streaks and patterns	Viruses p. 277
Leaves scorched in early spring	Frost p. 292
Leaves and/or other parts with powdery white coating	Powdery Mildew p. 204
Leaves and/or other parts with sticky black coating	Sooty Mould p. 209
Leaves with silver sheen; branches may die back	Silver Leaf p. 221
Leaves blistered, crumpled and reddish in early summer	Peach Leaf Curl p. 225

Leaves with more or less regular holes; no gummy branch lesions	Peach Shot Hole p. 268
Leaves with brown or black pustules beneath; small yellow spots above	Plum Rust p. 198
Leaves more or less bleached; veins remain dark green	Iron Deficiency p. 288
Leaves and shoots infested by small insects, often sticky and sooty	Aphids p. 104
Leaves discoloured, bronzing and drying, with numerous small mites on undersides	Glasshouse Red Spider Mites p. 173 Fruit Tree Red Spider Mite p. 175
Leaves with large irregular holes and pieces eaten away	Caterpillars p. 132
Branches and stems with brown, waxy scales, leaves often sticky and sooty	Scale Insects p. 124
Branches die back in absence of stem lesions; leaves silvery	Silver Leaf p. 221
Branches and/or stems with many gummy lesions; may die back and leaves have irregular holes	Bacterial Canker p. 218
Branches and/or stem with hard irregular swelling	Crown Gall p. 224
Trees generally unthrifty	Deficiencies of Nitrogen p. 284 Phosphorus p. 285 and Potassium p. 285

Aquatic Plants

Aquatic plants are seldom affected by pests, diseases or disorders although water-lilies are sometimes damaged by insects or affected by leaf spots (see **Nymphaea**). Insecticides should not be used on aquatic plants growing in ponds and streams since they kill fish and other aquatic animals.

Aquilegia

Leaves and/or other parts with powdery white coating	Powdery Mildew p. 204
Leaves and shoots infested by small insects, often sticky and sooty	Aphids p. 104

Araucaria (Monkey-puzzle). See **Conifers** and **Trees**

Arbor Vitae. See **Thuja**

Arbutus (Strawberry Tree). Also see **Trees**

Fruits eaten	Birds p. 179
Leaves with small irregular spots	Leaf Spots p. 258

Arctotis

Leaves, shoots and flowers infested by small insects; leaves often sticky and sooty	Aphids p. 104

Armeria

Leaves with brown pustules	Rust p. 191

Artemisia

Leaves and shoots with frothy masses of spit-like substance	Froghoppers p. 98

Symptom	Cause
Leaves and shoots infested by small insects, sometimes sticky and sooty	Aphids p. 104
Roots infested by small white insects; plants unthrifty	Root Aphid p. 120

Arum Lily. See **Zantedeschia**

Aruncus

Symptom	Cause
Leaves extensively eaten, often reduced to a skeleton of veins; caterpillars may be present	Spiraea Sawfly p. 158

Asclepias

Symptom	Cause
Leaves with yellowish mottling or other irregular patterns	Viruses p. 277

Ash. See **Fraxinus**

Asparagus (Vegetable)

Symptom	Cause
Leaves and stems eaten, grey/black larvae and/or yellow/black beetles may be present	Asparagus Beetle p. 167
Shoots eaten, slime trails present on or near plants	Slugs p. 90
Shoots with masses of brown powdery pustules	Rusts p. 191
Shoots blacken and die suddenly in spring	Frost p. 292
Shoots with fluffy grey mould growth	Grey Mould Rot p. 236
Plants die back with decay at base and/or on roots	Root and Foot Rots p. 242
Plants feeble and stunted; roots decayed with matted dark strands	Violet Root Rot p. 241

Asparagus (Ornamental). See **Glasshouse and House Plants**

Aspidistra. See **Glasshouse and House Plants**

Asplenium. See **Ferns**

Aster (China). See **Callistephus**

Aster (Michaelmas daisies)

Symptom	Cause
Flowers malformed, often killed, leaving rosettes of green calyces; young shoots distorted, lateral buds killed	Strawberry Mite p. 177
Leaves and shoot tips infested by small insects, often sticky and occasionally sooty	Aphids p. 104
Leaves with irregular holes	Caterpillars p. 132
Leaves and shoots with white froth covering wingless insects	Froghoppers p. 98
Leaves discoloured, growth stunted	Chrysanthemum Eelworm p. 86
Leaves and/or other parts with powdery white coating	Powdery Mildew p. 204
Leaves wilt; stem interior with brown or black streaks	Wilt p. 211
Shoots eaten near soil, slime trails present on or near plants	Slugs p. 90

Aubergine (Egg Plant)

Symptom	Cause
Leaves discoloured, bronzing and drying, numerous small mites on undersides	Glasshouse Red Spider Mites p. 173
Leaves and/or other parts variously crumpled and distorted	Viruses p. 277

Aubrieta. See **Bedding Plants**

Auricula. See **Primula**

Autumn Crocus. See **Colchicum**

Azalea. See **Rhododendron**

Barberry. See **Berberis**

Bay Laurel. See **Laurus**

Beans (Dwarf or French, Runner and Broad)

Symptom	Cause
Seeds fail to germinate and/or seedlings grow poorly and may die	Mice p. 185 Slugs p. 90 Bean Seed Fly p. 151 Millepedes p. 92
Plants stunted and deformed, sometimes collapsing	Stem Eelworm p. 84
Pods of broad beans with triangular pieces pecked out and beans removed	Jays p. 182
Pods rotted and with fluffy grey mould growth	Grey Mould Rot p. 236
Pods with rounded greasy spots (runner and French beans only)	Halo Blight p. 261
Pods with rounded reddish spots; reddish veins on undersides of leaves (runner and French beans only)	Anthracnose p. 222
Seeds with rounded dark brown lesions within; plant unthrifty	Manganese Deficiency p. 289
Leaves discoloured, yellowing, bronzing and dying, many small mites on undersides	Glasshouse Red Spider Mites p. 173
Leaves and shoots infested by small black insects, sometimes sticky and sooty	Black Bean Aphid p. 112
Leaves infested by small white insects, sometimes sticky and sooty	Glasshouse Whitefly p. 102
Leaves with small semi-circular notches eaten out of edges, producing a scalloped effect	Pea and Bean Weevils p. 169
Leaves with reddish veins beneath; pods with rounded reddish spots (runner and French beans only)	Anthracnose p. 222
Leaves with dry lesions surrounded by marked yellow halo; pods may have greasy spots (runner and French beans only)	Halo Blight p. 261
Leaves with chocolate brown spots (broad beans only)	Chocolate Spot p. 261
Leaves crumpled and/or with irregular yellowish patterns	Viruses p. 277
Leaves wilt (oldest first); stem with dark streaks within, extending well above ground level	Wilt p. 211
Leaves wilt; stem rotted at base; no dark streaks within stem well above ground level	Root and Foot Rots p. 242
Leaves with scorched margins; oldest affected first	Potassium Deficiency p. 285
Leaves turn blue-green or yellowish and may wilt	Copper Deficiency p. 290
Stems streaked; leaves with reddish veins beneath (runner and French beans only)	Anthracnose p. 222
Stems and roots rotted and blackened at base	Root and Foot Rots p. 242
Stemms rotted at base; white cottony mould present	Sclerotinia Disease p. 247
Stem with long dark streaks within; leaves wilt	Wilt p. 211
Roots blackened and decayed	Root and Foot Rots p. 242
Roots with small nodular swellings	Root Nodules p. 276

Bean Tree. See **Catalpa**

Bedding Plants

Ornamental annuals and biennials that are grown for summer bedding need special care if they are to do well during their short period of growth. They are often raised in warmth and, if not adequately hardened-off, the soft, succulent growth will be susceptible to rotting diseases. Handle fragile young plants gently when planting out and always try to keep a few plants in reserve to fill gaps caused by early losses. During their initial growth in frames and glasshouses young plants may be affected by many of the pests, diseases and disorders of **Glasshouse and House Plants** (see p. 47 for key) and of **Seedlings** (see p. 73). In addition, transplants or direct-sown plants growing outdoors may be damaged by soil pests, especially **Wireworms** (p. 163), **Leatherjackets** (p. 147), **Chafers** (p. 163), **Cutworms** (p. 136) and **Swift Moths** (p. 137) and soil-borne pathogens such as those causing **Root and Foot Rots** (p. 242), all of which may cause sudden wilting, collapse and death. Among diseases frequently found affecting the leaves of some genera are **Downy Mildews** (p. 202), **Powdery Mildews** (p. 204), **Grey Mould** (p. 232) and certain **Leaf Spots** (p. 258) and **Stem and Leaf Rots** (p. 252). **Slime Moulds** (p. 273) may occasionally infest bedding plants and the commonest disorder is probably **Magnesium Deficiency** (p. 287) which gives rise to pale interveinal areas on the leaves. Other troubles are noted under the main plant genera.

Beech. See **Fagus**

Beet (Spinach and Beetroot)

Leaves pale and toughened with grey-purple mould on undersides	Downy Mildew p. 202
Leaves toughened, crumpled and/or with abnormal colouration	Viruses p. 277
Leaves with inter-veinal yellowing and sometimes dead patches also; edges may roll upwards; older leaves affected first	Manganese Deficiency p. 289
Leaves infested by small black insects	Black Bean Aphid p. 112
Leaves with conspicuous brown blotch mines	Beet Leaf Miner Fly p. 149
Roots with irregular holes and cavities	Cutworms p. 136 Swift Moths p. 137
Roots decayed with mottled dark strands; plants often feeble	Violet Root Rot p. 241
Roots with scab-like patches of corky tissue	Common Scab p. 229
Roots with rough surface patches and dark patches or rings within flesh	Boron Deficiency p. 289
Roots with irregular swellings	Crown Gall p. 224
Plants run to flower prematurely	Bolting p. 297

Beetroot. See **Beet**

Begonia. Also see **Bulbs etc., Bedding Plants** and **Glasshouse and House Plants**

Leaves with irregular mottling; plants may be stunted	Viruses p. 277
Leaves and/or other parts with powdery white coating	Powdery Mildew p. 204
Leaves wilted; stem interior with brown or black streaks	Wilt p. 211
Leaves with rough warty outgrowths on undersides	Oedema p. 297
Leaves infested by small white winged insects; plants sometimes sticky and sooty	Glasshouse Whitefly p. 102
Leaves infested by green or yellow insects, sometimes sticky and sooty	Aphids p. 104
Leaves with yellow to dark-brown or black areas between veins	Chrysanthemum Eelworm p. 86

Symptom	Cause
Leaves distorted, puckered, slightly thickened and with margins curled downwards; sometimes with rusty colour; flowers malformed	Tarsonemid Mites p. 176
Leaves and stems with colonies of soft-bodied insects covered with white wax powder and filaments	Glasshouse Mealybugs p. 127
Leaves with discoloured areas, yellowing and silvering; small narrow-bodied insects present	Thrips p. 129
Leaves with brown scales on undersides; foliage sticky and sooty	Scale Insects p. 124
Plants unthrifty; roots with numerous irregular hard lumps	Root-Knot Eelworms p. 88
Roots, tubers and rhizomes eaten; small C-shaped legless larvae present	Vine Weevil p. 170

Betula (Birches). Also see **Trees**

Symptom	Cause
Leaves with irregular holes and pieces eaten away	Caterpillars p. 132 Weevils p. 168 Sawflies p. 154
Leaves with irregular yellowish streaks and patterns	Viruses p. 277
Branches with masses of proliferating shoots like large birds' nests	Witches' Brooms p. 227
Stem and/or branches with dry, crumbly rot; fungal brackets may be present	Stem Rot p. 252

Biennials. See **Bedding Plants**

Bilberry. See **Vaccinium**

Birch. See **Betula**

Blackberry, Dewberry

Symptom	Cause
Fruit rotted and with fluffy grey mould growth	Grey Mould p. 232
Fruits malformed and maggoty	Raspberry Beetle p. 165
Flowers killed suddenly	Frost p. 292
Leaves and young shoots with masses of spit-like substance	Froghoppers p. 98
Leaves with light mottling, insect moult skins often on undersides	Leafhoppers p. 98
Leaves with small tattered holes	Capsid Bugs p. 97
Leaves and/or other parts with powdery white coating	Powdery Mildew p. 204
Leaves with orange-yellow and/or black pustules on undersides	Rusts p. 191
Leaves with greyish circular purple-bordered spots and no pustules beneath	Purple Blotch p. 262
Stems with orange, slit-like lesions	Common Rust p. 191
Stems with greyish elliptical purple-bordered spots	Cane Spot or Purple Blotch p. 262
Stems with hard, irregular swellings	Crown Gall p. 224
Roots with hard, irregular swellings	Crown Gall p. 224

Black Currants. See **Currants**

Bluebell. See **Endymion**

Box. See **Buxus**

Brassicas (Broccoli, Brussels Sprouts, Cabbages, Cauliflowers, Chinese Cabbages, Kale and Kohlrabi)

Symptom	Cause
Leaves and/or other parts with powdery white coating	Powdery Mildew p. 204
Leaves with brownish angular patches and greyish mould beneath	Downy Mildew p. 202

Symptom	Cause
Leaves variously spotted	Leaf Spot p. 258
Leaves and/or other parts with small, often concentric clusters of creamy droplets	White Blister p. 210
Leaf blades narrow; leaves appearing whip-like; esp. cauliflower	Molybdenum Deficiency p. 290
Leaves with blue-green colouration, often marginal scorching and plant generally unthrifty. On older leaves first	Potassium Deficiency p. 285
Leaves small, pale but with yellow, red or purplish tints, on older leaves first; plant generally unthrifty but no obvious root damage	Nitrogen Deficiency p. 284
Leaves stunted and brittle and, when cut, brownish patches in cauliflower curds and stem	Boron Deficiency p. 289
Leaves within cabbage heads and Brussels sprout buttons with small dark patches (internal browning)	Calcium Deficiency p. 286
Leaves with inter-veinal yellowing; usually on older leaves first	Manganese Deficiency p. 289
Leaves with inter-veinal yellowing giving pronounced marbled effect	Magnesium Deficiency p. 287
Leaves and/or stem with rough warty outgrowths	Oedema p. 297
Leaves variously affected with irregular yellowish or dark green patterns, crinkling and/or crumpling	Viruses p. 277
Leaves wilting, plants collapsing and dying, usually in dry weather after transplanting; white maggots feeding on roots	Cabbage Root Fly p. 150
Leaves infested by small white-winged insects and oval yellow scales, especially on undersides; leaves sticky and sooty	Cabbage Whitefly p. 103
Leaves infested by dense colonies of grey-green insects covered in white powdery wax	Cabbage Aphid p. 113
Leaves pecked and torn, often reduced to a skeleton of veins	Birds p. 179
Leaves of young plants with many small circular holes and pits	Flea Beetles p. 165
Leaves with irregular holes and pieces eaten away; caterpillars present, often eating into hearts	Cabbage Caterpillars p. 138
Leaves with fine white flecking, small elongate insects present	Thrips p. 129
Leaves with irregular holes eaten out, slime trails present on or near plants	Slugs and Snails p. 90
Heads with soft and slimy decay; usually no mould growth	Bacterial Soft Rot p. 234
Heads with soft rot and fluffy grey mould growth	Grey Mould Rot p. 236
Curds with dark internal patches	Downy Mildew p. 202 or Boron Deficiency p. 289 Former tends to give black patches and the latter brown
Curds fail to form	Blindness p. 297
Stem with dark internal patches (esp. cauliflower)	Boron Deficiency p. 289
Stem with rough warty outgrowths	Oedema p. 297 or

	Herbicide Damage p. 301
Stems eaten at soil level, plants collapsing and dying	Cutworms p. 136
Stems and roots with rounded irregular hollow outgrowths (galls) containing legless white larvae	Turnip Gall Weevil p. 169
Roots with irregular swellings not containing caterpillars or holes	Clubroot p. 223
Seedlings die, usually in patches. Roots and/or stem base rotted	Damping-off p. 243
Seedlings unthrifty and with tough wiry stems	Wirestem p. 243
Seedlings with yellow specks on upper leaf and cotyledon surfaces and off-white mould beneath	Downy Mildew p. 202
Plants run to flower	Bolting p. 297

Broad Beans. See **Beans**

Broccoli. See **Brassicas**

Brussels Sprouts. See **Brassicas**

Buddleia

Leaves narrowed, crumpled or otherwise distorted	Viruses p. 277
Leaves with small, tattered holes, especially on young shoots	Capsid Bugs p. 97
Leaves distorted, growth of young shoots checked, buds sometimes killed	Chrysanthemum Eelworm p. 86

Bulbocodium. See **Bulbs etc.**

Bulbs, Corms, Rhizomes and Tubers

Bulbs, corms, rhizomes and tubers should always be carefully examined before planting, to detect any signs of pests and diseases which might prove difficult to eradicate after planting. The most important symptoms at this stage are:

Bulbs feel soft when squeezed and show circles of brown discoloured tissues when cut across with a knife	Stem Eelworm p. 84
Bulbs feel soft when squeezed, rotting cavity in centre, often with fly maggot present	Large Narcissus Fly p. 152
Bulbs, corms, rhizomes or tubers otherwise soft and slimy	Bacterial Soft Rot p. 234
Bulbs, corms, rhizomes or tubers affected by decay; often with some mould growth present	Fungal Rot p. 231
Bulbs with red markings around necks and showing internal red discolouration of scales when cut across with knife	Tarsonemid Mites p. 176

The main symptoms appearing after planting are:

Leaves weak, distorted and discoloured, sometimes with small yellow bumps; flowers weak and distorted	Stem Eelworm p. 84
Leaves thin and grass-like; flowers weak and distorted	Large Narcissus Fly p. 152
Bulbs, corms, rhizomes or tubers with irregular holes and pieces eaten away below and above ground; slime trails present	Slugs p. 90
Bulbs, corms, rhizomes or tubers with small round holes; long, narrow, yellow insect larvae present	Wireworms p. 163
Bulbs and bases of stems eaten, stems sometimes severed at ground level; caterpillars in soil	Cutworms p. 136

Bulbs, corms, rhizomes or tubers with base and roots rotted with matted dark strands — Violet Root Rot p. 241

Corms and rhizomes eaten; small C-shaped, legless white larvae present — Vine Weevil p. 170

Plants fail to flower — Blindness p. 297

Also see separate entries under main plant genera

Busy Lizzie. See **Impatiens**

Buxus (Box). Also see **Trees** and **Hedges**

Leaves at tips of shoots forming tight clusters, like miniature cabbages — Box Sucker p. 101

Cabbage. See **Brassicas**

Cacti and Succulents

These plants are generally trouble-free, providing they are well grown in good conditions. They can survive long periods of drought but may be damaged by over-watering, which encourages rotting of soft tissues (see p. 252). The main pests are those that commonly affect **Glasshouse and House Plants** (p. 47) and the commonest disorder is the rough warty condition of stems and/or leaves brought about by Oedema (p. 297).

Calceolaria

Leaves irregularly mottled — Viruses p. 277

Plants grown indoors in houses and glasshouses are likely to be attacked by pests of **Glasshouse and House Plants** (see p. 47) and those grown outdoors may be affected by the main groups of pests attacking **Alpine Plants** (p. 20) and **Bedding Plants** (p. 27).

Calendula. Also see **Bedding Plants**

Leaves and/or other parts with powdery white coating — Powdery Mildew p. 204

Leaves with circular, gradually darkening spots — Smuts p. 199

Stems with irregular swellings — Crown Gall p. 224

Callistephus (China aster). Also see **Bedding Plants**

Leaves wilt; stem interior with brown or black streaks — Wilt p. 211

Leaves with irregular mottling and yellowing; flowers malformed — Viruses p. 277

Calluna (Heather)

Stem and branches with irregular, small, usually greyish growths — Lichen p. 273

Stem and branches overgrown with leafless, twining, reddish shoots — Dodder p. 275

Stem and branches die back; leaves sparse and yellowed; some death of roots, especially older ones close to stem — Phytophthora Root Death p. 251

Shoots grazed — Rabbits p. 183

Camellia

Leaves and/or flowers and buds scorched or killed suddenly — Frost p. 292

Leaves more or less bleached; veins remain dark green — Iron Deficiency p. 288

Leaves and/or shoots with rough warty outgrowths — Oedema p. 297

Leaves with irregular mottling — Viruses p. 277

Leaves with flat yellow or brown scales on undersides, often sticky and sooty on upper surfaces — Scale Insects p. 124

Flowers pecked and torn — Birds p. 179

Stems infested by wingless insects covered in white wax powder and filaments; leaves often sticky and sooty	Mealybugs p. 127
Roots eaten by C-shaped, white legless grubs	Vine Weevil p. 170

Campanula

Leaves and shoots with irregular holes, slime trails present on or near plants	Slugs and Snails p. 90
Leaves with irregular yellowish mosaic and distortion	Viruses p. 277
Stem rotted at base; white cottony mould present	Sclerotinia Disease p. 247
Stems and shoots with small masses of froth covering wingless insects	Froghoppers p. 98

Capsicum (Pepper)

Fruit with dark, toughened areas at blossom end (blossom end rot)	Calcium Deficiency p. 286
Leaves and/or stem with rough warty outgrowths	Oedema p. 297
Leaves discoloured, bronzing and drying, numerous small mites on undersides	Glasshouse Red Spider Mites p. 173
Leaves and shoots infested by small insects; leaves sometimes sticky and sooty	Aphids p. 104

Caraway

Stem rotted at base; white cottony mould present	Sclerotinia Disease p. 247

Carnation. See **Dianthus**

Carpinus (Hornbeam). Also see **Trees**

Carrot

Leaves reddened and with fine yellowish mottling; plants stunted	Viruses p. 277
Leaves infested by small green insects, foliage sometimes distorted and discoloured	Willow-Carrot Aphid p. 114
Root tunnelled by maggots, often with secondary rotting; foliage discoloured, growth stunted	Carrot Fly p. 149
Roots with larger holes eaten in them, grey-brown or white caterpillars in soil	Cutworms p. 136 Swift Moth p. 137
Roots with elongate crater-like spots (cavity spot)	Calcium Deficiency p. 286
Roots split	Splitting p. 298
Roots with soft and slimy rot	Bacterial Soft Rot p. 234
Roots (in store) with white cottony mould growth	Sclerotinia Disease p. 247
Roots decayed and with matted dark strands to which soil adheres	Violet Root Rot p. 241

Caryopteris

Leaves with small ragged holes, especially at tips of shoots	Capsid Bugs p. 97

Castanea (Sweet Chestnut). Also see **Trees**

Leaves yellow and wilt in absence of root damage	Wilt p. 211

Branches die back, leaves sparse and yellowed; tissue at stem base may be blackened and decayed — Phytophthora Root Death p. 251

Catalpa (Indian bean-tree). Also see **Trees**

Leaves turn yellow and wilt in absence of root damage — Wilt p. 211

Cattleya. See **Orchids**

Cauliflower. See **Brassicas**

Ceanothus. Also see **Trees**

Leaves and/or flowers scorched or killed — Frost p. 292

Leaves more or less bleached; veins remain dark green — Iron Deficiency p. 288

Stems with brown or white scales, leaves sticky and sooty — Scale Insects p. 127

Cedar (Cedrus). See **Conifers** and **Trees.**

Cedrus (Cedar, deodar). See **Conifers** and **Trees**

Celeriac. See **Celery**

Celery, Celeriac

Leaves irregularly mottled or yellowed and crumpled — Viruses p. 277

Leaves variously spotted — Leaf Spot p. 258

Leaves yellowed; leaf stalks discoloured and split; no root damage — Boron Deficiency p. 289

Leaves with yellow-brown blotch mines — Celery Fly p. 149

Stalks with irregular pieces eaten out, slime trails present — Slugs p. 90

Plants collapsing, stems eaten through at soil level — Cutworms p. 136

Plants collapsing, roots and bases of stems tunnelled by maggots — Carrot Fly p. 149

Leaf stalks with soft and slimy decay — Bacterial Soft Rot p. 234

Leaf stalks with soft rot at base and white cottony mould growth — Sclerotinia Disease p. 247

Leaf stalks rotted and with patches of fluffy grey mould growth — Grey Mould Rot p. 236

Leaf stalks split but not discoloured — Splitting p. 298

Leaf stalks split and with brownish patches; leaves yellowed — Boron Deficiency p. 289

Leaf stalks and centre of crown blackened (black heart) — Calcium Deficiency p. 286

Roots and stem base rotted and/or with black lesions below soil level — Root Rot p. 242

Roots decayed with matted dark strands — Violet Root Rot p. 241

Seedlings die in patches — Damping-off p. 243

Plants run to flower — Bolting p. 297

Centaurea

Leaves and/or other parts with powdery white coating — Powdery Mildew p. 204

Leaves with pale yellowish patches and whitish mould growth beneath — Lettuce Downy Mildew p. 202

Cercis (Judas tree). Also see **Trees**

Branches die back; masses of small, usually pink pustules present — Coral Spot p. 216

Chaenomeles (Japanese Quince)

Symptom	Cause
Leaves with irregular yellowish streaks and patterns and/or crumpled	Viruses p. 277
Leaves more or less bleached; veins remain dark green	Iron Deficiency p. 288
Flowers pecked and torn	Birds p. 179
Shoots exude slime and die back; flowers and/or leaves may shrivel	Fireblight p. 217

Chamaecyparis (False Cypress). For true cypresses see **Cupressus.** Also see **Conifers** and **Trees**

Symptom	Cause
Leaves yellowed and sparse; shoots may die back; roots close to stem base may die and patches of dead bark develop on stem	Phytophthora Root Death p. 251

Cheiranthus (Wallflower). Also see **Trees**

Symptom	Cause
Flowers of dark coloured types with pale streaks; leaves may be malformed	Viruses p. 277
Leaves with brownish angular patches and greyish mould growth beneath	Downy Mildew p. 202
Leaves wilted; stem interior with brown or black streaks	Wilt p. 211
Leaves and/or other parts with small, often concentric clusters of creamy droplets	White Blister p. 210
Leaves and shoots eaten, slime trails present on and near plants	Slugs p. 90
Leaves of young plants with numerous small round holes and pits	Flea Beetles p. 165
Leaves with irregular holes	Caterpillars p. 132
Plants collapsing, roots eaten by maggots	Cabbage Root Fly p. 150
Stem with irregular swellings	Crown Gall p. 224
Roots with irregular swellings not containing larvae or holes	Clubroot p. 223

Cherry (fruiting and flowering ornamental). Also see **Trees**

Symptom	Cause
Fruit eaten when ripe	Birds p. 179
Fruit with soft brown rot and usually off-white cottony pustules	Brown Rot p. 235
Fruit with dark green, velvety spots	Scab p. 228
Fruit split	Splitting p. 298
Flower buds eaten in winter, branches with bare lengths devoid of flowers in spring	Bullfinch p. 179
Flowers and/or leaves scorched or killed suddenly	Frost p. 292
Leaves scorched and/or killed suddenly in spring	Frost p. 292
Leaves with dark green, velvety spots	Scab p. 228
Leaves curled and reddened in early summer	Leaf Curl p. 222
Leaves at tips of shoots tightly curled and infested by colonies of black insects; foliage sticky and sooty	Cherry Blackfly p. 111
Leaves with irregular holes and pieces eaten away	Caterpillars p. 132
Leaves wilt in absence of root damage or other stress	Wilt p. 211
Leaves with silvery sheen; branches may die back	Silver Leaf p. 221
Leaves and/or other parts with sticky black coating	Sooty Mould p. 209
Leaves more or less bleached; veins remain dark green	Iron Deficiency p. 288
Leaves with yellow-brown blotches; later wither and remain hanging on tree over winter	Leaf Scorch p. 264

Leaves with more or less regular holes	Peach Shot Hole p. 268
Leaves with irregular patterns or variously malformed	Viruses p. 277
Leaves wither and tip of terminal shoot droops	Wither Tip p. 235
Branches die back in absence of stem lesions; leaves silvery	Silver Leaf p. 221
Branches die back; root and stem base decayed; toadstools and bootlace-like strands may be present	Honey Fungus p. 249
Branches and/or stem oozing gum; may be some dieback and also spotting and holes in leaves	Bacterial Canker p. 218
Branches otherwise dying back	Diebacks p. 214
Branches with masses of proliferating shoots	Witches' Brooms p. 227
Stem with decay at base; toadstools and/or bootlace-like strands may be present and branches die back	Honey Fungus p. 249
Stem with hard irregular swelling	Crown Gall p. 224
Trees generally unthrifty	Deficiencies of Nitrogen p. 284 Phosphorus p. 285 and Potassium p. 285

Chestnut. See **Castanea.** For **Horse Chestnut** see **Aesculus**

Chicory

Leaves and crown blackened and stunted	Calcium Deficiency p. 286
Plants wilted; stem rotted at base; white cottony mould present	Sclerotinia Disease p. 247

China Aster. See **Callistephus**

Chinese Cabbage. See **Brassicas**

Chionodoxa. Also see **Bulbs etc.**

Chives

See **Onion**; many of the problems on onions affect chives also

Chlorophytum (Spider plant)

Also see **Glasshouse and House Plants**

Leaves with brown, dead tips – a common problem of unknown origin but see	Dry Air p. 291

Christmas Rose. See **Helleborus**

Christmas Tree. See **Picea**

Chrysanthemum (including glasshouse Chrysanthemums and Marguerite). Also see **Bedding Plants** and **Perennials**

Many different pests, diseases and disorders affect chrysanthemums, especially those that are grown for exhibition, either outdoors or indoors, and those that are grown as decorative glasshouse and house plants. Much published information is available on these popular plants and in Britain the National Chrysanthemum Society publishes a booklet dealing with the main pests and diseases.

Flowers with ragged holes eaten in petals	Earwigs p. 94
Flowers with large pieces eaten out of petals	Caterpillars p. 132

Symptom	Cause
Flowers discoloured, with fine light flecking; many small, narrow-bodied insects present	Thrips p. 129
Flowers malformed, flower buds sometimes killed	Capsid Bugs p. 97
Flowers and/or buds rotted and with fluffy grey mould growth	Grey Mould p. 232
Leaves with brown pustules beneath; pale yellowish spots above	Rust p. 191
Leaves with dirty-white pustules beneath; pale yellowish spots above	White Rust p. 191
Leaves and/or other parts with powdery white coating	Powdery Mildew p. 204
Leaves variously spotted with dark more or less circular lesions	Leaf Blotch p. 262
Leaves wilt; stem interior with brown or black streaks	Wilt p. 211
Leaves with brown or black areas between veins, older leaves dying	Chrysanthemum Eelworm p. 86
Leaves discoloured, bronzing and dying, many small mites on undersides	Glasshouse Red Spider Mites p. 173
Leaves with sinuous white mines	Chrysanthemum Leaf Miner p. 153
Leaves with irregular holes and pieces eaten away	Caterpillars p. 132
Leaves with small ragged holes, especially at tips of shoots, buds sometimes killed	Capsid Bugs p. 97
Leaves with small white winged insects on undersides, foliage sticky and sooty	Glasshouse Whitefly p. 102
Leaves, stems, buds and flowers infested by small winged and wingless green, yellow, brown or red insects; foliage sticky and sooty	Aphids p. 104
Shoots eaten when young, leaves with holes, slime trails present on or near plants	Slugs p. 90
Stem keels over at point of decay lesion; fluffy grey mould present	Stem Rot p. 252
Stem rotten, usually at base; cottony white mould present	Sclerotinia Disease p. 247
Stem with irregular swellings	Crown Gall p. 224
Plants generally unthrifty; roots blackened and/or decayed	Root and Foot Rots p. 242

Cineraria (*Senecio cruentus*). Also see **Glasshouse and House Plants**

Symptom	Cause
Leaves and/or other parts with powdery white coating	Powdery Mildew p. 204
Leaves with pale yellowish spots and whitish mould growth beneath	Lettuce Downy Mildew p. 202
Leaves and/or other parts with blisters and small orange and white pustules or cup-like bodies	Rust p. 191
Leaves variously spotted	Leaf Spot p. 258
Leaves, flowers, buds and stems infested by colonies of winged and wingless yellow, green or pink insects; foliage sticky and sooty	Aphids p. 104
Leaves with sinuous white mines	Chrysanthemum Leaf Miner p. 153
Leaves with small white winged insects on undersides; foliage sticky and sooty	Glasshouse Whitefly p. 102

Citrus. See **Glasshouse and House Plants**

Clematis. Also see **Climbing Plants**

Leaves and/or other parts with powdery white coating	Powdery Mildew p. 204
Leaves variously mottled or malformed	Viruses p. 277
Leaves wilt; shoots and entire plant may die back	Diebacks p. 214
Leaves sticky and sooty, leaves and stems infested by colonies of small wingless and winged insects	Aphids p. 104
Leaves sticky and sooty, stems and undersides of leaves infested by brown or yellow scales	Scale Insects p. 124
Leaves with small notches eaten out of edges	Weevils p. 168
Leaves with small ragged holes, especially at tips of shoots, buds sometimes killed	Capsid Bugs p. 97
Flowers with ragged holes eaten in petals	Earwigs p. 94
Shoots eaten at or just above soil level, leaves with irregular holes, slime trails present	Slugs and Snails p. 90

Climbing Plants

Temperatures are often slightly higher near walls, especially if these are part of a heated building, and plants climbing on them may be affected by some of the pests and diseases that attack **Glasshouse and House Plants** (p. 47). They may also be susceptible to drought if they are protected from prevailing winds and rain. Young plants are often attacked by **Slugs and Snails** (p. 90), **Earwigs** (p. 94) and **Woodlice** (p. 93) that thrive near walls, especially if there are many crevices and some accumulations of organic debris to shelter them. Some climbing plants such as Clematis, Honeysuckle and Ivy may themselves cause trouble if they are allowed to grow over other plants.

Cobnut. See **Corylus**

Codiaeum (Croton). See **Glasshouse and House Plants**

Colchicum (Autumn Crocus). See **Bulbs etc.**

Coleus. See **Glasshouse and House Plants**

Conifers

Most conifers are relatively free from pests and diseases. This may be partly due to the comparative toughness of their leaves and to the production of resin, which may repel pests and seal wounds. Young trees may need protection from **Deer** (p. 187), **Squirrels** (p. 184), **Rabbits** (p. 183), and **Voles** (p. 186), all of which can cause serious damage by stripping bark from the base of stems. Older trees are mainly susceptible to attack by **Adelgids** (p. 120), a group of pests that is restricted to conifers, by some **Aphids** (p. 104) and by **Caterpillars** (p. 132) of moths and **Sawflies** (p. 154). The premature shedding of leaves occurs fairly commonly and is discussed under **Needle Casts** (p. 210) while the masses of proliferating shoots known as **Witches' Brooms** (p. 227) are also seen sometimes. Trunks of mature trees are often affected by a number of rotting diseases such as **Honey Fungus** (p. 249), while one of the commonest causes of death of cypresses in gardens is **Phytophthora Root Death** (p. 251). **Mistletoe** (p. 276) grows sometimes on conifers in parts of Europe while the growth of toadstools under trees is often an indication of the beneficial presence of **Mycorrhiza** (p. 276) on the roots.

Also see separate entries for the main plant genera and for **Trees**

Conophytum. See **Cacti and Succulents**

Convallaria (Lily-of-the-Valley)

Symptom	Cause
Leaves with soft brown region at base with mould growth	Paeony Grey Mould Blight p. 254
Rhizomes eaten by large white caterpillars	Swift Moths p. 137

Coreopsis. See **Bedding Plants** and **Perennials**

Corms. See **Bulbs etc.**

Cornflower. See **Centaurea**

Corylus (hazel, cobnut, filbert). Also see **Trees**

Symptom	Cause
Nuts cracked open and eaten	Squirrels p. 184
Leaves with powdery white coating	Powdery Mildew p. 204
Leaves with irregular holes and pieces eaten away	Caterpillars p. 132
Buds abnormally enlarged	Nut Gall Mite p. 178

Cosmos. See **Bedding Plants**

Cotinus

Symptom	Cause
Leaves wilt; stem interior with brown or black streaks	Wilt p. 211

Cotoneaster

Symptom	Cause
Fruits eaten	Birds p. 179
Leaves sticky and sooty, stems and leaves infested by brown or grey scales	Scale Insects p. 124
Leaves sticky and sooty, shoots infested by small wingless and winged insects	Aphids p. 104
Leaves with irregular holes, foliage sometimes drawn together with silk webbing	Caterpillars p. 132 esp. Hawthorn Webber p. 143
Shoots exude slime and die back; flowers and/or leaves shrivelled	Fireblight p. 217
Stems with tufts of white wax wool covering small dark wingless insects	Woolly Aphid p. 108

Courgette. See **Cucumber**

Crassula. Also see **Cacti and Succulents**

Symptom	Cause
Stem decayed	Stem Rot p. 252
Roots eaten by C-shaped white legless larvae	Vine Weevil p. 170

Crataegus (Hawthorn). Also see **Trees** and **Hedges**

Symptom	Cause
Leaves and/or other parts with powdery white coating	Powdery Mildew p. 204
Leaves silvery; branches may die back	Silver Leaf p. 221
Leaves with irregular holes and pieces eaten away	Caterpillars p. 132
Branches and/or stem with hard irregular swelling	Crown Gall p. 224
Branches and/or stem with canker lesions; may die back beyond lesion	Apple Canker p. 215
Branches with parasitic leathery plant growing from them	Mistletoe p. 276

Cress

Symptom	Cause
Seedlings die in patches	Damping-off p. 243

Crinum. Also see **Bulbs etc.**

Symptom	Cause
Leaves turn yellow and shrivel; young shoots and/or other parts with gradually spreading brown blotches	Narcissus Leaf Scorch p. 267

Crocosmia. See **Bulbs etc.**

Crocus. For **Autumn Crocus** see **Colchicum.** Also see **Bulbs etc.**

Shoots eaten off, often carried away	Squirrels p. 184 Mice p. 185
Leaves yellowed; sheaths decayed at ground level and masses of tiny black bodies present	Corm Rot p. 231

Croton (Codiaeum). See **Glasshouse and House Plants**

Cucumber (also Courgette, Marrow, Melon, Pumpkin, Squash and Zucchini)

These plants are most susceptible to pests when grown under glass in glasshouses or frames and are generally less likely to be attacked when grown in the open garden.

Fruit not formed or warty	Viruses p. 277
Fruit with sunken lesions	Anthracnose p. 222
Leaves and young shoots infested by colonies of green, yellow, pink or black winged and wingless insects; growth sometimes distorted, foliage sticky and sooty	Aphids p. 104
Leaves with small white winged insects on undersides; foliage sticky and sooty	Glasshouse Whitefly p. 102
Leaves discoloured, yellowing, bronzing and dying; many small mites on undersides, sometimes with fine silk webbing	Glasshouse Red Spider Mites p. 173
Leaves and/or other parts with powdery white coating	Powdery Mildew p. 204
Leaves wilt; stem interior with black or brown streaks	Wilt p. 211
Leaves crumpled and/or with irregular yellowish mottling	Viruses p. 277
Leaves and/or other parts thickened, twisted or otherwise distorted	Hormone Herbicide Injury p. 301
Leaves with very pale green, often translucent spots	Anthracnose p. 222
Stem with patches of soft rot and fluffy grey mould growth	Stem and Fruit Rots p. 252
Stem and/or other parts thickened, twisted or otherwise distorted	Hormone Herbicide Injury p. 301
Stem rotted at base; cottony white mould growth present	Sclerotinia Disease p. 247
Stem with soft irregular swelling	Crown Gall p. 224
Stem and/or other parts with soft and slimy rot; no mould growth	Bacterial Soft Rot p. 234
Roots decayed; sometimes with tough unaffected core; plants unthrifty	Black Root Rot or other Root and Foot Rots p. 242
Plants unthrifty, roots with irregular solid swellings	Root Knot Eelworm p. 88
Plants unthrifty; no stem lesions but roots decayed	Black Root Rot or other Root and Foot Rots p. 242
Plants wilt in absence of stem or root lesions	Drought p. 291
Plants more or less covered in slimy, cushion-like bodies of varying colour	Slime Mould p. 273

Cupressus (Cypress). Also see **Conifers** and **Trees**

Leaves yellowed and sparse; shoots may die back; roots close to stem may die and patches of dead bark develop on stem	Phytophthora Root Death p. 251

Currants (Black, Red and White)

Symptom	Cause
Fruits eaten as they ripen	Birds p. 179
Leaves sticky and sometimes sooty, often with red or yellow blisters and other distortions; small green or yellow wingless and winged insects present on undersides of leaves and on young shoots	Aphids p. 104
Leaves with small tattered holes, especially on younger leaves at tips of shoots	Capsid Bugs p. 97
Leaves at tips of shoots twisted, failing to develop normally	Blackcurrant Leaf Midge p. 146
Leaves scorched suddenly in spring	Frost p. 292
Leaves silvery; branches may die back	Silver Leaf p. 221
Leaves with small, irregular brownish spots or blotches	Leaf Spot p. 258
Leaves and/or other parts with deep orange or red pustules	Gooseberry Cluster-Cup Rust p. 196
Leaves and/or other parts with powdery white or felted brown coating	American Gooseberry Mildew p. 206
Leaves with inter-veinal yellowing	Manganese Deficiency p. 289
Buds abnormally enlarged in spring, dying later	Blackcurrant Gall Mite p. 178
Stems and branches infested by brown, waxy scales, sometimes with conspicuous tufts of white wax wool	Scale Insects p. 124
Branches die back; leaves with silver sheen	Silver Leaf p. 221
Branches die back; may be toadstools and bootlace-like strands at stem base; root decayed close to stem	Honey Fungus p. 249
Branches die back; masses of small, usually pink pustules present	Coral Spot p. 216
Branches die back in absence of lesions or other damage	Grey Mould Dieback p. 220
Branches and/or stem with hard, irregular swelling	Crown Gall p. 224

Cyclamen

Hardy outdoor cyclamen are not seriously affected by pests, diseases or disorders, although they may suffer from some of the conditions noted under **Alpine and Rock Garden Plants.** For conditions affecting pot cyclamen also see **Glasshouse and House Plants** and **Bulbs etc.**

Symptom	Cause
Flowers and/or buds shrivelled and with fluffy grey mould	Grey Mould p. 232
Leaves wilt; stem interior with black or brown streaks	Wilt p. 211
Corm with soft and slimy rot	Bacterial Soft Rot p. 234
Plants unthrifty; roots decayed	Root and Foot Rots p. 242

Cymbidium. See **Orchids**

Cypress. See **Chamaecyparis** and **Cupressus**

Cypripedium. See **Orchids**

Daffodil. See **Narcissus**

Dahlia

Symptom	Cause
Flowers and/or buds shrivelled and with fluffy grey mould growth	Grey Mould p. 232
Flowers with tattered petals	Earwigs p. 94
Flowers with light flecking on petals, many small long-bodied winged and wingless insects present	Thrips p. 129
Leaves with numerous pale spots	Smuts p. 199
Leaves variously crumpled or with irregular, pale yellowish patterns	Viruses p. 277
Leaves wilt; stem interior with brown or black streaks	Wilt p. 211
Leaves with irregular holes and pieces eaten away; no slime trails present on or near plants	Caterpillars p. 132
Leaves with irregular holes and pieces eaten away; slime trails present on or near plants	Slugs and Snails p. 90
Leaves with small tattered holes, especially at tips of shoots; buds sometimes killed and flowers distorted	Capsid Bugs p. 97
Leaves discoloured, yellowing, bronzing and dying; many small mites on undersides of leaves and sometimes on dry shoots, with fine silk webbing	Glasshouse Red Spider Mites p. 173
Leaves, shoots and flowers infested by colonies of black, green or yellow wingless and winged insects; foliage sticky and sometimes sooty	Aphids p. 104
Stem with soft, irregular swelling	Crown Gall p. 224
Stem base rotted; cottony white mould growth present	Sclerotinia Disease p. 247

Damson. See **Plum**

Daphne

Symptom	Cause
Leaves and young shoots infested by colonies of small winged and wingless insects; leaves sticky	Aphids p. 104

Datura. See **Glasshouse and House Plants**

Day Lily. See **Hemerocallis**

Delphinium (including Larkspur)

Symptom	Cause
Leaves and/or other parts with powdery white coating	Powdery Mildew p. 204
Leaves with bituminous black blotches in absence of stem rot	Black Blotch p. 271
Leaves and flowers with irregular holes and pieces eaten away	Caterpillars p. 132 Earwigs p. 94
Leaves and young shoots eaten; slime trails present on or near plants	Slugs and Snails p. 90
Leaves, shoots and flowers infested by yellow, green or pink wingless and winged insects; foliage sticky, sometimes sooty	Aphids p. 104
Leaves variously crumpled or with irregular yellowish patterns	Viruses p. 277
Stem base rotted; cottony white mould growth present	Sclerotinia Disease p. 247
Stem base and/or roots rotted	Root and Foot Rots p. 242
Roots eaten by large white caterpillars in soil	Swift Moths p. 137

Dendrobium. See **Orchids**

Deodar. See **Cedrus**

Dewberry. See **Blackberry**

Dianthus (Carnations, pinks and sweet williams). Also see **Glasshouse and House Plants**

Symptom	Cause
Flowers distorted; anthers filled with dark powdery mass	Carnation Anther Smut p. 200
Flowers, flower buds and young shoots eaten and spun together with fine silk webbing; caterpillars usually present	Carnation Tortrix Moth p. 142
Flower petals with light flecking, sometimes withering, small narrow-bodied insects present	Thrips p. 129
Flowers, buds, leaves and stems infested by colonies of yellow, green or dark-coloured wingless and winged insects; foliage sticky and sooty	Aphids p. 104
Leaves with small yellow-brown pustules	Rust p. 191 (Carnation)
Leaves and/or other parts with powdery white coating	Powdery Mildew p. 204
Leaves distorted and/or with irregular yellowish mottling	Viruses p. 277
Leaves wilt; stem interior with brown or black streaks	Wilt p. 211
Leaves discoloured, yellowing, bronzing and dying; many small mites present, sometimes with fine silk webbing	Glasshouse Red Spider Mites p. 173
Roots rotted; plants unthrifty	Root and Foot Rots p. 242
Plants unthrifty, roots infested by small white wingless insects	Root Aphids p. 120

Digitalis (Foxglove)

Symptom	Cause
Leaves and/or other parts with powdery white coating	Powdery Mildew p. 204

Dogwood. See **Cornus**

Doronicum

Symptom	Cause
Leaves and/or other parts with powdery white coating	Powdery Mildew p. 204

Egg Plant. See **Aubergine**

Elaeagnus. Also see **Trees**

Symptom	Cause
Branches die back; masses of small, usually pink pustules present	Coral Spot p. 216

Elderberry. See **Sambucus**

Elm. See **Ulmus**

Epiphyllum. See **Cacti and Succulents** and **Glasshouse and House Plants**

Eranthis (Winter Aconite)

Symptom	Cause
Flowers and flower buds pecked	Birds p. 179
Flowers, flower buds, leaves and stems infested by small insects; foliage sticky and sooty	Aphids p. 104

Erica (Heath, Heather)

Symptom	Cause
Leaves and young shoots grazed	Rabbits p. 183

Symptom	Cause
Stem and branches with irregular, small, usually greyish growths	Lichen p. 273
Stem and branches die back; leaves sparse and yellowed; some death of roots, especially older ones close to stem	Phytophthora Root Death p. 251

Escallonia

Symptom	Cause
Leaves with various irregular pale streaks and mottles or distortions	Viruses p. 277

Eucalyptus. Also see **Trees**

Symptom	Cause
Leaves and/or shoots scorched or killed	Frost p. 292

Euonymus. Also see **Trees**

Symptom	Cause
Leaves and/or other parts with powdery white coating	Powdery Mildew p. 204
Leaves with yellowish mosaic or mottle patterns	Viruses p. 277
Stem with hard, irregular swelling	Crown Gall p. 224
Leaves, shoots and young stems infested by small black insects; foliage sticky and sooty	Black Bean Aphid p. 112

Euphorbia (including **Poinsettia**). See **Glasshouse and House Plants**

Fagus (Beech). Also see **Trees**

Symptom	Cause
Leaves scorched in early spring	Frost p. 292
Leaves yellowed and sparse; shoots may die back; roots close to stem may die and patches of dead bark develop	Phytophthora Root Death p. 251
Leaves with irregular holes and pieces eaten away	Caterpillars p. 132 Weevils p. 168
Leaves mined, browning and curling	Weevils p. 168
Leaves with tufts of white wax wool on undersides covering yellow-green insects; foliage sticky and sooty	Beech Aphid p. 119
Leaves with small yellow or green active winged and wingless insects on undersides	Leafhoppers p. 98
Branches die back; masses of usually pink pustules present	Coral Spot p. 216
Stems and trunks with conspicuous areas of white wax wool covering minute insects	Beech Scale p. 126
Roots close to stem die; patches of dead bark on stem; shoots may die back and leaves become yellowed and sparse	Phytophthora Root Death p. 251

Fatsia. See **Glasshouse and House Plants**

Ferns

Ferns growing outdoors are generally free from serious troubles but ferns growing in glasshouses and houses may be affected by some of the pests, diseases and disorders of **Glasshouse and House Plants** (p. 47). Variously-coloured, but usually brown pustules on the fronds (not to be confused with the fern spore masses which are also brown but usually regularly arranged) occur fairly commonly and are the symptoms of **Rust** (p. 191).

Fern (Asparagus). See **Glasshouse and House Plants**

Ficus (Rubber Plant). See **Glasshouse and House Plants**

Fig. Also see **Trees**

Fruit rotted and with fluffy grey mould growth	Grey Mould Rot p. 236
Leaves scorched in spring	Frost p. 292
Leaves with irregular yellow-green blotches	Viruses p. 277
Branches die back; masses of small, usually pink pustules present	Coral Spot p. 216

Filbert. See **Corylus**

Fir. For true firs see **Abies**; for Douglas Fir see **Pseudotsuga**

Flag. See **Acorus**

Forget-Me-Not. See **Myosotis**

Forsythia

Flowers and flower buds pecked	Birds p. 179
Leaves with small ragged holes, especially at tips of shoots	Capsid Bugs p. 97
Leaves with yellowish banding along veins; may be some distortion	Viruses p. 277
Shoots with firm irregular swellings	Gall p. 224

Foxglove. See **Digitalis**

Fraxinus (Ash). Also see **Trees**

Leaves with irregular yellowish streaks and patterns	Viruses p. 277
Stems encrusted by colonies of white scales; foliage sticky and sometimes very sooty	Willow Scale p. 126
Trees overgrown with evergreen climbing plant	Ivy p. 275

Freesia. Also see **Bulbs** and **Glasshouse and House Plants**

Flowers and/or buds shrivel; fluffy grey mould growth present	Grey Mould p. 232
Flowers, flower buds, stems and leaves infested by small insects; foliage sticky, sometimes sooty	Aphids p. 104
Flowers and leaves with large irregular holes; slime trails present on or near plants	Slugs p. 90
Flowers and leaves with large irregular holes; no slime trails present	Caterpillars p. 132
Leaves discoloured; many small mites present on undersides	Glasshouse Red Spider Mites p. 173
Leaves with rows of tiny white flecks	Viruses p. 277
Leaves with gradually enlarging brown or other coloured spots	Iris Leaf Spot p. 266

Fritillary (Fritillaria). See **Bulbs etc.**

Fuchsia

Symptom	Cause
Leaves with small winged insects and yellow scales on undersides; foliage sticky and sooty	Glasshouse Whitefly p. 102
Leaves and stems infested by green, yellow or pink wingless and winged insects; foliage sticky and sooty	Aphids p. 104
Leaves discoloured, yellowing, bronzing and dying; many small mites on undersides of leaves	Glasshouse Red Spider Mites p. 173
Leaves with small tattered holes, especially at tips of young shoots	Capsid Bugs p. 97

Gaillardia

Symptom	Cause
Leaves with pale yellowish spots and whitish mould beneath	Lettuce Downy Mildew p. 202

Galanthus (including Snowdrop). Also see **Bulbs etc.**

Symptom	Cause
Flowers pecked and torn	Birds p. 179
Leaves turn yellow and shrivel; young shoots and/or other parts with gradually spreading brown blotches	Narcissus Leaf Scorch p. 267
Leaves turn yellow and decay at ground level where masses of tiny black bodies are present on them	Bulb Rot p. 231
Leaves become brown and rotten; plants stunted and fail to flower; bulbs turn soft and pulpy	Grey Mould Blight p. 218
Bulbs with many small sunken lesions, visible when scales removed	Bulb Rot p. 231

Galtonia. Also see **Bulbs etc.**

Symptom	Cause
Leaves with fine mottling of white and green	Viruses p. 277

Garlic. See **Onion**

Gerbera

Symptom	Cause
Flowers and leaves with large irregular holes; slime trails on or near plants	Slugs p. 90
Leaves, flower buds and shoots infested by small yellow, green, pink or dark-coloured wingless and winged insects; foliage sticky and sooty	Aphids p. 104
Leaves with small white winged insects on undersides; foliage sticky and sooty	Glasshouse Whitefly p. 102
Stem and/or roots rotted; plants unthrifty	Root and Foot Rots p. 242

Gladiolus. Also see **Bulbs etc.**

Symptom	Cause
Flowers with disrupted colour pattern	Viruses p. 277
Flowers and leaves discoloured, with light flecking, later withering and dying; many small narrow-bodied insects present, especially under leaf bases	Gladiolus Thrips p. 130
Leaves, flowers, buds and shoots infested by small black, green or yellow wingless and winged insects; foliage sticky and sooty	Aphids p. 104
Leaves and flowers with irregular holes; slime trails present on or near plants	Slugs and Snails p. 90
Leaves and flowers with irregular holes; no slime trails present	Caterpillars p. 132
Leaves variously streaked or mottled with pale markings	Viruses p. 277

Leaves with gradually enlarging brown spots	Iris Leaf Spot p. 266
Leaves turn yellow and decay at ground level where masses of tiny black bodies are present on them	Corm Rots p. 231
Corms with rounded pale yellow spots	Corm Rots p. 231
Roots eaten by white caterpillars in soil	Swift Moths p. 137

Glasshouse and House Plants

The special conditions in which glasshouse and house plants are grown favour many pests and some diseases. Some of the pests are native species that thrive when they are protected from extremes of climate and from the predators and parasites that attack them outdoors and some are species that have been accidentally introduced from tropical and sub-tropical countries, usually without the parasites and predators that check them in their original environment. High temperatures and humidities may also encourage the development and spread of diseases and, in addition, pot-grown plants are especially liable to drought, waterlogging, and other disorders. During winter, plants may be chilled or frosted if temperatures fall too low and in summer they may be scorched by strong sun if not adequately shaded.

Good hygiene and careful routine inspection of plants can prevent much trouble and, if chemicals must be used, it is generally easier to treat glasshouse and house plants than it is to treat outdoor plants. Fumigation is effective in glasshouses, providing they are reasonably air-tight, and biological control of some pests may also be feasible. The following key can be used to identify the main causes of trouble:

Plants infested by small, wingless and winged, green, yellow, brown or black insects, often in dense colonies on leaves, young shoots, stems, buds and flowers; plants sticky, often sooty, growth checked and sometimes distorted	Aphids p. 104
Plants infested by small, white, winged insects, especially on undersides of young leaves; plants sticky, sometimes sooty	Glasshouse Whitefly p. 102
Plants infested by soft-bodied, wingless insects covered in white wax powder and filaments, often forming clusters in leaf axils and on stems; plants sticky, sometimes sooty	Glasshouse Mealybugs p. 127
Plants infested by brown, yellow or white, flat or raised scales, especially on undersides of leaves and also on stems; foliage sticky, sometimes sooty	Scale Insects p. 124
Plants infested by small winged and wingless yellow-green insects feeding on undersides of leaves and causing coarse light mottling on upper surfaces; empty moult skins often remain attached to leaves	Glasshouse Leafhoppers p. 99
Plants infested by small green or red-brown mites, especially on undersides of leaves; fine light flecking on upper surfaces later turns yellow and leaves may dry out and die; fine silk webbing may cover affected parts	Glasshouse Red Spider Mites p. 173
Plants infested by narrow-bodied yellow, brown or black wingless and winged insects, especially on leaves and in flower buds and flowers; leaves and flowers with fine white flecking and other discolourations	Thrips p. 129

Symptom	Cause
Plants with irregular holes and pieces eaten out of leaves and flowers; stems and buds sometimes damaged; slime trails present on or near plants	Slugs and Snails p. 90
Plants with irregular holes and pieces eaten out of leaves, buds and flowers; tips of shoots sometimes drawn together with fine silk webbing; no slime trails present	Caterpillars p. 132
Plants with young growth distorted; leaves sometimes thickened and curled, buds killed and flowers disfigured; very small brown mites and white eggs present in buds and growing points	Tarsonemid Mites p. 176
Plants with roots, corms or tubers eaten by C-shaped legless grubs, especially in pots	Vine Weevil p. 170
Plants with roots developing irregular hard swelling, sometimes affecting most of root system; plants growing poorly	Root Knot Eelworm p. 88
Plants with many small dark flies running over surface of soil or potting medium; white, legless larvae with dark heads sometimes present among roots and at bases of stems	Sciarid Flies p. 147
Plants with minute, wingless insects jumping from surface of soil or potting compost, especially when plants are grown in pots	Springtails p. 94
Flowers and/or buds fail to form or drop prematurely	See under Drought p. 291
Flowers and/or buds rotten with fluffy grey mould growth present	Grey Mould p. 232
Leaves generally dull; later wilted, toughened and turning brown	Drought p. 291
Leaves yellowed; sometimes with dry angular blotches and generally stunted; roots may become rotten	Waterlogging p. 295 but see also Root and Foot Rots p. 242 and Light p. 294
Leaves and/or other parts with powdery white coating	Powdery Mildew p. 204
Leaves and/or other parts rotten and bearing fluffy grey mould growth	Grey Mould (Follow guidelines on p. 232)
Leaves variously spotted or malformed	See Leaf Spot p. 258 and discussion under Localised Pollutants p. 299
Also check Plates 21–22 giving symptoms of	Mineral Nutrient Deficiency
Roots rotten; plants generally unthrifty	Root and Foot Rots p. 242

Also see **Cockroaches** (p. 95) and **Woodlice** (p. 93), which are sometimes troublesome in glasshouses and see separate entries for important plants **(Begonia, Chrysanthemum, Senecio (Cineraria), Dianthus, Freesia, Fuchsia, Primula, Rhododendron (Azalea), Saintpaulia).**

Globe Artichoke

Symptom	Cause
Flower heads shrivelled and with fluffy grey mould growth	Grey Mould p. 232
Leaves with pale yellowish spots and whitish mould growth beneath	Lettuce Downy Mildew p. 203

Globe Flower. See **Trollius**

Gloxinia. See **Sinningia**

Godetia

Symptom	Cause
Leaves of seedlings and young plants with small holes and pits	Flea Beetles p. 165
Leaves wilt; stem interior with brown or black streaks	Wilt p. 211

Golden Rod. See **Solidago**

Gooseberry

Symptom	Cause
Fruit rotted and with fluffy grey mould growth	Grey Mould Rot p. 236
Fruit scorched following hot weather	High Temperature Injury p. 294
Flowers die suddenly; leaves may be scorched	Frost p. 292
Buds pecked out during winter and early spring	Birds p. 179
Leaves with irregular holes and pieces eaten away, sometimes stripped to veins	Gooseberry Sawfly p. 156 Magpie Moth p. 135
Leaves and shoot tips infested by small grey-green insects; leaves curled	Gooseberry Aphid p. 112
Leaves with small tattered holes, especially at tips of shoots	Capsid Bugs p. 97
Leaves and/or other parts with orange or red pustules	Cluster-Cup Rust p. 196
Leaves and/or other parts with powdery white or felted brown coating	American Mildew p. 206
Leaves with pale yellow banding along veins	Viruses p. 277
Leaves scorched suddenly in spring	Frost p. 292
Leaves silvery; branches may die back	Silver Leaf p. 221
Leaves variously spotted	Currant Leaf Spot p. 265
Leaves with inter-veinal yellowing	Manganese Deficiency p. 289
Branches die back; leaves with silvery sheen	Silver Leaf p. 221
Branches die back in absence of lesions or other damage	Grey Mould Dieback p. 218
Branches die back; masses of small, usually pink pustules present	Coral Spot p. 216
Branches and/or stem with hard, irregular swelling	Crown Gall p. 224
Branches die back; may be toadstools and bootlace-like strands at stem base; root decayed close to stem	Honey Fungus p. 249

Gorse. See **Ulex**

Grape Hyacinth. See **Muscari**

Grape-Vine

Symptom	Cause
Fruits partially eaten as they ripen; skin punctured and contents removed	Wasps p. 161
Fruit rotted and with fluffy grey mould growth present	Grey Mould Rot p. 236
Fruit with pale pustules and some rotting	Bitter Rot p. 234
Fruit scorched after hot weather or when close to glass in glasshouse	High Temperature Injury p. 294
Flowers killed suddenly; leaves may be scorched	Frost p. 292

Leaves and/or other parts with powdery white coating	Powdery Mildew p. 204
Leaves with rough, warty outgrowths on undersides	Oedema p. 297
Leaves discoloured, yellowing, bronzing and dying, sometimes falling prematurely; many small mites on undersides	Glasshouse Red Spider Mites p. 173
Leaves showing red discolourations, followed by rapid collapse and death of plants; small yellow insects on roots (extremely rare in Britain)	Vine Phylloxera p. 123
Leaves and stems infested by yellow and brown waxy scales; foliage sticky and sooty	Scale Insects p. 124
Stems with clusters of soft-bodied wingless insects covered in white wax powder and filaments; foliage sticky and sooty	Glasshouse Mealybugs p. 127
Shoots with rough, warty outgrowths	Oedema p. 297
Stem with hard, irregular swelling	Crown Gall p. 224
Stem with toadstools and/or bootlace-like strands at base; roots close to stem may be decayed and branches die back	Honey Fungus p. 249
Roots decayed close to stem; toadstools and/or bootlace-like strands may be present	Honey Fungus p. 249

Gypsophila

Stem rotted at base; cottony white mould growth present	Sclerotinia Disease p. 247

Hawthorn. See **Crataegus**

Hazel Nuts. See **Corylus**

Heaths and Heathers. See **Erica** and **Calluna**

Hebe. See **Veronica**

Hedera (Ivy). Also see **Climbing Plants** and **Glasshouse and House Plants**

Leaves spotted	Leaf Spot p. 258

Hedges

Most hedging plants are sufficiently robust to be little affected by pests, although they may be regularly infested by **Caterpillars** (p. 132), **Aphids** (p. 104), **Leafhoppers** (p. 98) and other groups of pests. Some diseases may be more prevalent in hedges, since close contact of roots and other parts may favour rapid transmission. Diseases commonly affected by this type of transmission, which results in death of patches of the hedge while the remainder stays healthy, are **Honey Fungus** (p. 249) and **Phytophthora Root Death** (p. 251). Leakage of pollutants, such as gas from an underground source or the dumping of road salt on streets, can give rise to similar effects (see p. 299).

Also see separate entries for the main plant genera.

Helenium

Leaves and shoots distorted; leaf blades narrowed and curled	Stem Eelworm p. 84
Leaves drawn together at tips of shoots with fine silk webbing protecting small caterpillars	Tortrix Moths p. 142
Shoots and leaves eaten when young; slime trails present on or near plants	Slugs and Snails p. 90
Leaves wilt; stem interior with brown or black streaks	Wilt p. 211

Helianthus (Sunflower)

Symptom	Cause
Flowers shrivelled and with fluffy grey mould growth present	Grey Mould p. 232
Leaves at base of plants with irregular holes and pieces eaten away, sometimes reduced to a skeleton of veins; slime trails present on or near plants	Slugs and Snails p. 90
Stem rotted at base; cottony white mould growth present	Sclerotinia Disease p. 247

Helichrysum

Symptom	Cause
Leaves with pale yellowish spots and whitish mould growth beneath	Lettuce Downy Mildew p. 202

Helleborus (including Christmas rose)

Symptom	Cause
Flowers and leaves infested by pale green insects; leaves sticky, sometimes sooty	Aphids p. 104
Leaves with large, more or less circular, concentrically marked brown blotches	Leaf Spot p. 258

Hemerocallis (Day Lily)

Symptom	Cause
Leaves with gradually enlarging brown spots	Iris Leaf Spot p. 266

Hemlock. See **Tsuga**

Herbs. See entries for main plant genera

Hibiscus. See **Glasshouse and House Plants**

Hippeastrum. See **Glasshouse and House Plants**

Holly. See **Ilex**

Hollyhock. See **Althaea**

Honeysuckle. See **Lonicera**

Hornbeam. See **Carpinus**

Horse Chestnut. See **Aesculus**

Horse Radish

Symptom	Cause
Leaves and/or other parts with small, often concentric clusters of creamy droplets	White Blister p. 210
Leaves with large, yellow blotches or yellowish mosaic	Viruses p. 277
Roots with irregular swellings not containing caterpillars or holes	Clubroot p. 223

Houseleek. See **Sempervivum**

House Plants. See **Glasshouse and House Plants**

Hosta

Symptom	Cause
Leaves and young shoots eaten away at tips	Rabbits p. 183
Leaves and young shoots eaten, leaves with irregular holes; slime trails present on or near plants	Slugs and Snails p. 90

Hoya

Symptom	Cause
Leaves with various yellowish mosaic-like patterns	Viruses p. 277

Hyacinthus

Symptom	Cause
Leaves with fine mottling of white and green	Viruses p. 277
Bulbs with soft and slimy rot	Bacterial Soft Rot p. 234
Roots blackened and rotted; decay not usually extending into bulb	Root and Foot Rot p. 242
Plants grown in water culture covered with pale yellowish slimy mass	Slime Mould p. 273

Hydrangea

Symptom	Cause
Flowers shrivelled and with fluffy grey mould growth	Grey Mould p. 232
Flowers stunted and remain green (note that hydrangea flowers are normally green before they open fully)	Viruses p. 277
Leaves with many small ragged holes, especially at tips of shoots; buds sometimes killed	Capsid Bugs p. 97
Leaves twisted and distorted, especially at tips of shoots; stems scarred, growth stunted	Stem Eelworm p. 84
Leaves and/or other parts with powdery white coating	Powdery Mildew p. 204
Leaves with yellowish mottled and/or irregular patterns	Viruses p. 277
Leaves and/or stems with patches of rot bearing fluffy grey mould growth	Stem and Leaf Rots p. 252
Leaves more or less bleached; veins remain dark green	Iron Deficiency p. 288
Roots and/or stem base blackened and rotten	Root and Foot Rots p. 242

Also see **Glasshouse and House Plants** for conditions affecting pot hydrangeas

Ilex (Holly). Also see **Trees**

Symptom	Cause
Leaves with brown and yellow blotch mines	Holly Leaf Miner p. 154
Leaves with brown or yellow scales on undersides; foliage sticky and sooty	Scale Insects p. 124
Leaves with greyish spots	Leaf Spot p. 258

Impatiens (including Busy Lizzie). Also see **Glasshouse and House Plants**

Symptom	Cause
Flowers and/or buds shrivelled and with fluffy grey mould growth present	Grey Mould p. 232
Leaves with pale brown blotches	Leaf Spot p. 258

Ipomoea (Morning Glory). See **Climbing Plants**

Iris. Also see **Bulbs etc.**

Symptom	Cause
Flowers of dark coloured types with streaks of paler colour	Viruses p. 277
Leaves spotted with brown or grey	Leaf Spot p. 258
Leaves yellowed or mottled; may be general stunting and disruption of flower colour	Viruses p. 277
Leaves with yellow but darkening streaks; terminal parts turn red-brown and shrivel (bulbous irises only)	Bulb Rot p. 231
Leaves with irregular holes and pieces eaten; slime trails present on or near plants	Slugs and Snails p. 90
Leaves eaten, sometimes extensively; no slime trails present	Caterpillars p. 132
Bulbs or rhizomes with soft and slimy rot	Bacterial Soft Rot p. 234
Bulbs with black patches or streaks; may be extensive decay	Bulb Rot p. 231

Ivy. See **Hedera**

Ixia. Also see **Bulbs etc.**

Symptom	Cause
Corms with dry rot and with soil adhering to whitish mould when dug up; plants emerge feebly	Corm Rot p. 231

Japanese Quince. See **Chaenomeles**

Jasmine. See **Jasminum**

Jasminum (Jasmine)

Symptom	Cause
Leaves with yellow variegation	Viruses p. 277
Leaves and young shoots infested by small insects; foliage sticky and sooty	Aphids p. 104

Jerusalem Artichoke

Symptom	Cause
Stem base and/or tubers rotted and with cottony white mould growth present	Sclerotinia Disease p. 247
Tubers holed and tunnelled, often extensively	Slugs p. 90 Swift Moths p. 137

Judas Tree. See **Cercis**

Juglans (Walnut). Also see **Trees**

Symptom	Cause
Leaves with blister-like growths (galls)	Gall Mites p. 177
Leaves with brown or yellowish blotches; may be dark blotches on green nuts also	Leaf Blotch p. 262
Leaves scorched in early spring	Frost p. 292
Branches die back; masses of small, usually pink pustules present	Coral Spot p. 216
Branches and/or stem with hard, irregular swelling	Crown Gall p. 224
Branches with masses of proliferating shoots (witches' brooms)	Viruses p. 277

Juniper. See **Juniperus**

Juniperus (Juniper). Also see **Trees** and **Conifers**

Symptom	Cause
Leaves discoloured, yellowing and browning; small mites present, producing some silk webbing	Conifer Spinning Mite p. 175
Leaves and stems with small, round, grey-white scales, sometimes forming extensive encrustations	Scale Insects p. 124

Kalanchoe. See **Cacti and Succulents**

Kale. See **Brassicas**

Kohl-Rabi. See **Brassicas**

Laburnum. Also see **Trees**

Symptom	Cause
Leaves with powdery white coating	Powdery Mildew p. 204
Leaves with brown blotch mines	Laburnum Leaf Miner p. 144
Leaves with regular, almost semicircular pieces cut away	Leaf Cutter Bees p. 162
Branches die back; fungal fruit bodies may be present	Diebacks p. 214 or Silver Leaf p. 221

Lachenalia. Also see **Bulbs etc.**

Symptom	Cause
Leaves with fine mottling of white and green	Viruses p. 277
Leaves with yellow but darkening streaks; terminal parts turn red-brown and shrivel	Bulb Rot p. 233
Bulb softened and with rich brown rot spreading from basal ring	Bulb Rot p. 233
Bulbs with black patches or streaks; may be extensive decay	Bulb Rot p. 233

Larch. See **Larix**

Larix (Larch). Also see **Conifers** and **Trees**

Symptom	Cause
Leaves scorched in early spring; shoots may be killed	Frost p. 292
Leaves turn brown or pale-coloured and drop prematurely	See discussion under Needle Casts p. 210
Leaves and shoots with tufts of white wax wool covering small dark insects	Adelgids p. 120
Leaves eaten, especially at tips of shoots	Sawflies p. 154
Stem with some decay of wood; fungal brackets may be present	Stem Rot p. 248

Larkspur. See **Delphinium**

Lathyrus (Sweet Pea)

Symptom	Cause
Flowers pecked and torn	Birds p. 179
Flowers and leaves discoloured with light flecking and more extensive silvering; narrow bodied wingless and winged insects present	Thrips p. 129
Flowers, leaves and shoots infested by small winged and wingless green or yellow insects; plants sometimes sticky and sooty	Aphids p. 104
Flowers of dark coloured types with paler streaks	Viruses p. 277
Leaves with irregular holes; young shoots eaten; slime trails present on or near plants	Slugs and Snails p. 90
Leaves discoloured, yellowing and drying out; many small mites on undersides	Glasshouse Red Spider Mites p. 173
Leaves and/or other parts with powdery white coating	Powdery Mildew p. 204 but also see White Mould p. 256
Leaves wilt; stem interior with brown or black streaks	Wilt p. 211
Leaves with various mottle or mosaic patterns or otherwise distorted	Viruses p. 277
Stem with soft irregular swelling	Crown Gall p. 224
Stems with decay at ground level; may extend to roots	Root and Foot Rots p. 242
Stem with decay, usually at ground level and with cottony white mould growth	Sclerotinia Disease p. 247
Roots with many small, hard swellings	Root Nodules p. 276

Laurel, Bay. See **Laurus**

Laurel, Cherry. See **Prunus**

Laurel, Portugal. See **Prunus**

Laurus (Bay laurel). Also see **Trees**

Symptom	Cause
Leaves with edges curled and thickened; small insects present, usually covered with white wax wool	Bay Sucker p. 101

Leaves with flat yellow or brown scales on undersides; foliage sticky and sooty	Scale Insects p. 124

Lavandula (Lavender)

Flowers and/or buds shrivelled and with fluffy grey mould growth	Grey Mould p. 232
Shoots and stems with small masses of white froth covering wingless insects; growth sometimes distorted	Froghoppers p. 98

Lavatera (Tree-mallow)

Leaves and stem with raised, orange-brown pustules a few mm in diameter	Hollyhock Rust p. 196

Lavender. See **Lavandula**

Lawns

The establishment and maintenance of fine lawns is a specialised aspect of gardening which is dealt with in detail in many gardening books. Good control of pests and diseases is essential if consistently good results are to be achieved and this usually involves good management combined with some chemical treatments. The following key can be used to identify the main causes of trouble:

Seed removed from newly-sown areas	Birds p. 179
Soil scratched and newly-sown seed disturbed	Cats p. 188 Birds p. 179
Grass yellowing, browning and dying, often in patches	Leatherjackets p. 147 Chafers p. 163 Dogs p. 188 Lawn Turf Rots p. 244
Grass with gelatinous green bodies among leaves	Algae p. 274
Grass with white or greyish, often branched growths	Lichen p. 273
Grass smothered with variously coloured, slimy, often sponge-like bodies	Slime Moulds p. 273
Leaves with powdery white coating	Powdery Mildews p. 204
Mounds of loose soil thrown up on surface of lawns, up to about 10 cm high or higher	Moles p. 186
Mounds of fine soil thrown up on surface, up to about 10 mm high	Ants p. 160
Small casts of soil extruded from holes on surface	Earthworms p. 91

Leek

Leeks have many problems in common with **Onion** (q.v.) but a few, such as Rust and White Tip, are much commoner

Lettuce

Plants wilt and die; stem severed at soil level	Cutworms p. 136
Plants unthrifty; roots attacked by thin yellow-brown larvae	Wireworms p. 163
Plants unthrifty; roots infested by small white insects	Root Aphids p. 120
Leaves with pale yellowish or brown, angular spots and whitish mould growth beneath	Downy Mildew p. 202
Leaves with pale inter-veinal areas giving marbled effect	Viruses p. 277
Leaves irregularly blistered and distorted and with pale yellow bands along veins	Viruses p. 277
Leaves pecked and torn	Birds p. 179

Leaves infested by small green or yellow insects	Aphids p. 104
Leaves with irregular holes; slime trails present; seedlings may be killed	Slugs and Snails p. 90
Leaves with irregular holes; no slime trails present	Caterpillars p. 132
Heads with soft and slimy rot	Bacterial Soft Rot p. 234
Heads rotted and with fluffy grey mould growth present; stems may rot completely	Grey Mould p. 232 but also see Sclerotinia Disease p. 247 and Root and Foot Rots p. 242
Plants run to flower	Bolting p. 297

Ligustrum (Privet). Also see **Hedges**

Leaves turn yellow and wilt in absence of root damage	Wilt p. 211
Leaves with disfiguring brown blotch mines	Lilac Leaf Miner p. 144
Leaves with white flecking and silvery sheen; small, narrow-bodied insects present	Privet Thrips p. 131
Leaves rolled tightly and discoloured, especially at tips of shoots; leaves fall prematurely	Privet Aphid p. 118
Stems with encrustations of small white scales	Willow Scale p. 126
Branches or stem with irregular hard swellings	Crown Gall p. 224

Lilac. See **Syringa**

Lilium (Lily). Also see **Bulbs etc.**

Plants infested by red beetles and grubs; holes eaten in leaves, stems, buds, flowers and seed-capsules	Lily Beetle p. 167
Flowers distorted; leaves irregularly mottled; plants unthrifty	Viruses p. 277
Leaves with mottling or distortion	Viruses p. 277
Leaves and young shoots grazed	Rabbits p. 183
Leaves, young shoots and other parts infested by small insects; leaves sticky, sometimes sooty	Aphids p. 104
Bulbs dug up and eaten	Squirrels p. 184
Bulbs tunnelled; young shoots and leaves with irregular holes; slime trails present	Slugs and Snails p. 90
Bulbs (in store) with firm, dry rot and blue-green mould growth	Blue Mould Rot p. 232
Roots blackened and rotted; decay not usually extending into bulb	Root and Foot Rots p. 242

Lily. See **Lilium**

Lily-Of-The-Valley. See **Convallaria**

Lime. See **Tilia**

Lithops. See **Cacti and Succulents**

Lobelia. Also see **Bedding Plants**

Leaves mottled and/or distorted	Viruses p. 277

Loganberry. See **Raspberry**

Lonicera (Honeysuckle). Also see **Climbing Plants**

Leaves and young shoots infested by dense colonies of blue-green insects; growth distorted, foliage very sticky and sooty	Honeysuckle Aphid p. 118
Leaves with powdery white coating	Powdery Mildew p. 204

Lunaria	
Leaves and/or other parts with small, often concentric clusters of creamy droplets	White Blister p. 210
Roots with irregular swellings	Clubroot p. 223
Lupin. See **Lupinus**	
Lupinus (Lupin)	
Leaves and/or other parts with powdery white coating	Powdery Mildew p. 204
Leaves with dark green bands along veins or various irregular yellowish patterns	Viruses p. 277
Stem with irregular swellings	Crown Gall p. 224
Stem rotted at base; white cottony mould growth present	Sclerotinia Disease p. 247
Roots blackened and decayed; plant unthrifty	Root and Foot Rots p. 242
Roots with small nodular swellings	Root Nodules p. 276
Lychnis	
Leaves and young shoots infested by small insects; growth distorted	Aphids p. 104
Leaves, shoots and stems with small masses of white froth covering small wingless insects	Froghoppers p. 98
Magnolia	
Buds and flowers pecked or gnawed	Birds p. 179 or Grey Squirrel p. 184
Flowers or buds shrivel and die suddenly	Frost p. 292
Flowers and/or buds with powdery grey mould growth	Grey Mould p. 232
Leaves with tattered holes	Capsid Bugs p. 97
Leaves with irregular yellowish patterns	Viruses p. 277
Branches die back; masses of small, usually pink pustules present	Coral Spot p. 216
Mahonia	
Leaves with pale brown pustules on undersides	Rust p. 191
Maidenhair Fern. See **Ferns**	
Maize. See **Sweet Corn**	
Mallow (Tree). See **Lavatera**	
Malus. See **Apple.** Many of the problems affecting apples also occur on ornamental **Malus**	
Malva (Mallow). See **Althaea**	
Mammillaria. See **Cacti and Succulents**	
Maple. See **Acer**	
Marguerite. See **Chrysanthemum**	
Marigold. See **Calendula** and **Tagetes**	
Marrow. See **Cucumber**	
Matthiola (Stock)	
Flowers of dark coloured types with paler streaks and distortion; leaves may be mottled or distorted	Viruses p. 277
Leaves and/or other parts with small, often concentric clusters of creamy droplets	White Blister p. 210
Roots with irregular swellings	Clubroot p. 223
Leaves of young plants with small round holes and pits	Flea Beetles p. 165

Leaves of older plants with irregular holes and pieces eaten away — Caterpillars p. 132
Leaves and young shoots infested by small wingless and winged insects; foliage sticky and sooty — Aphids p. 104
Roots eaten by maggots; plants wilt — Cabbage Root Fly p. 150

Medlar. Also see **Trees**
Fruit with soft brown rot and usually off-white cottony pustules; associated twigs may die back — Brown Rot p. 235
Leaves with powdery white coating — Powdery Mildew p. 204
Leaves with irregular yellowish streaks and patterns and/or some distortion — Viruses p. 277

Melon. See **Cucumber**

Metasequoia. See **Conifers** and **Trees**

Michaelmas Daisy. See **Aster**

Mint
Plants distorted and bearing masses of small orange pustules — Rust p. 191

Monkey-Puzzle Tree (Araucaria). See **Conifers** and **Trees**

Monstera. See **Glasshouse and House Plants**

Montbretia. Also see **Bulbs etc**
Leaves turn yellow and decay at ground level where masses of tiny black bodies are present on them — Corm Rot p. 231
Leaves with yellow but darkening streaks; terminal parts turn red-brown and shrivel — Corm Rot p. 231

Morning Glory. See **Ipomoea**

Mountain Ash. See **Sorbus**

Mulberry. Also see **Trees**
Leaves with powdery white coating — Powdery Mildew p. 204
Branches die back; masses of small, usually pink pustules present — Coral Spot p. 216

Mullein. See **Verbascum**

Muscari (Grape Hyacinth). Also see **Bulbs etc.**
Bulbs with soft and slimy rot — Bacterial Soft Rot p. 234

Mushrooms (Cultivated)
Stalks and caps tunnelled by maggots — Sciarid Flies p. 147
Stalks and caps with irregular pieces eaten away; slime trails present — Slugs p. 90

Myosotis (Forget-me-not)
Plants infested by small green or pink wingless and winged insects; growth distorted, foliage sticky and sooty — Aphids p. 104
Flowers and/or buds with fluffy grey mould growth — Grey Mould p. 232
Leaves and/or other parts with powdery white coating — Powdery Mildew p. 204

Narcissus. Also see **Bulbs etc.**

Symptom	Cause
Bulbs soft at planting time, with internal brown discolouration and decay; growth poor and distorted	Stem Eelworm p. 84
Bulbs soft at planting time, with internal cavity tunnelled by maggots; leaves thin and weak and flowers fail to develop	Large Narcissus Fly p. 152
Bulbs in soil with holes eaten in from the outside, often extensively tunnelled	Slugs p. 90
Bulbs softened and with rich brown rot spreading from basal ring	Bulb Rot p. 231
Bulbs (in store) with firm, dry rot and blue-green mould growth	Bulb Rot p. 231
Leaves variously streaked or distorted, plants often unthrifty	Viruses p. 277
Leaves with red-brown scorch, spreading downwards from tip; gradually shrivel and die; flower stalks and flowers may also have brown discolouration	Leaf Scorch p. 264
Leaves turn brown at base; upper parts yellow and wilted and soon covered with fluffy grey mould	Smoulder p. 253
Roots blackened and rotted; decay not usually extending into bulb	Root and Foot Rots p. 242

Nasturtium. See **Tropaeolum**

Nectarine. See **Apricot**

Nemesia. See **Bedding Plants**

Nerine. See **Bulbs etc.**

Nerium (Oleander). Also see **Glasshouse and House Plants**

Symptom	Cause
Shoots and/or other parts with soft, spongy growth, canker lesions or other distortion	Gall p. 224

Nicotiana (including Tobacco). Also see **Bedding Plants**

Symptom	Cause
Leaves with irregular, yellowish streaks and patterns and/or various forms of distortion; plants generally unthrifty	Viruses p. 277

Nymphaea (Water lily). Also see **Aquatic Plants**

Symptom	Cause
Leaves with extensive irregular holes eaten by beetles and larvae on upper surfaces	Water-Lily Beetle p. 167

Oak. See **Quercus**

Odontoglossum. See **Orchids**

Oleander. See **Nerium**

Onion, Shallot, Chives, Garlic, Ornamental Allium, Leek

Symptom	Cause
Leaves turn yellow and die from tip downwards; various other leaf symptoms may occur also either simultaneously or later and include several types of mould growth. It is difficult to distinguish between the various different causes	See discussion under Leaf Rot p. 252
Leaves with dull streaks or blisters of dark powder; plants often distorted	Smuts p. 199

Symptom	Cause
Leaves and/or other parts with red-orange pustules (esp. on chives and leeks)	Rusts p. 191
Leaves with short yellow streaks at base and variously distorted	Viruses p. 277
Leaves swollen and distorted; bulbs soft, tending to crack at base	Stem Eelworm p. 84
Leaves wilting and yellowing; bulbs and stems tunnelled by maggots; young plants often killed	Onion Fly p. 151
Leaves with fine light flecking and more extensive silver sheen; small narrow-bodied insects present	Onion Thrips p. 130
Bulbs covered with white cottony mould in which are tiny black bodies (esp. on salad onions)	White Rot p. 245
Bulbs (in store) soften from neck downwards; fluffy grey mould growth present	Neck Rot p. 238
Bulbs with soft and slimy rot	Bacterial Soft Rot p. 234
Plants run to flower	Bolting p. 297

Opuntia. See **Cacti and Succulents**

Orchids. Also see **Glasshouse and House Plants**

Symptom	Cause
Flowers with brownish streaks and spots	Viruses p. 277
Leaves variously spotted	Leaf Spot p. 258
Leaves with irregular streaks and patterns and often distortion of entire plant	Viruses p. 277

Ornithogalum. See **Hyacinthus** and **Bulbs etc.**

Paeonia (Paeony)

Symptom	Cause
Leaves with irregular yellowish rings or patterns	Viruses p. 277
Leaves with grey-brown, reddish-bordered spots	Blotch p. 262
Leaves with soft brown region at base; stem base brown and decayed with fluffy grey mould growth	Grey Mould Blight p. 218
Leaves wilt; stem interior with brown or black streaks	Wilt p. 211
Leaves and young shoots distorted and discoloured and growth checked in early spring	Chrysanthemum Eelworm p. 86
Roots eaten by white caterpillars in soil	Swift Moths p. 137

Palms. See **Glasshouse and House Plants**

Pansy. See **Viola**

Papaver (Poppy)

Symptom	Cause
Flowers and/or buds shrivelled and with fluffy grey mould growth	Grey Mould p. 232
Leaves and/or other parts with powdery white coating	Powdery Mildew p. 204

Paphiopedilum. See **Orchids**

Parsley

Symptom	Cause
Leaves and/or other parts with powdery white coating	Powdery Mildew p. 204

Symptom	Cause
Leaves turning yellow and red; growth poor; fly maggots feeding on roots	Carrot Fly p. 149

Parsnip

Symptom	Cause
Leaves and/or other parts with powdery white coating	Powdery Mildew p. 204
Leaves with pale, brown-bordered spots	Cankers p. 214
Leaves with net-like veinal yellowing	Viruses p. 277
Leaf bases swollen and splitting, crowns rotting	Stem Eelworm p. 84
Leaves with yellow blotch mines	Celery Fly p. 149
Roots tunnelled by white maggots	Carrot Fly p. 149
Roots with soft and slimy rot	Bacterial Soft Rot p. 234
Roots (especially in store) with brown rot and cottony white mould growth; mainly around crown	Sclerotinia Disease p. 247
Roots rotted and with matted dark strands to which soil adheres	Violet Root Rot p. 241
Roots split but not usually decayed	Splitting p. 298
Roots with other forms of decay or lesion, especially around crown	Cankers p. 214

Parthenocissus (Virginia Creeper). Also see **Climbing Plants**

Symptom	Cause
Leaves with pale yellowish spots and whitish mould growth beneath	Grapevine Downy Mildew p. 202

Passiflora (Passion Flower). Also see **Climbing Plants**

Symptom	Cause
Leaves with irregular yellowish mosaics or patterns, crumpling and/or other distortion	Viruses p. 277

Passion Flower. See **Passiflora**

Pea

Symptom	Cause
Seeds removed before they germinate	Birds p. 179 Mice p. 185
Seeds with dark areas on cotyledons when pulled apart	Manganese Deficiency p. 287
Seedlings with pieces eaten away as they emerge through soil, often failing to establish	Slugs p. 90 Millepedes p. 92 Bean Seed Fly p. 151
Seedlings pecked and pulled out of soil	Birds p. 179
Pods with caterpillars inside, eating holes in peas	Pea Moth p. 139
Pods and leaves with light flecking and silvery sheen on surfaces, small narrow-bodied insects present	Pea Thrips p. 130
Pods with triangular pieces pecked away and peas removed	Birds p. 179
Pods, flower stalks and leaves with brown-yellow, sunken spots	Leaf and Pod Spots p. 258
Pods rotted, usually at flower end and with fluffy grey mould growth	Grey Mould p. 232
Leaves and/or other parts with powdery white coating	Powdery Mildew p. 204
Leaves wilt, stem interior with brown or black streaks extending well above ground level	Wilt p. 211
Leaves with blue-green tint; may later turn yellow and wilt	Copper Deficiency p. 290
Leaves with small semi-circular notches eaten out of edges, producing a scalloped effect	Pea and Bean Weevils p. 169

Leaves and shoots infested by colonies of green, pink or yellow winged and wingless insects; foliage sticky and growth sometimes checked	Aphids p. 104
Stem rotted at base with cottony white mould growth present	Sclerotinia Disease p. 247
Stem with brown or blackish lesions at base; roots blackened or rotten; plants unthrifty	Root and Foot Rots p. 242
Roots with small nodular swellings	Root Nodules p. 276
Seedlings die; often in groups	Damping-off p. 243

Peach. See **Apricot**

Pear. Also see **Apple** and **Trees**

Fruits pecked as they ripen; (peck-holes often extended by wasps)	Birds p. 179
Fruits distorted, with irregular bumps and scars	Capsid Bugs p. 97
Fruit with soft brown rot and usually off-white cottony pustules; associated twigs may die back	Brown Rot p. 235
Fruit with round, dark, saucer-like depressions; usually only in store	Bitter Rot p. 234
Fruit leathery and cracked; often on windfalls and low-hanging fruit	Leathery Rots p. 237
Fruit otherwise rotted, especially in store	Minor Rots p. 238
Fruit scorched following very hot weather	High Temperature Injury p. 294
Fruit with very dark brown more or less rounded corky patches	Scabs p. 228
Fruit with dark green mouldy patches on surface; easily wiped off	Sooty Blotch p. 271
Fruit dimpled; sometimes wholly misshapen	Viruses p. 277
Fruitlets enlarged and distorted, falling prematurely; small yellow or white maggots in cavities	Pear Midge p. 145
Flowers and/or buds die suddenly	Frost p. 292
Flowers and then spur leaves wilt	Brown Rot Blossom Wilt p. 235
Flowers and flower buds discoloured, failing to develop normally; small flattened insects present, foliage sticky and sooty	Pear Sucker p. 100
Leaves and shoots infested by small black or brown insects, often in dense colonies; foliage sticky and sooty	Aphids p. 104
Leaves with rashes of blister-like pustules, at first yellow but later turning dark brown	Pear Leaf Blister Mite p. 178
Leaves with irregular holes and pieces eaten away	Caterpillars p. 132
Leaves with surface tissues eaten away, exposing fine veins; shining black larvae present	Pear and Cherry Slugworms p. 155
Leaves with irregular yellowish streaks and patterns	Viruses p. 277
Leaves scorched at margins in spring	Frost p. 292
Leaves and/or other parts with powdery white coating	Apple Powdery Mildew p. 205
Leaves and/or other parts with sticky black coating	Sooty Mould p. 209
Leaves with irregular dark brown blotches	Scabs p. 228
Leaves with small brown blisters	Leaf Curl p. 222
Branches die back; stem base and roots decayed; toadstools and bootlace-like strands may be present	Honey Fungus p. 249
Branches with canker lesions; may die back beyond lesions	Cankers p. 214

Branches die back; masses of small, usually pink pustules present — Coral Spot p. 216
Branches and/or stem with hard irregular swelling — Crown Gall p. 224
Shoots exude slime and die back; flowers and/or leaves shrivelled — Fireblight p. 217
Stem base and roots decayed; toadstools and bootlace-like strands may be present and branches die back — Honey Fungus p. 249
Trees generally unthrifty — Deficiencies of Nitrogen p. 284, Phosphorus p. 285 and Potassium p. 285

Pelargonium. Also see **Bedding Plants** and **Glasshouse and House Plants**

Leaves with yellowish rings, streaks or other patterns — Viruses p. 277
Leaves with pale spots on uppersides and more or less rounded brown pustules beneath — Rusts p. 191
Leaves and/or stems with rough, warty outgrowths — Oedema p. 297
Stem, especially of cuttings, pinched and shrivelled just above ground level — Blackleg p. 246

Penstemon

Leaves and young shoots distorted and scarred; growth checked — Chrysanthemum Eelworm p. 86

Peperomia. Also see **Glasshouse and House Plants**

Leaves and/or stems with rough warty outgrowths — Oedema p. 297

Peppers. See **Capsicum**

Perennials

Ornamental plants grown as herbaceous perennials, usually in mixed borders and beds, remain on the same site for a number of years and may therefore suffer from a gradual build-up of pests and diseases as well as loss of vigour resulting from depletion of nutrients and competition between plants. Sustained good performance of these plants can often be encouraged by regular maintenance and renewal. Clear debris in autumn and winter; divide, reduce, mulch and support plants in spring and cultivate, manure and replant borders and beds when necessary, which may be every five years or so on light infertile soils but can be much longer on fertile soils. The following key can be used to identify the main causes of trouble and additional entries are given for some of the more important plant genera.

Leaves, buds, shoots, stems or flowers infested by small wingless and winged green, yellow, brown or pink insects; young growths sometimes checked and distorted; foliage sticky, sometimes sooty — Aphids p. 104
Leaves and young shoots distorted, sometimes discoloured; growth poor — Eelworms p. 84
Leaves and/or other parts with powdery white coating — Powdery Mildew p. 204
Leaves with various yellowish streaks and patterns — Viruses p. 277
Leaves variously spotted — Spots p. 258
Leaves and shoots with small masses of froth covering pink or white wingless insects; growth sometimes distorted — Froghoppers p. 98

Leaves with irregular holes and pieces eaten away; no slime trails present	Caterpillars p. 132
Leaves with irregular holes and pieces eaten away; young shoots eaten; flowers and buds sometimes attacked; slime trails on or near plants	Slugs and Snails p. 90
Leaves with small tattered holes, especially near tips of shoots; buds sometimes killed and flowers distorted	Capsid Bugs p. 97
Stem with irregular swellings	Crown Gall p. 224
Roots blackened and decayed; plants unthrifty	Root and Foot Rots p. 242
Roots and other underground parts eaten by white caterpillars living in soil	Swift Moths p. 137
Roots and other underground parts eaten by C-shaped white beetle larvae living in soil	Chafers p. 163
Roots and other underground parts eaten by grey-brown caterpillars living in soil; stems sometimes severed at soil level	Cutworms p. 136
Roots and other underground parts eaten by thin, long, wiry white or yellow bettle larvae living in soil; corms, tubers and rhizomes often with small cylindrical holes and tunnels	Wireworms p. 163

Petunia. Also see **Bedding Plants**

Leaves with irregular, yellowish streaks and patterns and/or various forms of distortion; plants generally unthrifty	Viruses p. 277

Philadelphus

Leaves with irregular yellowish streaks and patterns and/or distortion	Viruses p. 277
Leaves and young shoots infested by small black insects; growth distorted and checked	Black Bean Aphid p. 112

Philodendron. See **Glasshouse and House Plants**

Phlox (annual and perennial). Also see **Perennials** and **Bedding Plants**

Leaves and/or other parts with powdery white coating	Powdery Mildew p. 204
Leaves and young shoots of perennial phlox deformed; leaves reduced to narrow frills along midribs	Stem Eelworm p. 84
Stem with irregular swelling	Crown Gall p. 224

Phyllitis. See **Ferns**

Picea (Spruce). Also see **Conifers** and **Trees**

Leaves discolour and drop prematurely	See discussion under Needle Casts p. 210
Leaves discoloured, sometimes falling prematurely; small green insects present	Green Spruce Aphid p. 120
Leaves discoloured, yellowing and bronzing, sometimes falling prematurely; small mites and silk webbing present	Conifer Spinning Mite p. 175
Leaves and stems with tufts of white wax wool	Adelgids p. 120
Buds at tips of shoots enlarged and modified to form galls that resemble miniature pineapples	Spruce Gall Adelgids p. 121

Stem with some decay of wood; fungal brackets may be present — Stem Rot p. 252

Pine. See **Pinus**

Pink. See **Dianthus**

Pinus (Pine). Also see **Conifers** and **Trees**

Leaves discolour and drop prematurely — See discussion under Needle Casts p. 210

Leaves eaten, especially at tips of shoots, caterpillars usually present — Caterpillars p. 132 or Pine Sawflies p. 157

Leaves, shoots and stems with tufts of white wax covering small dark insects — Adelgids p. 120

Stem with some decay of wood, fungal brackets may be present — Stem or Heart Rot p. 252

Plane. See **Trees**

Platanus (Plane). See **Trees**

Pleione. See **Glasshouse and House Plants** and **Orchids**

Plum and Damson. Also see **Trees**

Fruit with small holes pecked from the outside as it ripens — Birds p. 179

Fruit with larger holes, often extending under the skin at edges — Wasps p. 161

Fruits and fruitlets tunnelled, often with external holes exuding wet brown frass; fruitlets fall prematurely — Plum Sawfly p. 155

Fruit with soft brown rot and usually off-white cottony pustules — Brown Rot p. 235

Fruit with green-brown, velvety spots — Scabs p. 228

Fruit split — Splitting p. 298

Fruit with dark green mouldy patches on surface; easily wiped off — Sooty Blotch p. 271

Fruit (red-coloured types) with dark bands and lines; (yellow and dark coloured types) with grooves and pits on surface — Viruses p. 277

Flowers and/or leaves scorched or killed suddenly — Frost p. 292

Flowers and then spur leaves wilt — Brown Rot Blossom Wilt p. 235

Leaves at tips of shoots tightly curled and distorted; colonies of small insects present inside curled leaves — Leaf-curling Plum Aphid p. 110

Leaves with dense colonies of green and yellow insects on undersides; upper surfaces often very sticky and sooty — Mealy Plum Aphid p. 110

Leaves with irregular holes and pieces eaten away — Caterpillars p. 132

Leaves at tips of shoots with small tattered holes; fruits sometimes misshapen and discoloured — Capsid Bugs p. 97

Leaves on foliar spur or terminal shoot wither — See Brown Rot Spur Blight and Wither Tip p. 235

Symptom	Cause
Leaves with brown or black pustules beneath; small yellow spots above	Plum Rust p. 198
Leaves with silver sheen; branches may die back	Silver Leaf p. 221
Leaves with irregular patterns or variously malformed	Viruses p. 277
Leaves with brown leaf spots and/or holes	Bacterial Canker p. 218
Leaves small and narrow with irregular margins and thickened blades; fruit sparse	Viruses p. 277
Branches die back in absence of stem lesions; leaves silvery	Silver Leaf p. 221
Branches die back; root and stem base decayed; toadstools and bootlace-like strands may be present	Honey Fungus p. 249
Branches and/or stem oozing gum; may be some dieback and also spotting and holes in leaves	Bacterial Canker p. 218
Branches with masses of proliferating shoots	Witches' Brooms p. 227
Stem with hard, irregular swelling	Crown Gall p. 224
Tree generally unthrifty	Deficiencies of Nitrogen p. 284, Phosphorus p. 285 and Potassium p. 285

Poinsettia (Euphorbia). See **Glasshouse and House Plants**

Polyanthus. See **Primula**

Poplar. See **Populus**

Poppy. See **Papaver**

Populus (Poplar). Also see **Trees**

Symptom	Cause
Leaves with surface tissues eaten away by metallic blue, red or green beetles and black-spotted larvae	Poplar Leaf Beetles p. 168
Leaves blistered; may be a powdery yellow coating	Leaf Curl p. 222
Leaves with silvery sheen; branches may die back	Silver Leaf p. 221
Leaf stalks of Lombardy poplars with conspicuous pouch-like growths (galls) enclosing colonies of small insects	Lettuce Root Aphid p. 114
Branches die back; leaves with silvery sheen	Silver Leaf p. 221
Branches with parasitic leathery plant growing from them (esp. on hybrid black poplars)	Mistletoe p. 276
Stems with flattened or sunken lesions; branches may die back	Cankers and Diebacks p. 214
Stems or branches with hard irregular swelling	Crown Gall p. 224

Potato

Symptom	Cause
Leaves discoloured, growth poor, plants often collapsing and dying; small white, yellow or brown cysts on roots	Potato Cyst Eelworm p. 89

Symptom	Cause
Leaves infested by small green, yellow or pink wingless and winged insects; foliage sticky, sometimes discoloured	Aphids p. 104
Leaves with small ragged holes, especially at tips of shoots	Capsid Bugs p. 97
Leaves eaten by black and yellow striped beetles and/or by pink-red larvae (rare in Britain)	Colorado Beetle p. 166
Leaves with black, soft patches bearing powdery white mould growth	Blight p. 214
Leaves browned or scorched at margins; plant unthrifty	Potassium Deficiency p. 285
Leaves small and pale (symptom spreading from lower to upper leaves); plant unthrifty; few tubers	Nitrogen Deficiency p. 284
Leaves rolled; shoots leggy; many very small tubers	Calcium Deficiency p. 286
Leaves rolled (lower first) stiff and brittle; may rattle if shaken	Viruses p. 277
Leaves rolled (upper first) and wilt; stem base black and slimy; roots rotten	Black Leg p. 246
Leaves with pronounced inter-veinal yellowing (lower first)	Manganese Deficiency p. 289
Leaves with dark streaks or spots along veins; leaves turn yellow and hang by thread	Viruses p. 277
Leaves roughened or puckered; yellow green mottling; few tubers	Viruses p. 277
Leaves with indefinite yellowish mottling or patterns	Viruses p. 277
Stem base black and slimy; tubers may be rotten and leaves rolled	Black Leg p. 246
Stem base rotten and with white cottony mould growth	Sclerotinia Disease p. 247
Stem with rough, brown and cracked lesions on underground parts	Blight p. 214
Tubers with small round holes and tunnels; thin yellow-brown larvae present in tubers and/or soil	Wireworms p. 163
Tubers with larger tunnels and holes, often extensively damaged	Slugs p. 90
Tubers with large pieces eaten out of their surface	Chafers p. 163, Cutworms p. 136, Swift Moths p. 137
(Note: Millepedes (p. 92) may often be present in damaged tubers but are usually of only secondary importance)	
Tubers turn green	Light p. 294
Tubers split or with internal hollows but not usually decayed and no mould growth present	Mechanical Injury p. 298 or Splitting p. 298
Tubers soft and rubbery when lifted	Drought p. 291
Tubers with silvery sheen; usually only apparent in store	Silver Scurf p. 268
Tubers with small brownish pimples	Skin Spot p. 258
Tubers soft and rotten; stem base black and slimy	Black Leg p. 246
Tubers (in store) with soft and slimy rot	Bacterial Soft Rot p. 234
Tubers with scabby spots of corky tissue	Common Scab p. 229 but also see Powdery Scab p. 230

Tubers with rough and warty outgrowths	Wart p. 226
Tubers (in store) with soft, brown rot and fluffy grey mould growth	Grey Mould p. 232
Tubers shrunken or wrinkled and with cracks or cavities lined with fluffy white, blue or pink mould (very common)	Dry Rot p. 239
Tubers with small thumb-print-like lesions from which rot extends	Gangrene p. 240
Tubers with rubbery consistency when cut; tissues turn pink within half an hour	Pink Rot p. 240
Tubers with indefinite dark patches within	Often caused by Frost p. 292 but there are several other causes including Viruses p. 277
Tubers with more or less definite dark lines or crescentic patterns within but no decay	Viruses p. 277
Plants with masses of proliferating shoots	Viruses p. 277

Primula (including Auricula and Polyanthus). Also see **Bedding Plants** and **Glasshouse and House Plants**

Flowers and flower buds pecked and torn	Birds p. 179
Leaves with irregular holes, especially near soil surface; slime trails present	Slugs p. 90
Leaves discoloured, yellowing and later bronzing, drying out and dying; small mites present	Glasshouse Red Spider Mites p. 173 or Bryobia Mites p. 176
Leaves, buds, stems and flowers infested by small green, yellow or pink wingless and winged insects; plants sticky and sooty	Aphids p. 104
Leaves with yellowish mosaic pattern; plant often stunted	Viruses p. 277
Stem base and/or roots rotted; plants unthrifty	Root and Foot Rots p. 242

Privet. See **Ligustrum**

Prunus. See separate entries for **Almond, Cherry** and **Plum.** Ornamental species and cultivars are generally affected by the same pests, diseases and disorders as those affecting their fruiting counterparts. Also see **Trees**

Pseudotsuga (Douglas Fir). Also see **Conifers** and **Trees**

Needles discolour and drop prematurely	See discussion under Needle Casts p. 210
Leaves and stems with tufts of white wax wool covering small dark insects; foliage sooty	Adelgids p. 120
Stem with decay of wood which breaks into cubical fragments; fungal brackets may be present	Stem Rot p. 252

Pumpkin. See **Cucumber**

Pyracantha

Leaves and stems with tufts of white wax wool	Woolly Aphids p. 108
Leaves eaten and sometimes drawn together with silk webbing	Caterpillars p. 132
Leaves and stems infested by brown, waxy scales; foliage sticky and sooty	Scale Insects p. 124

Shoots die back; masses of small, usually pink pustules present — Coral Spot p. 216

Shoots exude slime and die back; flowers and/or leaves shrivelled — Fireblight p. 217

Pyrus. See **Pear;** many of the problems affecting pears can occur on ornamental *Pyrus* species also

Quercus (Oak). Also see **Trees**

Leaves with powdery white coating — Powdery Mildew p. 204

Leaves with pink-purple blisters — Leaf Curl p. 222

Leaves with irregular holes and pieces eaten away — Caterpillars p. 132, Chafers p. 163

Leaves with yellow and brown mottling on uppersides, small yellow insects on undersides; leaves may fall prematurely — Oak Phylloxera p. 123

Leaves, buds, stems, acorns or roots with unusual growths (galls) of varied form — Gall Wasps p. 158

Branches with dormant buds bursting into leaf late in season — Disturbed Growth p. 297

Quince. For **Japanese Quince** see **Chaenomeles**

Flowers and/or buds die suddenly — Frost p. 292

Fruit with soft brown rot and usually off-white cottony pustules; associated twigs may die back — Brown Rot p. 235

Fruit with round, dark, saucer-like depressions; usually only in store — Bitter Rot p. 234

Leaves and/or other parts with powdery white coating — Apple Powdery Mildew p. 205

Leaves with silvery sheen; branches die back — Silver Leaf p. 221

Branch and/or stem with hard irregular swelling — Crown Gall p. 224

Branches die back; leaves with silvery sheen — Silver Leaf p. 221

Radish

Radishes have many problems in common with their close relatives, **Brassicas** (q.v.) although they also commonly have rough, corky patches on the roots caused by — Common Scab p. 229

Ranunculus

Leaves and/or other parts with powdery white coating — Powdery Mildew p. 204

Raspberry and **Loganberry**

Fruits malformed and infested by small white beetle larvae — Raspberry Beetle p. 165

Fruit rotted and with powdery grey mould growth — Grey Mould p. 232

Flowers killed suddenly — Frost p. 292

Leaves and/or other parts with powdery white coating — Strawberry Powdery Mildew p. 208

Leaves with yellowish mosaics or mottles; plants may be unthrifty — Viruses p. 277

Leaves with yellow pustules on uppersides or orange and/or black pustules beneath — Rusts p. 191

Leaves more or less bleached; veins remain dark green — Iron Deficiency p. 288

Leaves wilt; canes with blue striping on one side — Wilt p. 211

Leaves, canes and/or other parts with purple grey-centred spots	Cane and Leaf Spots p. 258
Leaves and shoots infested by small green or yellow wingless and winged insects; foliage sticky and sooty	Aphids p. 104
Leaves with light flecking, sometimes with more extensive discolouration; small yellow insects and cast skins on undersides	Leafhoppers p. 98
Leaves with irregular holes and pieces eaten away, sometimes reduced to a skeleton of veins	Caterpillars p. 132 or Sawflies p. 154
Leaves with small tattered holes, especially near tips of shoots	Capsid Bugs p. 97
Shoots and leaves with white froth covering small wingless insects	Froghoppers p. 98
Canes with small pink or orange-red larvae under discoloured areas of bark, especially near cracks and wounds	Raspberry Cane Midge p. 146
Canes with dark, cracked patches just above soil level	Cane Blight p. 219
Canes with dark purple patches in summer; silvery sheen in winter	Spur Blight p. 219
Canes with hard, irregular swellings	Crown Gall p. 224
Canes die back; roots and stem base decayed; toadstools and boot-lace-like strands may be present	Honey Fungus p. 249

Red Currants. See **Currants**

Rhizomes. See **Bulbs etc.**

Rhododendron (including **Azalea**)

Flowers and/or buds shrivelled and with fluffy grey mould growth	Grey Mould p. 232
Flower buds covered with numerous tiny black pinhead-like structures	Bud Blast p. 232
Leaves mottled yellow on uppersides with rusty brown deposits on undersides; insects present on undersides during summer	Rhododendron Bug p. 96
Leaves with small white winged insects and yellow scales on undersides, especially at tips of shoots; foliage sticky and sooty	Rhododendron Whitefly p. 103 or Azalea Whitefly p. 103
Leaves with small iregular notches eaten out of edges, especially on lower leaves	Vine Weevil p. 170
Leaves variously spotted	Leaf Spot p. 258
Leaves and buds infested by winged insects with conspicuous red stripes on green wing cases	Rhododendron Leafhopper p. 99
Shoots with irregular small, usually greyish growths	Lichen p. 273
Branches die back; leaves sparse and yellowed; tissues at stem base may be blackened and decayed	Phytophthora Root Death p. 251
Stem with large, irregular, woody swellings	Crown Gall p. 224

Rhubarb

Leaves with mosaic patterns or irregular yellowish streaks	Viruses p. 277
Leaves wilt; crown with brown or black streaks within	Wilt p. 211
Leaves discoloured and distorted, crowns soft and rotten	Stem Eelworm p. 84

- Roots and crown base rotted; toadstools and bootlace-like strands may be present — Honey Fungus p. 249
- Roots eaten by white caterpillars in soil — Swift Moths p. 137

Rhus (Sumach). Also see **Trees**
- Buds and/or leaves shrivelled or scorched suddenly — Frost p. 292
- Leaves wilt in absence of obvious damage or stress factors — Wilt p. 211

Ribes. For ornamental *Ribes* see **Currants**

Robinia (False acacia). Also see **Trees**
- Leaves wilt in absence of obvious damage or stress factors — Wilt p. 211
- Branches with parasitic, leathery plant growing from them — Mistletoe p. 276

Rosa (Roses)
- Flowers, flower buds and leaves with irregular holes and pieces eaten away — Caterpillars p. 132; Chafers p. 163
- Flowers with fine light flecking; narrow-bodied insects present — Thrips p. 129
- Flowers and/or buds shrivelled and with fluffy grey mould growth — Grey Mould p. 232
- Leaves, buds, shoots and stems infested by green, pink or brown wingless and winged insects; foliage sticky, sometimes sooty — Aphids p. 104
- Leaves with fine white mottling, sometimes causing extensive discolouration; small green or yellow insects and their cast skins present on undersides — Leafhoppers p. 98
- Leaves with small tattered holes, especially at tips of shoots — Capsid Bugs p. 97
- Leaves with regular, almost semicircular pieces removed from edges — Leaf-Cutter Bee p. 162
- Leaves with surface tissues eaten away, exposing veins; green or yellow larvae present — Rose Slug Sawfly p. 156
- Leaves with leaflets tightly rolled along their length and drooping — Leaf-Rolling Rose Sawfly p. 157
- Leaves discoloured, yellowing, bronzing and sometimes dying; small mites present on undersides — Glasshouse Red Spider Mites p. 173
- Leaves and/or other parts with powdery white coating — Powdery Mildew p. 204
- Leaves with dark, blackish spots or blotches — Black Spot p. 270
- Leaves and/or other parts with bright orange pustules — Rusts p. 191
- Leaves with small yellow or black pustules on undersides — Rusts p. 191
- Leaves with various irregular yellowish streaks and patterns — Viruses p. 277
- Leaves more or less bleached; veins remain dark green — Iron Deficiency p. 288
- Leaves wilt in absence of obvious damage or stress factors — Wilt p. 211
- Leaves with silvery sheen; branches may die back — Silver Leaf p. 221
- Shoots with hard, irregular swelling (*Note:* Such swellings associated with graft unions or on heavily and regularly pruned stems may well be normal) — Crown Gall p. 224
- Shoots with various types of canker lesions and/or dieback — Cankers p. 214

Plants generally unthrifty	Deficiencies of Nitrogen p. 284, Phosphorus p. 285 and Potassium p. 285

Rose. See **Rosa**

Rowan. See **Sorbus**

Rubber Plant (Ficus). See **Glasshouse and House Plants**

Rudbeckia. See **Perennials**

Saintpaulia (African Violet). Also see **Glasshouse and House Plants**

Flowers distorted, growth poor; small mites present in buds and growing points	Tarsonemid Mites p. 176
Leaves and/or stems rotted; sometimes mould growth present	Stem and Leaf Rots p. 252
Note: Correct diagnosis of the varied symptoms shown by saintpaulias can prove difficult. If in doubt, seek expert advice.	

Salix (Willow). Also see **Trees**

Leaves with irregular holes and pieces eaten away, sometimes reduced to a skeleton of veins	Caterpillars p. 132, Sawflies p. 154 or Willow Leaf Beetles p. 168
Leaves with conspicuous hard raised yellow or bright red bean-like growths (galls)	Willow Bean-Gall Sawfly p. 157
Leaves discoloured, yellowing, bronzing, drying out and often falling prematurely; small mites, eggs and silk webbing present	Red Spider Mites p. 172
Leaves and shoots infested by small yellow or green wingless and winged insects; foliage sticky and sooty	Aphids p. 104
Leaves with black, bitumen-like spots	See Acer Tar Spot p. 260
Leaves with silvery sheen; branches may die back	Silver Leaf p. 221
Leaves with small red-brown spots; small lesions on twigs; entire tree dies back (esp. weeping willow)	Anthracnose p. 222
Stems and branches infested by dense colonies of grey-brown wingless insects; foliage usually very sticky and sooty and attractive to wasps	Large Willow Aphid p. 119
Stems infested by small white scales; foliage sticky and sooty	Willow Scale p. 126
Branches with hard irregular swellings	Crown Gall p. 224
Branches with parasitic leathery plant growing from them (esp. on *Salix fragilis*)	Mistletoe p. 276

Salsify

Leaves and/or other parts with powdery white coating	Powdery Mildew p. 204

Salvia. Also see **Glasshouse and House Plants** and **Bedding Plants**

Leaves with small tattered holes, especially at tips of shoots	Capsid Bugs p. 97

Sambucus (Elderberry)
Leaves with various yellowish streaks and patterns and/or distortion — Viruses p. 277

Sansevieria. See **Glasshouse and House Plants**

Savoy. See **Brassicas**

Saxifraga (Saxifrage). See **Cacti and Succulents**

Scabiosa (Scabious)
Leaves and/or other parts with powdery white coating — Powdery Mildew p. 204

Scabious. See **Scabiosa**

Schizanthus. Also see **Glasshouse and House Plants**
Leaves and/or other parts with powdery white coating — Powdery Mildew p. 204

Schizostylis. See **Bulbs etc.**

Scilla (Squill). See **Bulbs etc.**

Scorzonera
Leaves and/or other parts with powdery white coating — Powdery Mildew p. 204

Sea Kale. See **Brassicas**

Sedum. See **Cacti and Succulents**

Seedlings

Young seedlings are especially susceptible to pests and diseases and may also suffer from disorders, especially those caused by under- or over-watering and by low temperatures during germination and establishment. Diagnosis of the causes of trouble may be difficult since seedlings quickly die and rot away, leaving no symptoms, but the following key can be used to identify the main causes of trouble.

Seedlings pulled out of soil; pecked and torn — Birds p. 179
Seedlings scratched out of soil — Cats p. 188
Seedlings collapse and die; stems eaten into at soil level, roots damaged — Cutworms p. 136, Leatherjackets p. 147, Wireworms p. 163
Seedlings collapse and die, usually in patches, and with blackening and decay of the stem base and/or fluffy grey mould growth present — Damping-off p. 243
Seedlings with leaves yellowed, sometimes with dry angular blotches, and generally stunted; roots may rot — Waterlogging p. 295
Seedlings with leaves variously discoloured – check Plates 21–22 giving symptoms of Mineral Nutrient Deficiency
Seedlings with leaves and growing points eaten away — Slugs p. 90, Woodlice p. 93, Cockroaches p. 95
Seedlings, especially of brassicas, with small round pits and holes; jumping beetles present — Flea Beetles p. 165
Seedlings with leaves minutely pitted; minute, wingless jumping insects present — Springtails p. 94

Sempervivum (Houseleek). See **Cacti and Succulents**

Senecio For *Senecio cruentus* see **Cineraria** and for succulent forms see **Cacti and Succulents.** Also see **Bedding Plants**
Leaves and/or other parts with powdery white coating — Powdery Mildew p. 204

Sequoia, Sequoiadendron (Redwood). See **Conifers** and **Trees**

Shallot. See **Onion**

Shrubs

Ornamental shrubs are generally robust, once established, but may be affected by some of the pests, diseases and disorders noted under **Trees.** Also see separate entries for the main plant genera.

Sidalcea

Leaves and/or stem with raised orange-brown pustules	Hollyhock Rust p. 196

Sinningia (Gloxinia). See **Glasshouse and House Plants**

Skimmia

Leaves more or less bleached; veins remain dark green	Iron Deficiency p. 288
Leaves scorched suddenly in spring; blossom may be killed	Frost p. 292

Snapdragon. See **Antirrhinum**

Snowdrop. See **Galanthus**

Solanum

Ornamental *Solanum* species may be expected to have many problems in common with **Potato** *(S. tuberosum)* q.v., esp.:

Leaves with irregular, yellowish streaks and patterns and/or various forms of distortion; plants generally unthrifty	Viruses p. 277

Solidago (Golden rod). Also see **Perennials**

Leaves and/or other parts with powdery white coating	Powdery Mildew p. 204

Solomon's Seal. See **Polygonatum**

Sorbus (including Mountain Ash). Also see **Trees**

Berries eaten	Birds p. 179
Leaves with yellow or brown blister-like growths	Pear Leaf Blister Mite p. 178
Leaves with irregular pieces eaten away	Caterpillars p. 132
Shoots exude slime and die back; flowers and/or leaves shrivelled	Fireblight p. 217

Sparmannia. See **Trees**

Spider Plant. See **Glasshouse and House Plants**

Spinach (including Spinach Beet)

Leaves with brown blotch mines	Beet Leaf Miner p. 149
Leaves with small black wingless and winged insects	Black Bean Aphid p. 112
Leaves with pale yellowish spots and grey-purple mould growth beneath	Downy Mildew p. 202
Leaves yellowed and curled or otherwise distorted; symptoms on inner leaves first; entire plant may later wilt and die	Viruses p. 277
Leaves yellowed between veins; symptoms on outer leaves first which may curl upwards at edges	Manganese Deficiency p. 289
Plants run to flower	Bolting p. 297

Spruce. See **Picea**

Squash. See **Cucumber**

Squill. See **Scilla**

St John's Wort. See **Hypericum**

Stapelia. Also see **Glasshouse and House Plants**

Symptom	Cause
Leaves with yellowish mottling or other irregular patterns	Viruses p. 277

Stephanotis. Also see **Glasshouse and House Plants**

Symptom	Cause
Leaves with yellowish mottling or other irregular patterns	Viruses p. 277

Sternbergia. Also see **Bulbs etc.**

Symptom	Cause
Leaves with red-brown scorch, spreading downwards from tip; gradually shrivel and die; flower stalks and flowers may also have brown discolouration	Narcissus Leaf Scorch p. 267

Stock. See **Matthiola**

Stranvaesia. Also see **Trees**

Symptom	Cause
Shoots exude slime and die back; flowers and/or leaves shrivelled	Fireblight p. 217

Strawberry

Symptom	Cause
Fruits pecked and eaten	Birds p. 179
Fruits with large pieces eaten out; slime trails present on and near plants	Slugs and Snails p. 90
Fruits with small cavities, seeds eaten, black beetles present under trusses and straw	Strawberry Beetles p. 164
Fruit with soft rot and fluffy grey mould growth	Grey Mould p. 232
Fruit leathery, brown and shrivelled; fruit stalks shrivelled	Leathery Fruit Rot p. 237
Flowers killed suddenly; young leaves may be scorched	Frost p. 292
Flowers deformed and with green colouration	Mycoplasma p. 277
Leaves and/or other parts with powdery white coating; leaves curl upwards at margins	Powdery Mildew p. 204
Leaves and/or other parts variously spotted	Leaf Blotch, Leaf Scorch or Leaf Spot p. 258
Leaves more or less bleached; veins remain dark green	Iron Deficiency p. 288
Leaves with yellow margins in late summer; plants stunted	Viruses p. 277
Leaves with various yellowish patterns or streaks, distortion and/or crumpling	Viruses p. 277
Leaves wilt, (outer first); stem interior with brown or black streaks	Wilt p. 211
Leaves and shoots infested by small green or yellow wingless and winged insects; foliage sticky and sooty	Aphids p. 104
Leaves discoloured, yellowing, bronzing and dying; small mites and silk webbing present	Glasshouse Red Spider Mite p. 173
Leaves crumpled and distorted; white marks alongside veins; growth stunted	Eelworms p. 84
Stems eaten through at ground level; plants wilt and die	Cutworms p. 136
Plants wilt and die; roots eaten by small white legless larvae in soil	Vine Weevil p. 170
Plants stunted; older leaves turn brown and hang down; root with black regions	Root Rot p. 242

Plants stunted; central leaves small; outer, brown and stiff; central core of roots (other than in summer) appears red	Red Core p. 248

Strawberry Tree. See **Arbutus**

Streptocarpus. See **Glasshouse and House Plants**

Succulents. See **Cacti and Succulents**

Sunflower. See **Helianthus**

Sumach. See **Rhus**

Swede, Turnip

Leaves and/or other parts with powdery white coating	Powdery Mildew p. 204
Leaves with pale yellowish patches and greyish mould beneath	Crucifer Downy Mildew p. 202
Leaves with yellowish inter-veinal mottling, crinkling and stunting	Viruses p. 277
Leaves with tiny more or less circular dirty white spots with purplish border	White Spot p. 263
Leaves and/or other parts with small, often concentric clusters of creamy droplets	White Blister p. 210
Leaves of seedlings with small circular holes and pits	Flea Beetles p. 165
Stems eaten through at ground level; plants wilt and die	Cutworms p. 136
Roots with holes eaten out by white caterpillars in soil	Swift Moths p. 137
Roots tunnelled by white maggots	Cabbage Root Fly p. 150
Roots decayed with matted dark strands	Violet Root Rot p. 241
Roots with soft and slimy rot	Bacterial Soft Rot p. 234
Roots with irregular fairly soft swellings and often some decay; plants may be stunted	Clubroot p. 223
Roots with hard irregular swellings; no decay; plants otherwise normal	Hybridisation Nodules p. 276
Roots (in store) with soft rot and grey fluffy mould growth	Grey Mould p. 232
Roots with scab-like patches of corky tissue	Common Scab p. 229

Sweet Corn (and ornamental maize)

Seeds removed from soil after sowing	Birds p. 179
Leaves with yellow streaks, later fraying; fly maggots tunnelling in shoots, killing growing points and checking growth	Frit Fly p. 148
Cobs malformed and containing black powder	Smuts p. 199
Cobs fail to develop; whitish stripes on leaves	Boron Deficiency p. 289

Sweet Pea. See **Lathyrus**

Sweet William. See **Dianthus**

Sycamore. See **Acer**

Syringa (Lilac). Also see **Trees**

Leaves with powdery white coating	Powdery Mildew p. 204

Symptom	Cause
Leaves with yellowish patterns or streaks and/or malformation	Viruses p. 277
Leaves with brown blotch mines	Lilac Leaf Miner p. 144
Leaves with semi-circular pieces cut out of edges	Leaf Cutter Bee p. 162
Stems infested by small white scales; foliage sticky and sooty	Willow Scale p. 126

Tigridia (Tiger Flower). See **Bulbs etc.**

Taxus (Yew). Also see **Conifers** and **Trees**

Symptom	Cause
Leaves eaten away, leaving bare sections on shoots, often with bark removed	Weevils p. 168
Shoot tips enlarged to form growths (galls) like miniature artichokes	Yew Gall Midge p. 152
Stems with hemispherical brown scales; leaves often sticky and sooty	Scale Insects p. 124
Branches die back; leaves sparse and yellowed; tissues at stem base may be blackened and decayed	Phytophthora Root Death p. 251

Tagetes (African marigold). See **Bedding Plants**

Tilia (Lime). Also see **Trees**

Symptom	Cause
Leaves and buds infested by small green or yellow wingless and winged insects; foliage often very sticky and sooty	Aphids p. 104
Leaves with bright red growths (galls) projecting from upper surfaces	Nail Gall Mite p. 179
Leaves with irregular holes and pieces eaten away	Caterpillars p. 132
Leaves discoloured, yellowing, bronzing and dying; small mites and silk webbing present; trunks sometimes covered in glistening sheets of webbing during late summer and autumn	Red Spider Mites p. 172
Leaves and/or other parts with sticky black coating	Sooty Mould p. 209
Leaves wilt in absence of obvious damage or stress factors	Wilt p. 211
Branches die back; masses of small, usually pink pustules present	Coral Spot p. 216
Branches with parasitic leathery plant growing from them	Mistletoe p. 276
Branches die back; leaves sparse and yellowed; tissues and stem base may be blackened and decayed	Phytophthora Root Death p. 251

Tobacco. See **Nicotiana**

Tomato

Symptom	Cause
Fruit split; no rotting or mould growth	Splitting p. 298
Fruit with small white spots; esp. late in season	Ghost Spotting p. 272
Fruit with soft and slimy rot (usually in store); no mould growth	Bacterial Soft Rot p. 234
Fruit with tough dryish rot and sometimes white mould growth; may be dark blotches on leaves and stems	Blight p. 219 but also see Stem and Fruit Rot p. 252

Symptom	Cause
Fruit with hard, dark patch at blossom end ('blossom-end rot')	Calcium Deficiency p. 286
Fruit with hard dark green or sometimes yellow patches when remainder ripens	High Temperature p. 294
Fruit ripen with irregular patches of ripe and unripe tissue	Viruses p. 277 Potassium Deficiency p. 285 or Drought p. 291
Fruit hollow	Drought p. 291, Potassium Deficiency p. 285 or Hormone Herbicide Injury p. 301
Flowers and/or buds shrivelled and with fluffy grey mould growth	Grey Mould p. 232
Flowers fail to set fruit satisfactorily	Viruses p. 277 or Drought p. 291
Leaves and shoots infested by green or pink-brown wingless and winged insects; leaves and fruits sticky and sooty	Aphids p. 104
Leaves with white winged insects and yellow scales on undersides; foliage and fruits sticky and sooty	Glasshouse Whitefly p. 102
Leaves with irregular white spots; yellow insects and cast skins on undersides	Glasshouse Leafhoppers p. 99
Leaves discoloured, yellowing, bronzing and dying; small mites on undersides	Glasshouse Red Spider Mite p. 173
Leaves discoloured, plants wilting and dying; small white, yellow or brown cysts on roots	Potato Cyst Eelworm p. 89
Leaves wilting, growth poor; roots with hard irregular growths (galls)	Root-Knot Eelworm p. 88
Leaves with sinuous white mines	Leaf Miner p. 144
Leaves with dark blotches which may bear white mould growth; fruit may also be rotted (usually outdoor plants only)	Blight p. 219
Leaves with pale yellow patches on upper surface with grey-brown mould beneath (usually glasshouse plants only)	Leaf Mould p. 256
Leaves and/or other parts, thickened, twisted or otherwise distorted	Hormone Herbicide Injury p. 301 but also see Viruses p. 277
Leaves (undersides) and/or stems with rough warty outgrowths	Oedema p. 297
Leaves with yellowish mottling and/or distortion	Viruses p. 277
Leaves wilt in absence of obvious damage or stress factors; no dark streaking in stem	Viruses p. 277 or Drought p. 291
Leaves wilt; stem interior with brown or black streaks well above soil level	Wilt p. 211
Leaves wilt; stem undamaged except possibly at base; roots blackened or decayed	Root and Foot Rots p. 242
Leaves with irregular silvery sheen	Silvering p. 298
Leaves curl in absence of obvious damage or stress factors plant otherwise normal – this is quite normal especially on outdoor tomatoes and no action is necessary	

Leaves turn blue-green, then yellow and wilt; plants unthrifty	Copper Deficiency p. 290
Leaves with marked interveinal yellowing on older leaves first (Note however that this symptom can arise on tomatoes quite normally as leaves begin to age and decline and/or are deeply shaded)	Magnesium Deficiency p. 287
Stem with patches of rot and grey mould growth esp. around leaf scars and pruning cuts	Grey Mould Stem Rot p. 236
Stem with large irregular swelling	Crown Gall p. 224
Roots blackened and/or decayed; plants unthrifty	Root and Foot Rots p. 242
Roots with rough and warty appearance	Potato Powdery Scab p. 230

Tradescantia. See **Glasshouse and House Plants**

Trees. Also see **Conifers** and individual entries for the main tree genera.

Young trees may be seriously damaged during their early growth by **Rabbits** (p. 183), **Hares** (p. 184), **Voles** (p. 186) and some other mammals that strip bark from the stems just above soil level. Mechanical barriers, such as spiral card or plastic tree protectors or wire netting should be used to prevent damage in areas where these pests are known to be present. Growth of young trees may also be checked by **Aphids** (p. 104) and **Caterpillars** (p. 132) feeding on buds, leaves and young shoots. The most important symptoms are:

Stems of young plants with bark stripped away at or above soil level	Voles p. 186, Rabbits p. 183, Hares p. 184, Deer p. 187, Squirrels p. 184
Leaves with irregular holes and pieces eaten away, sometimes reduced to a skeleton of veins	Caterpillars p. 132, Sawflies p. 154, Chafers p. 163
Leaves, buds and young shoots infested by small wingless and winged insects, especially on undersides of leaves; foliage sticky and sooty	Aphids p. 104
Leaves, buds or other parts with abnormal growths (galls) of varied form	Gall Midges p. 152, Gall Mites p. 177, Gall Wasps p. 158
Leaves with powdery white coating	Powdery Mildew p. 204
Leaves with sticky black coating	Sooty Mould p. 209
Leaves wilt in absence of obvious damage or stress factors	Wilt p. 211
Foliage of large part of tree, esp. facing prevailing wind, browned	Wind Scorching p. 296
Branches die back; masses of small, usually pink pustules present	Coral Spot p. 216
Branches with masses of proliferating shoots like large birds' nests	Witches' Brooms p. 227

Branches die back; leaves sparse and yellowing; tissues and stem base may be blackened and decayed	Phytophthora Root Death p. 251
Branches die back; roots and stem base decayed; toadstools and bootlace-like strands may be present	Honey Fungus p. 249
Branches with leathery parasitic plants growing from them	Mistletoe p. 276
Branches with some gross abnormality, e.g. twisted, flattened, or deeply fluted	Disturbed Growths p. 297
Branches with bark stripped, buds eaten and/or fruits damaged	Squirrels p. 184
Stems and/or branches with hard, irregular swelling	Crown Gall p. 224
Stems shattered, often for total height of tree	Lightning p. 295
Stems and/or branches broken off	Wind p. 296
Stems with some decay of wood; fungal brackets may be present.	Tree and Shrub Rots p.248
Trees with green or greyish growth on bark	Lichen p. 273, Algae p. 274
Trees overgrown by climbing plants	Ivy p. 275, Honeysuckle p. 275, Clematis p. 275
Trees with brown or purple scaly leafless plants growing beneath	Toothworts p. 274
Trees with toadstools or fungal brackets growing from or beneath them	Tree and Shrub Rots p. 248, Mycorrhiza p. 276
Trees generally unthrifty	See discussion under Mechanical Injury p. 298

Trillium. See **Bulbs etc.**

Tropaeolum (Nasturtium)

Leaves with irregular holes and pieces eaten away	Cabbage Caterpillars p. 138
Leaves and stems infested by small black insects	Black Bean Aphid p. 112

Tsuga (Hemlock). Also see **Conifers** and **Trees**

Needles turn brown and drop prematurely	See discussion under Needle Casts p. 210

Tubers

Tubers with soft and slimy rot	Bacterial Soft Rot p. 234
Tubers rotted and with matted dark strands	Violet Root Rot p. 241
Tubers with decay and blue-green mould growth	Fungal Rot p. 231

Also see individual entries under main plant genera, especially under **Potato**, and see **Bulbs etc.**

Tulipa (Tulip). Also see **Bulbs etc.**

Flowers, leaves and stems distorted	Stem Eelworm p. 84
Flowers of dark coloured types with pale streaks	Viruses p. 277
Leaves variously streaked and/or distorted	Viruses p. 277
Leaves with regular patterns of holes in early spring; slime trails may be present	Slugs p. 90
Shoots, buds and/or other parts withered and with fluffy grey mould growth	Fire Disease p. 257
Bulbs in store eaten	Mice p. 185
Bulbs in store infested by brown or yellow wingless insects, especially on shoots	Tulip Bulb Aphid p. 118

Bulbs dug up after planting	Squirrels p. 184
Bulbs with dry rot and with soil adhering to whitish mould when dug up; plants emerge feebly	Bulb Rot p. 231
Roots blackened and rotted; decay not usually extending into bulb	Root and Foot Rots p. 242

Turf. See **Lawns**

Turnip. See **Swede**

Ulmus (Elm). Also see **Trees**

Leaves wilt, turn yellow and die; entire tree becomes unthrifty and dies back; no root damage but many galleries visible when bark peeled from trunk	Dutch Elm Disease p. 212
Leaves with green or brown blisters	Leaf Curl p. 222
Leaves with various irregular yellowish streaks or mottles	Viruses p. 277
Leaves with rashes of small blister-like growths (galls)	Gall Mites p. 177
Bark of dead trees tunnelled by larvae making characteristic radiating galleries	Elm Bark Beetles p. 171
Branches die back; leaves wilt; turn yellow and die; entire tree becomes unthrifty; no root damage but many galleries visible when bark peeled from trunk	Dutch Elm Disease p. 212
Branches die back; masses of small, usually pink pustules present	Coral Spot p. 216
Branches with deeply grooved bark	Winged Cork p. 298
Stem rotten or hollowed extensively; fungal brackets may be present; decay often associated with wounds	Tree and Shrub Rots p. 248
Stem and sometimes entire crown overgrown by evergreen climbing plant	Ivy p. 275
Stem with large irregular swelling	Crown Gall p. 224

Valeriana (Valerian)

Leaves and/or other parts with powdery white coating	Powdery Mildew p. 204

Vallota. See **Bulbs etc.**

Vanda. See **Orchids**

Verbascum (Mullein)

Leaves and/or other parts with powdery white coating	Powdery Mildew p. 204

Verbena. See **Bedding Plants**

Veronica (including Hebe)

Leaves variously spotted; shoots may die back and plants become unthrifty	Leaf Spot p. 258

Viburnum. Also see **Trees**

Flowers and/or buds shrivelled and with fluffy grey mould growth	Grey Mould p. 232
Flowers and/or buds killed suddenly; leaves may be scorched	Frost p. 292
Leaves of *Viburnum tinus* sticky and sooty; white-fringed black scales on undersides	Viburnum Whitefly p. 103

Vine. See **Grape Vine** for both fruiting and ornamental types, and see **Parthenocissus** for **Virginia Creeper**

Viola (Viola, Violet, Pansy)

Leaves and/or other parts with powdery white coating	Powdery Mildew p. 204
Leaves with various irregular yellowish mottles, crumpling and/or other distortions	Viruses p. 277
Leaves with edges rolled and thickened; white or orange larvae present inside	Violet Leaf Midge p. 152
Leaved discoloured, yellowing, bronzing and dying; small mites present on undersides, sometimes with silk webbing	Glasshouse Red Spider Mite p. 173
Leaves, buds and shoots infested by green, yellow or pink wingless and winged insects; foliage sticky and sooty	Aphids p. 104
Leaves with irregular holes and pieces eaten away; slime trails present on or near plants	Slugs and Snails p. 90
Stem base and/or roots blackened and decayed	Root and Foot Rots p. 242

Violet. See **Viola** and for **African Violet** see **Saintpaulia**

Virginia Creeper. See **Parthenocissus**

Vitis (Vines). See **Grape Vine** for both fruiting and ornamental types

Wallflower. See **Cheiranthus**

Water-Lily. See **Nymphaea**

Willow. See **Salix**

White Currants. See **Currants**

Wistaria. Also see **Climbing Plants**

Flowers pecked and torn	Birds p. 179
Leaves with yellowing of veins or yellowish mottling	Viruses p. 277
Branches die back; masses of small, usually pink pustules present	Coral Spot p. 216

Yew. See **Taxus**

Yucca. Also see **Cacti and Succulents** and **Glasshouse and House Plants**

Leaves with ovoid, dark brownish spots	Leaf Spot p. 258

Zantedeschia (Arum Lily). Also see **Bulbs etc.** and **Glasshouse and House Plants**

Leaves and/or other parts with grey-black, thumb-print like spots	Leaf Spot p. 258
Leaves irregularly mottled or with yellowish streaks and patterns and distortion	Viruses p. 277
Corms and/or other parts with soft slimy rot	Bacterial Soft Rot p. 234
Roots and/or stem base blackened and decayed	Root and Foot Rots p. 242

Zinnia. Also see **Bedding Plants**

Flowers and/or buds shrivelled and with fluffy grey mould	Grey Mould p. 232

Zucchini. See **Cucumber**

Pests

The pests that are dealt with in this section are either vertebrate or invertebrate animals. Of the vertebrates, only a few species of birds and mammals are important pests in gardens. Invertebrate animals are generally much more numerous than vertebrates, both in numbers of individuals and in numbers of species, and it is therefore not surprising to find that most pests are invertebrates. Of these, the majority are insects which, with a world total of about a million species described, and possibly as many yet to be recognised and described, far outnumber all other groups of animals. Fortunately only a small proportion of all insects are pests but the list of pest species is still a very long one. In addition to insects, a few smaller groups of invertebrates, especially eelworms, slugs and snails, millepedes, woodlice and mites, contain some pest species.

Pests mainly affect garden plants by feeding directly on living plant tissues, either by biting, chewing and ingesting them or by piercing them to feed on sap. In most cases only the immature stages feed on plants but sometimes the adults do also. Symptoms vary considerably and all parts of plants may be affected by some pest or other. In a few instances whole plants may be eaten or killed but damage is usually restricted to some particular part (leaf, stem, bud, flower, fruit, etc.). Damage done to flowers, to fruits and to vegetables at or near harvest is of obvious importance, since it has a direct effect on both the quantity and the quality of garden produce, but less conspicuous damage to leaves, stems and roots may impair growth and may also make plants more susceptible to invasion by pathogens. Some pests may also produce special effects, such as the development of galls, which are abnormal growths of plant tissues, or of leaf-mines.

Pests also have important indirect effects on plants, especially by transmitting viruses and some other organisms that cause diseases, and also by fouling plants with excretions. The sticky honeydew that is excreted by aphids and other sap-feeding insects is a particular nuisance since it encourages the growth of sooty moulds on plants and this, in addition to making plants look unsightly, must also reduce photosynthetic activity by cutting off light from leaves.

Because of the great range in size, from gall mites that are less than 0.25 mm long to fallow deer that stand about a metre high, and because of similar great variation in the biology of different groups of pests, their impact on plants and also the methods used to prevent or minimise damage differ substantially from group to group. In the following pages basic information about the most important garden pests is summarised. Eelworms, slugs and snails, earthworms, millepedes and woodlice are dealt with first, followed by the main groups of insects, which take up most of this section, then mites, birds and finally mammals.

EELWORMS

(Plate 1)

Also known as nematodes (Nematoda). Microscopic, usually 1–2 mm long, about 0.1 mm wide, just visible against a dark background. Seen through a microscope they look like miniature translucent eels (Pl. 1). Head end is relatively blunt, with characteristic minute internal mouth-spear in many species. Tail tapers. Female cyst eelworms swell to form spherical brown cysts about 0.5 mm diameter (Pl. 1) and root-knot eelworms swell to pear shape. Males are generally smaller than females. World-wide distribution with many different species living in soil, water, animals (some as important parasites) and in living and dead plant tissues. Plant parasitic species feed internally or externally on plant tissues by puncturing cells with the mouth-spear and extracting fluid contents. This causes discolouration, distortion and death of affected plants. Some species also transmit virus diseases (see p. 277). Females lay minute eggs in plant tissues or in soil. Larvae usually hatch within a few days and feed, grow and moult to adults in 2–3 weeks. Populations increase rapidly in favourable conditions and a single infested plant may contain many millions of active eelworms. Normal development only proceeds in fluid environments but non-feeding dormant larvae and dormant eggs in cysts can survive desiccation for many years. Plant parasitic eelworms can move a few metres a year through soil but are mostly spread in infested plants, plant debris and soil carried by man, animals, wind or water.

STEM EELWORM *Ditylenchus dipsaci* Pl. 1

Also known as stem and bulb eelworm and some of its biological races are referred to as narcissus eelworm, tulip eelworm, onion eelworm and phlox eelworm. This species has been recorded from more than 400 different species of wild and cultivated plants. World-wide distribution.

Symptoms. Diagnosis of stem eelworm attack on symptoms alone is not always easy since similar symptoms may be produced by other pests and by some diseases and disorders. Doubtful cases should be referred to specialists, if possible.

Fruit. Only strawberries are seriously damaged. Plants growing slowly in spring are stunted and leaves are crinkled, crumpled and brittle. Leaf and flower stalks are thickened, often with brown cores. Ripening fruits develop light coloured soft patches. Leaf eelworms (p. 87), tarsonemid mites (p. 176) and virus diseases (p. 277) cause similar symptoms.

Vegetables. Onions: plants swell at base in spring and early summer. Leaves are swollen and distorted, producing the condition known as onion bloat (Pl. 1). Bulbs crack and rot, plants die. Similar symptoms develop on shallots, chives, garlic and leeks. Parsnips: crowns rot, dry and split; leaf bases swell and split. Symptoms may be confused by presence of other pests and diseases. Similar symptoms develop on carrots in some areas. Beans: severe attacks on broad beans stunt and malform plants and distort pods. Light infestations produce red to black patches at bases of stems causing collapse of plants at soil level. French and runner beans are also occasionally attacked. Stems swell, blister and brown and severely damaged plants are stunted, with leaves tightly bunched together. Rhubarb: crowns of young plants rot at ground level in spring. Stalks swell at base, split and rot. A bacterium, *Erwinia rhapontici*, is sometimes said to be associated with this condition. Also occasionally attacks peas, potatoes, lettuce, spinach and swedes, producing various similar symptoms.

Ornamentals. Narcissus, tulips, hyacinths, scillas and snowdrops are often seriously damaged. Infested bulbs feel soft, especially at necks, and show discoloured brown rings of dead tissue when cut across with a knife (Pl. 1). Plants grown from infested bulbs are malformed, with distorted leaves and flowers (Pl. 1) and may not grow at all. Exact symptoms vary considerably. Daffodil leaves develop characteristic small green or yellow bumps ('spickels') (Pl. 1). Tulip leaves tend to split longitudinally, flower stalks bend and petals stay green. Perennial phlox show progressive narrowing of upper leaves which are reduced to a mid-rib with a narrow, frilly leaf blade. Similar symptoms develop on oenotheras. Aubrietias, campanulas, gypsophilas, heleniums, heucheras, hydrangeas, irises and many other ornamentals may also be attacked and show similar symptoms.

Biology. Adults, 1–2 mm long, move in soil and enter plants through small wounds and natural openings (stomata and lenticels). They feed inside plant tissues, moving freely among damaged cells. Females lay many eggs which soon hatch. Development from egg to adult takes only 2–3 weeks at summer temperatures. When infested plants decay, eelworms leave and move through soil to find new host plants. In dry conditions they become dormant and may survive for several years before reactivation by water. Masses of dormant 'eelworm wool' often form on infested bulbs in bulb stores. Various biological races are known, each race attacking a particular group of plants. Interactions of races and plants are complex and not fully understood.

Treatment. Prevent establishment and spread of eelworms by good hygiene, adequate rotation of crops and efficient weed control. Obtain new plants from reputable suppliers. Buying cheap planting material (especially bulbs) is a false economy since a few infested plants will quickly contaminate a whole garden. Destroy soft, discoloured bulbs by burning immediately and keep suspect plants in isolation until they can be checked for eelworm. If infestations develop, despite these precautions, restrict spread by removal of all affected plants. Destroy by burning or by burying in a deep hole well away from main garden. Also collect up leaves and other plant debris and prevent spread by wind, on shoes and on implements and containers. Do not grow susceptible hosts on affected areas for 2–3 years and control weeds, which can maintain eelworm populations.

Onion eelworm attacks may be avoided by growing from healthy seed rather than from sets and by rotating crops so that onions and related vegetables are only grown on the same site once every three years.

Infested stocks of perennial phlox should be propagated by taking true root cuttings since eelworms do not penetrate the roots. Avoid reinfestation by growing on a site well away from infested areas.

Commercial growers use hot water treatment to maintain healthy stocks of bulbs and this treatment is sometimes used by gardeners. Dormant narcissus bulbs are immersed in water maintained at 44.5°C (112°F) for three hours. The temperature is critical as it must be high enough to kill eelworms inside the tissues without killing the bulbs. Fine thermostatic control is therefore essential. Chemicals used by commercial growers for stem eelworm control are too toxic for garden use.

CHRYSANTHEMUM EELWORM

Aphelenchoides ritzemabosi **Pl. 1**

Also known as leaf and bud eelworm. Particularly damaging on late-flowering outdoor and glasshouse chrysanthemums but can attack more than 150 different plant species. Widespread distribution.

Symptoms. *Ornamentals.* Chrysanthemums are attacked at any stage of growth, from young cuttings to mature plants. Most attacks develop during cool wet summers or in autumn. Leaves are discoloured, hang limply against stems and eventually die, starting with lower leaves and spreading up plants (Pl. 1). Exact symptoms vary but usually some leaves show discrete dark areas between veins where tissues have been killed. Buds are also damaged, checking growth, and if the terminal bud is killed lateral shoots develop. Blooms growing from damaged buds are distorted and stems may be scarred. Cuttings are stunted and usually killed. Poor growth and leaf discolourations are also caused by some diseases and nutritional disorders. Eelworm diagnosis may be confirmed by breaking affected leaves into small pieces and leaving in water in a glass tube for half an hour. Eelworms, if present, will move out of the leaves and collect into a wriggling mass in the bottom of the tube. They should not be confused with leaf hairs which look very like eelworms but do not move. Seek expert advice in doubtful cases. Other ornamentals attacked include asters (both china and perennial), buddleias, calceolarias, dahlias, delphiniums, doronicums, lavenders, paeonies, penstemons, phlox, pyrethrums, rudbeckias, saintpaulias, verbenas, wallflowers and zinnias. Symptoms vary considerably but generally show as stunted growth and discoloured leaves.

Fruit. Strawberries show symptoms in early spring and again in autumn. Leaves are crumpled and distorted and have characteristic white marks along veins on upper surface where eelworms have fed. Severe attacks kill the growing point and multiple crowns develop; flower trusses are killed and fruiting is seriously affected. The same symptoms are also produced by leaf eelworm (p. 87) and both eelworms may be present together. Association of these eelworms with a bacterium causes severe stunting and swelling of leaf and flower stalks which is known as 'cauliflower' disease of strawberries. Blackcurrants are also attacked by chrysanthemum eelworm in winter and early spring. Eelworms feed in buds causing distortion of developing leaves and checking growth. Buds are sometimes killed.

Biology. Very similar to stem eelworm (p. 84) but feeds and breeds externally in buds, leaf axils and similar situations as well as internally in plant tissues. Eelworms move over wet surfaces of leaves and stems by swimming in films of water. They tend to move upwards, invading healthy leaves by entering stomata, and move 5 cm or more a night. Development from egg to adult takes 3–4 weeks in favourable conditions and eelworms survive in dead leaves and other plant tissues for about three months. Long-term persistence (up to three years) is possible in dry plant debris but is not typical of natural environments, which seldom stay dry for so long. Survival in soil is not important but survival as breeding populations in weeds is. Many are alternative hosts, especially groundsel, sowthistle, chickweed, goosegrasses, speedwells and buttercups.

Treatment. Avoid introducing infested plants into gardens. Obtain plants from reputable sources and scrutinise all new introductions carefully before planting. If any plants look suspect, grow them in isolation away from the main garden. Despite these precautions, chrysanthemum eelworms may be carried into gardens in wind-blown plant debris and they may also be present on weeds. If established plants show symptoms it is usually best to destroy them immediately by burning or by burying in a deep hole. Valuable stocks of chrysanthemums can be disinfested by hot water treatment of the stools before taking cuttings. Trim plants and wash all soil off stools before treatment then immerse in hot water at 46°C (115°F) for 5 minutes or at 43.5°C (110°F) for 20–30 minutes. Plunge stools into clean, cold water to end treatment and then box up to grow on for cuttings well away from infested material. Alternatively, take tip cuttings from infested stocks and grow them on rapidly in a heated frame or glasshouse. After some weeks take further cuttings from the tips of these cuttings and root them in sterile compost. Resultant plants should be free from infestation since eelworms will have been unable to keep up with rapid new growth. Always keep plants well ventilated and relatively dry to limit spread of eelworms in water on leaf and stem surfaces. Spread of eelworm on larger chrysanthemum plants may also be restricted by applying bands of vaseline or vegetable grease (*not* car grease) around bases of stems. No chrysanthemum cultivars are entirely immune to eelworm but 'Orange Peach Blossom', 'Delightful', 'Amy Shoesmith', 'Covent Garden' and 'New Princess' are partially resistant.

Strawberry runners may be treated by immersing in hot water at 46°C (115°F) for 10 minutes but this treatment is not suitable for other host plants. No chemicals are readily available for eelworm control in gardens and hosts other than chrysanthemum and strawberries must therefore be treated by removing and destroying infested plants and by maintaining good hygiene.

LEAF EELWORM *Aphelenchoides fragariae*

Also known as fern eelworm and strawberry eelworm. Closely related to chrysanthemum eelworm (p. 86). Widespread distribution.

Symptoms. Produces similar symptoms to chrysanthemum eelworm on ornamentals, on strawberries and on mint. Discoloured areas develop between main veins, especially on ferns. Usually most apparent in winter. Begonia leaves turn yellow and transparent, starting at the edges. Similar symptoms develop on coleus, gloxinias, lilies, paeonies, primulas, saintpaulias, violets and many other plants. Buds and terminal shoots are also attacked, with resultant stunting, distorting and scarring of young growth.

Biology. Similar to chrysanthemum eelworm but has not been studied to the same extent.

Treatment. Good hygiene, combined with maintenance of relatively dry conditions, will limit eelworm movements in glasshouses. Infested strawberry, fern, begonia and mint plants may be given hot water treatment. Immerse strawberry runners in water at 46°C (115°F) for 10 minutes. Treat ferns at 43.5°C (110°F) for 10–15 minutes; small pot begonias at

48°C (118°F) for 30 minutes and mint runners at 46°C (115°F) for 10 minutes (which will also kill mint rust disease). These temperatures and times are critical and if they are exceeded plants will be seriously damaged. At the end of the treatment plunge plants into cold water and then grow them in sterile potting compost away from any possible sources of re-infestation.

ROOT-KNOT EELWORMS *Meloidogyne* spp. Pl. 1

At least 17 different species occur in western Europe. Some are native species but others have been accidentally introduced with plants from the tropics and sub-tropics and are now established in heated glasshouses. All attack roots, tubers and corms and more than 800 different plant hosts have been recorded.

Symptoms. Galls develop on roots (Pl. 1). Size of individual galls varies from about 1 mm to 2 cm or more. Galls are sometimes regular but often coalesce into irregular growths. Severe attacks interfere with normal root function, plants show signs of malnutrition, wilt and may die. Pot plants in glasshouses and houses are especially susceptible but plants growing in soil, both under glass and outdoors, are also affected. Plants commonly attacked include begonias, cacti, carnations, chrysanthemums, coleus, cyclamen, gloxinias and plumbagos. Also cucumbers, tomatoes, lettuce, French beans, and occasionally carrots, parsnips and beetroot. Attacks are generally worst on light soils and at high temperatures. All galls on plant roots are not necessarily caused by root-knot eelworms. Confirm diagnosis in doubtful cases by breaking open galls and examining with a lens for presence of female eelworms (see below), or submit specimens to an expert.

Biology. Minute eelworm larvae move through soil and invade root tissues. They feed internally for 1–2 months and as they feed the plant cells enlarge and proliferate to form the galls. Some species are parthenogenetic and only produce females. Mature females are pear-shaped, white and 0.5–1 mm long, either embedded in plant tissues or protruding from roots. Each lays 300–1,000 eggs over 2–3 months and these hatch into larvae which extend infestations by moving through the roots or the soil to new feeding sites. Eggs and larvae survive for only a few weeks in dry soil if no suitable host plants are available but can survive for months in moist soil at 10°C (50°F). In parthenogenetic species survival of a single egg is sufficient to start a new infestation.

Treatment. Do not introduce suspect soil or suspect plants into gardens. Examine roots of all newly acquired plants, especially pot plants and young lettuce, cucumber, cabbage and tomato plants. Destroy infested plants immediately by burning or burying and observe strict hygiene to prevent spread of eggs and larvae in soil, potting compost, staging gravel and on pots and implements. Sterilise pots, seed-trays, garden tools and potting composts by steaming, if possible, and grow seedlings and cuttings in sterile compost. There are no chemicals suitable for use in gardens.

YELLOW POTATO CYST EELWORM

Globodera rostochiensis (=*Heterodera rostochiensis*) **Pl. 1**

Also known as potato root eelworm and sometimes as golden nematode. Widespread in temperate regions and one of the most damaging pests of potatoes. Other very similar species also attack potatoes.

Symptoms. Roots of potatoes and tomatoes are infested by eelworms in the soil. Growth is checked and yields reduced. In severe attacks plants yellow and die, often in conspicuous patches of plants growing on infested areas of soil. White, yellow or shiny brown cysts, about 0.5 mm diameter, are usually present on roots and are easily seen with a hand lens or magnifyin glass (Pl. 1).

Biology. Each cyst is the dead, swollen body of a female eelworm and contains 200–600 eggs. These remain dormant within the cysts in the soil for up to 10 years but most hatch within a year or so when potatoes, tomatoes or related weeds grow near them. The roots of these plants release chemicals which diffuse through the soil and stimulate eggs to hatch. Young eelworms then move through the soil, locate and penetrate the roots, and start to feed. Females growing within roots swell and eventually burst through the outer tissues and protrude with their heads still attached to the plant. They are then fertilised by the smaller, thinner males and mature into spherical brown cysts which break away and lie free in the soil. Populations of cysts increase very rapidly in favourable conditions. On main-crop potatoes there may be an overall increase of 25 times the initial number in one growing season, which leaves many millions of cysts to overwinter and infest subsequent crops.

Treatment. Cysts are present in most soils but usually remain at undetectable low levels until susceptible plants are grown. Avoid undue build-up of the pest by not growing potatoes or tomatoes too often on the same site. Tomatoes are best grown in soil-less media without direct contact with the soil and if good hygiene is observed they should not create an eelworm problem. Potato crops must be rotated. Soil and situation have some effect so strict rules can be misleading but main-crop potatoes should not be grown on the same site more than once every five years. Early crops may be taken more frequently, about once every three years, as they take less time to grow and therefore give eelworms less time to multiply. There are no satisfactory chemical treatments for infested soils and the only way to bring seriously affected areas back into use is to refrain from growing potatoes or tomatoes on them for at least six years. Some eelworm resistant potato cultivars are available but should be used under expert professional guidance as they are not immune to all strains of the eelworm and their unsupervised use could actually increase eelworm. 'Maris Piper', 'Maris Anchor', 'Pentland Javelin', 'Pentland Lustre' and 'Pentland Meteor' are resistant to the yellow potato cyst eelworm, which can be recognised by the yellow colour of its cysts in July and early August but these cultivars are not resistant to the other species, the white potato cyst eelworm, which does not produce yellow cysts. Weeds are not of any real importance in maintaining populations of this eelworm although it can occur on wild species of *Solanum*.

SLUGS AND SNAILS

(Plate 1)

Soft-bodied, unsegmented gastropod molluscs (Mollusca: Gastropoda), moving on large, slimy, muscular foot. Snails have conspicuous hard shells into which the body retracts but slugs do not have this protection. Most species are widely distributed in Europe.

Symptoms. Effects of various species of slugs and snails are similar since they all feed by rasping plant tissues with a toothed tongue (radula). Irregular holes are eaten in roots, bulbs, corms, tubers, stems, leaves, buds, flowers, seed-capsules and fruits of many different plants. Most feed at night. Characteristic slime trails persist on plants and soil and indicate the extent of nocturnal activity. Damage to outdoor plants is generally most severe during warm humid periods in spring and autumn but in glass-houses and frames high temperatures and humidity prolong activity and increase damage.

Fruit. Ripening strawberries are eaten by slugs and snails but most other fruits escape attack.

Vegetables. Often seriously damaged. Pea and bean seeds are eaten soon after sowing, especially if they germinate slowly in cold weather. Seedlings, especially brassicas and lettuces, are eaten through at soil level, both outdoors and in seed boxes under glass. Tubers of Jerusalem artichokes and potatoes (Pl. 1) are extensively holed by subterranean slugs and damage is usually worst on main-crop potatoes. Leaf stalks of celery and chicory are often attacked by slugs and both slugs and snails feed on stems and leaves of cabbages, cauliflowers, Brussels sprouts and other brassicas, and on lettuces.

Ornamentals. Campanula zoysii, Omphalodes luciliae and *Phyteuma comosum* are so attractive to slugs that it may be quite impossible to grow these plants successfully. Other ornamental plants regularly attacked include anemones, coreopsis, daffodils and narcissi, dahlias, delphiniums, gerberas, heleniums, hostas, hyacinths, irises, lilies, primulas, rudbeckias, sweet peas, tulips and violas but many others are also attacked occasionally. Most damage is done in early spring by slugs and snails feeding above ground on seedlings, new shoots and crowns of plants and by slugs feeding in the soil on bulbs, corms and tubers. Leaves and stems of tulips are often extensively damaged as they grow up through the soil and similar symptoms may appear on other bulbous plants.

Biology. Individual slugs and snails are truly hermaphrodite, functioning both as male and female, but cross-mating is usual and courtship and mating behaviour is often very elaborate. Clusters of 10–50 spherical, opaque or transparent eggs (Pl. 1) are laid in small cavities in or on soil and each individual lays about 500 eggs during adult life, which may last for months or years. Eggs normally hatch within a month of laying in spring and summer but some species lay in autumn and eggs then lie dormant in soil until the following spring. They are often exposed when gardens are dug in winter. Young slugs and snails are miniature versions of adults and they feed for up to a year before maturing. Young and adults feed on dead, decaying organic matter, such as decaying leaves, as well as on living plants.

Slugs are most abundant in soils containing decaying organic matter, such as composts and manures. Snails are commonest on calcareous soils. The main pest species in gardens are the garden slug, *Arion hortensis*, (Pl. 1); the field slug, *Deroceras reticulatum*; the black slug, *Arion ater*; keeled slugs, *Milax* spp.; the garden snail, *Helix aspersa*; the strawberry snail, *Trichia striolata* and the banded snails, *Cepaea nemoralis* and *C. hortensis*.

Treatment. Moist soils with high organic content support large populations of slugs and if conditions in a garden are particularly favourable it may be impossible to prevent damage to plants. Some relief is given by cultivating frequently and thoroughly to expose eggs, young and adult slugs to predators and weather; by limiting use of organic fertilisers, such as manures and composts; by restricting use of mulches around plants and by generally maintaining good garden hygiene. In addition, slugs may be trapped by laying old lettuce or cabbage leaves, grapefruit skins, old sacking, bran and various other materials on soil surfaces. Warm humid evenings give best catches. Inspect traps early next morning and kill slugs by dropping into a bucket containing a strong solution of salt or very hot water. Slugs can also be trapped by sinking shallow dishes to soil level and filling them with beer, which attracts them, intoxicates them and drowns them. Beer remains effective for 2–3 nights. Alternatively, use poison baits containing either metaldehyde or methiocarb. These are sold as slug pellets which are placed in strategic positions near susceptible plants. Pellets remain effective for 3–4 days and repeat applications may be necessary. Methiocarb pellets are expensive but generally give best results and 1 kg of pellets should be sufficient to treat about 1 hectare. Follow manufacturer's instructions for use carefully. Keep children and pets away from treated areas and do not use edible crops until at least a fortnight after treatment.

Areas where celery or potatoes are to be grown are best treated before planting to reduce the local slug population so far as possible. Susceptible potato cultivars, especially 'Redskin', 'Maris Piper', 'Desirée', 'Glade', 'King Edward', 'Record' and 'Pentland Crown' should not be grown where slugs are troublesome and main-crop potatoes should be lifted and stored as soon as possible, not left in the soil at the end of the growing season. Protect seedlings of ornamental plants and vegetables growing in seed trays or in the open ground by sprinkling slug pellets, weathered ashes or soot around them and use the same treatment to protect the young growing points of susceptible plants in the spring.

Snails are generally less troublesome than slugs. Where they are pests they can be dealt with in the same way and it is also possible to pick them off plants by hand.

EARTHWORMS

Segmented worms (Annelida: Oligochaeta). Widespread distribution; many species. Generally have beneficial effects on soil fertility and drainage but some species are a nuisance in lawns and sports turf.

Symptoms. Casts of excreted soil appear on soil surface, especially in spring and autumn when earthworms are most active. Casts make mowing difficult, damage cutting edges of cylinder mowers, provide sites for colonisation of lawns by weeds, and make lawns muddy and slippery in wet weather.

Biology. Earthworms live in the soil and feed by ingesting soil and decaying plant material, especially leaves. They do not feed on living plants but are attracted to dead and dying plants and are therefore often found when such plants are uprooted. Most earthworms live in the top 50 cm and populations in grassland often exceed 5 million worms per hectare. In cold or dry weather earthworms move down a metre or more in the soil and remain inactive until conditions improve. Individuals are hermaphrodite, functioning both as male and female, and they mate either on the soil surface or in burrows in the soil. 20–30 eggs are laid in cocoon-like capsules made from mucus secreted by the clitellum, which is the smooth broad band around the middle of the body of mature worms. After 1–6 months, young worms hatch from eggs. They mature about a year later and may then live for some years as adults. The main pest species in lawns are *Allolobophora longa* and *A. nocturna*.

Treatment. Earthworms cannot thrive in acid soils and may therefore be discouraged by managing lawns so that acid conditions (pH 5 or lower) are maintained. This is done by removing all cut grass and by using top dressings of peat, sulphate of ammonia or sulphate of iron. Do not use top dressings containing lime or heavy dressings of organic matter, such as compost. If this treatment is not feasible, it may be possible simply to disperse worm casts by sweeping with a birch or similar broom before mowing. Many different chemicals are recommended for earthworm control and they vary considerably in effectiveness. The safest to use are expellents, such as derris dust or potassium permanganate solution. These bring worms to the surface but do not kill them and the expelled worms must be collected up and destroyed. Derris is usually applied as a 1% dust at the rate of 25 g/sq. metre and must be well watered in after application and potassium permanganate is applied at the rate of 4 g per litre of water to every square metre. Potassium permanganate is especially useful on lawns near ponds and streams as it is not toxic to fish. Both derris and potassium permanganate are non-persistent and repeat treatments may have to be made every six months. Worm killers based on chlordane are much more toxic and persistent and should only be used when there is no adequate alternative. This chemical kills earthworms within the soil, so there is no disposal problem, and although it is relatively expensive, it will control earthworms and other soil pests for a year or more after application. All worm killers are best applied in warm, humid weather in spring and autumn since worms are near the surface then, and label instructions for correct use should always be followed. Keep children and pets off treated areas for at least two weeks after applying chlordane.

MILLEPEDES

(Plate 1)

Segmented arthropods (Diplopoda) with up to 50 articulated segments and two pairs of legs per segment. World-wide distribution with many species. Mostly live in soil and leaf litter. Move slowly and smoothly, like snakes, and curl into tight coils when at rest. Feed mainly on dead and decaying plant material.

(*Note:* Centipedes are often confused with millepedes but have only one pair of legs per segment and move rapidly. They are mainly carnivorous, feeding on small insects, earthworms, slugs and other invertebrates, and are beneficial.)

Symptoms. Although millepedes generally feed on dead plants they sometimes eat seeds and young seedlings and often extend wounds on roots, bulbs, corms and tubers that have been caused by other pests, such as slugs, or by pathogens. Pea and bean seeds and seedlings are especially susceptible in early spring. Other plants commonly affected are strawberries, carrots, cucumbers, potatoes, lilies, daffodils and tulips. In all cases the plants are attacked at or below soil level and the symptoms are indistinct. Soft tissues are eaten and rots quickly establish. Careful examination of damaged plants and the adjoining soil will usually reveal numbers of millepedes. The main species associated with garden plants are the black millepedes, *Cyclindroiulus londinensis* and *Tachypodiulus niger*, and the spotted millepede, *Blaniulus guttulatus*, (Pl. 1).

Biology. Millepedes breed in spring and summer and females lay 50–100 eggs in small chambers that they excavate in the surface layers of the soil. Eggs hatch after 2–3 weeks. Young millepedes resemble adults but are much smaller and have fewer body segments. As they grow they moult periodically and the number of segments increases until they reach the full adult complement. Adults remain inactive in the soil in winter and may live for 2–3 years.

Treatment. Millepedes thrive in moist soils with a high content of organic matter and are especially favoured by undisturbed accumulations of decaying plant debris and other rubbish. Good hygiene and thorough cultivation will therefore reduce their numbers and may often be sufficient to prevent serious damage. Good hygiene is particularly important in glasshouses and frames where millepedes breeding under seed trays and pots may attack seedlings growing in them. Susceptible seeds, seedlings, bulbs and corms may be protected by working a little HCH dust into the soil just before sowing or planting and established plants can be treated by watering a spray-strength solution of HCH onto the roots. Use of HCH should however be kept to a minimum, especially in vegetable gardens where heavy applications may taint potatoes and other root crops. There is of course little point in controlling millepedes when they are not the primary cause of damage. In such cases the pest, disease or disorder responsible for the initial damage should be identified and treated.

WOODLICE

(Plate 1)

Terrestrial crustaceans (Isopoda). Bodies with hard, jointed exoskeleton and up to 7 pairs of legs. Up to 2 cm long. Many species, widely distributed and common in leaf litter, rotting wood and other decaying organic matter. The commonest species in gardens are *Oniscus asellus*, *Porcellio scaber* and *Armadillidium vulgare*. Other species, especially *Armadillidium nasutum*, *Porcellio laevis* and *Androniscus dentiger* are commoner in glasshouses.

Symptoms. Seedlings in seed boxes in glasshouses and frames are eaten off at soil level and irregular holes are eaten in leaves; stems, fruits and roots of older plants sometimes gnawed. Cacti, chrysanthemums, cucumbers, cyclamen, lupins, pansies and petunias are especially susceptible. Roots of ferns and orchids may also be attacked. Most damage is done at night but woodlice can usually be found during the day hiding near damaged plants under seed boxes, pots, stones and pieces of wood.

Biology. Females lay batches of 20 or more eggs in brood pouches under the body. Eggs soon hatch into young woodlice, which are miniature, light-coloured replicas of the adults, and they stay in the brood pouch for the first week or so after hatching. They then disperse and feed for about a year before maturing. Females of most species produce a number of broods in early summer but will reproduce at other times if conditions are favourable. Woodlice cannot survive dry conditions and therefore tend to concentrate in moist, cool situations with an abundance of plant debris and plenty of shelter. They are therefore abundant in overgrown neglected gardens. Their main source of food is dead organic matter, not living plants.

Treatment. First clear up accumulations of plant debris, old seed-boxes, stacks of unwashed pots, piles of rubble and rotting wood and any other possible breeding sites. Any woodlice found in such places may be killed by dusting with HCH or carbaryl or by simply pouring boiling water on them. Baits of bran, dried blood, boiled potato, turnip, cheese or sugar may then be used to attract survivors and HCH or carbaryl dust may be mixed with the bait to kill woodlice when they feed on it. These pests do not move very far from their breeding sites and a concerted campaign against them in a glasshouse or garden in winter or early spring should reduce the local population for the rest of the season.

SPRINGTAILS

Small (1–5 mm long) wingless arthropods (Class: Collembola) often abundant in soil and leaf litter, sometimes aggregating in large masses containing thousands of individuals. They jump by flicking a forked terminal appendage against the ground and are sometimes mistaken for fleas, especially when they occur on house plants. Most species feed on fungal spores and mycelium or on decaying plant tissues. Some occasionally attack living plants but are rarely of any importance in gardens.

GRASSHOPPERS

Grasshoppers are serious pests of plants in many parts of the world but not in Britain or in the cool and humid conditions of northern Europe.

EARWIGS

(Plate 2)

Insects (Dermaptera), up to 25 mm long. Body ending in horny forceps. Large, delicate hind-wings fold tightly into short wing cases formed from modified fore-wings. The common earwig, *Forficula auricularia* is the only species of general importance in Britain and northern Europe but other species may be locally troublesome in glasshouses and also outdoors in southern areas with warmer climates.

Symptoms. Ragged holes are eaten in petals of chrysanthemums (Pl. 1), cinerarias, clematis, dahlias, delphiniums, pansies, violas, zinnias and some other ornamental flowers. Most damage is done between June and September outdoors. Earwigs hide within damaged flowers during the day and feed mainly at night. Leaves and buds are also damaged and young buds may be killed. Earwigs are often found in cavities in fruits, especially peaches and apples, and in distorted leaves. In such cases they are not usually the main cause of the damage but are simply using these sites as hiding places.

Biology. Females overwinter in soil under stones, wood and other debris. In December and January each female lays 50–100 eggs in a small chamber excavated in the soil and she remains with them until they hatch in February–March. Females then remain with the small, white earwig nymphs, tending them and feeding them with regurgitated food, until they mature and disperse in May–June. Further egg batches may then be laid, giving rise to a second generation of adults by September. Although they have wings, adults do not normally fly and mainly disperse by crawling relatively short distances from their breeding sites. Most of the earwigs present in a garden during the summer are therefore likely to be from local breeding in the previous winter and spring.

Although earwigs undoubtedly damage plants, they also feed on aphids and other small insects and may have some beneficial effect by limiting pest populations.

Treatment. Tidy up accumulations of rubbish, maintain good garden hygiene and cultivate thoroughly to destroy breeding sites. Trap earwigs under old sacking, planks or cardboard placed on soil surface or in upturned flower pots stuffed with straw and positioned on the top of canes or stakes. Treat infested plants by spraying with HCH or malathion and treat known breeding and hiding sites with HCH or carbaryl dust. Insecticides are best applied late in the evening or after dark when earwigs are most active. Pot chrysanthemums that have stood in the open during late summer and early autumn should be examined carefully before they are moved into glasshouses. If earwigs are present, spray before moving or fumigate with HCH as soon as they have been moved into glasshouse.

COCKROACHES

Medium to large insects (Dictyoptera: Blattodea), up to 4 cm long with long antennae and tough fore-wings lying horizontally on flattened body and covering hind-wings. Native European species are small and of no importance as pests but four larger species have been introduced from warmer climates and are now well established in heated glasshouses and in bakeries, kitchens and other warm buildings. Of these the Australian cockroach, *Periplaneta australasiae*, is the species most likely to damage plants in glasshouses.

Symptoms. Tops eaten off seedlings, seeds are destroyed and roots, stems, leaves and flowers of older plants are chewed. Cinerarias, chrysanthemums, pot cyclamen, nicotianas, orchids and schizanthus are particularly prone to attack but many other glasshouse plants may also be damaged, especially when populations of cockroaches are high. Most damage is done at night and the presence of cockroaches can usually be confirmed by inspecting glasshouses 2–3 hours after sunset.

Biology. Cockroaches hide during the day in plant debris, pipe ducts, crevices in walls and woodwork, under pots and seed trays and in soil. They come out to feed at night and eat almost any organic matter. They seldom fly but run quickly and erratically. Females lay eggs in tough, brown, purse-like cases (oothecae) which are either deposited on the ground or carried by females until eggs hatch. Each female produces up to 30 oothecae over 3–12 months and each contains about 15 eggs. Eggs usually hatch in 1–3 months at high temperatures but may not hatch for a year or more at low temperatures. Young cockroaches resemble adults but lack wings and wing cases. They take 9–12 months to mature and develop most rapidly above 21°C (70°F).

Treatment. Cockroaches are usually most troublesome in old glasshouses run at high temperatures as these usually contain plenty of food and cover and therefore favour rapid breeding. Limit potential breeding by removing accumulations of rubbish and by repairing old brickwork and woodwork. Then apply dusts of HCH or malathion to pipe ducts, paths, brickwork and other surfaces on which cockroaches will walk at night and renew at intervals of a week or so until the population is reduced. Baits of bran, bread, beer, sugar, treacles and various other materials can be used to trap cockroaches in jars or wide-mouthed bottles sunk flush with soil surface. A little bait in the bottom of each container attracts cockroaches which fall in and are then unable to scramble out. Insecticide may be mixed with bait or trapped cockroaches may be killed by pouring very hot water into containers. Persistent trapping for a few weeks will give good control but eggs may continue to hatch for up to a year and repeated trapping may be necessary.

LACE BUGS

(Plate 2)

Small insects (Hemiptera: Tingidae), up to 6 mm long. Adults have unusual lace-like fore-wings and extensions from the thorax. Nymphs and adults feed on plant sap but only one species is of importance as a pest of garden plants.

RHODODENDRON BUG *Stephanitis rhododendri* Pl. 2

Symptoms. Upper surfaces of rhododendron leaves mottled yellow and undersides with characteristic rusty brown discolourations (Pl. 2). Nymphs are present on young leaves from May onwards. Foliage of severely infested plants droops and is extensively discoloured. Plants growing in open, dry positions are more susceptible than plants growing in shade and hybrids of *Rhododendron arboreum*, *R. campanulatum*, *R. campylocarpum*, *R. catawbiense* and *R. caucasicum* are generally more susceptible than hybrids of other species.

Biology. Probably a North American species. First recorded in Britain in

1901 and now widely established in southern England and Wales and in parts of northern Europe. Eggs laid in autumn alongside leaf mid-ribs hatch from May onwards. Nymphs feed on undersides of leaves in groups of 10–50. Adults mature from June onwards and females move up onto youngest leaves to lay eggs. Adults have wings but do not fly and colonies therefore remain relatively static on the same plants year after year. Adults die out in early winter but eggs survive.

Treatment. Do not grow susceptible species and hybrids if this pest is known to be troublesome and avoid growing rhododendrons in exposed, dry sunny conditions, if possible. If plants are attacked, prune out and burn affected branches in March, if feasible, to destroy overwintering eggs, and spray with contact insecticides, such as HCH, malathion or nicotine, or with systemic insecticides, such as dimethoate or heptenophos, on two or three occasions at about three-week intervals from mid-June. Spray thoroughly to contact colonies of bugs on the undersides of leaves.

Light infestations on small plants may be dealt with in spring and summer simply by shaking or picking off nymphs and adults by hand.

CAPSID BUGS

(Plate 2)

Small, active insects (Hemiptera: Miridae), up to 6 mm long. Adults with fore-wings hardened, hind-wings membranous, legs, antennae and proboscis long. Nymphs similar but without wings. Colour varies with species from pale yellow and green to red-brown, often with subsidiary markings in other colours. Many different species are common and widespread in Britain and northern Europe, mostly feeding on plants. Nymphs and adults pierce plant tissues with fine stylets, inject saliva and feed on sap. Saliva of main pest species kills plant tissues. Some species of capsid bugs prey on mites, aphids, caterpillars and other small invertebrates and may have some beneficial effect by reducing pest populations.

Symptoms. Small ragged holes appear in young leaves, followed by characteristic tattering (Pl. 2). Buds and shoots may be killed and flowers developing from damaged buds are deformed (Pl. 2). Careful examination of affected plants may detect capsids but they are elusive and quickly drop to the ground or fly away when disturbed. Most damage is done in late spring and during the summer and many different garden plants are affected.

Injury on apples often shows as bumps and other irregularities on developing fruits (Pl. 2) and other plants that are commonly affected in various ways include pears, plums, black and redcurrants, gooseberries, raspberries, strawberries, potatoes, runner beans, asters, arctotis, buddleias, caryopteris, ceanothus, chrysanthemums, dahlias, forsythias, fuchsias, hydrangeas, magnolias, nasturtiums, pelargoniums, poppies, roses, salvias, sunflowers, venidiums and zinnias.

The main pest species in gardens are the common green capsid, *Lygocoris pabulinus*; the tarnished plant bug, *Lygus rugulipennis*; the potato capsid, *Calocoris norvegicus* and the apple capsid, *Plesiocoris rugicollis.* Adults of the tarnished plant bug hibernate in leaf litter under hedges, in herbaceous borders and in similar situations but the other three species overwinter as eggs inserted in twigs and branches of woody plants. Populations of nymphs and adults are usually highest in June and July but breeding may continue until the autumn.

Treatment. Capsids tend to be rather elusive and control is not always easy but when damage is expected populations of nymphs and adults should be reduced before attacks develop. This is best done by a combination of chemical and non-chemical methods. In winter tidy under hedges by raking out leaf litter and clear up any other accumulations of plant debris and coarse herbage that may provide overwintering sites for the tarnished plant bug and, if necessary, spray with non-systemic insecticides, such as fenitrothion, malathion or nicotine, in spring, summer and autumn, when the pests are active. Spray strawberries, raspberries and loganberries immediately before flowering and treat apples, pears, plums, currants and gooseberries immediately after flowering. Ornamental plants should be treated in spring and early summer, if necessary, and may also need protection later in the year if capsids are abundant.

FROGHOPPERS

(Plate 2)

Medium-sized sap-feeding insects (Hemiptera: Cercopidae), up to 6 mm long. Rather frog-like, with prominent eyes and powerful hind legs, with which adults jump when disturbed. Pale-coloured nymphs feed on stems, leaves and roots of cultivated and wild plants under conspicuous coverings of froth, commonly known as 'cuckoo spit' (Pl. 2). Many species with widespread distribution in Britain and northern Europe but only the common froghopper, *Philaenus spumarius*, and the red and black froghopper, *Cercopis vulnerata*, are pests in gardens.

Symptoms. Froth masses appear on plants from May onwards. Young growths may be distorted and occasionally wilt but damage is seldom severe. Blackberries, raspberries, perennial asters, campanulas, chrysanthemums, coreopsis, geums, lavender, lychnis, phlox, roses, rudbeckias and solidagos growing outdoors are especially susceptible but many other plants may be attacked. Glasshouse plants are sometimes infested, especially chrysanthemums taken under glass after standing outside.

Biology. Females lay eggs in batches of about 30 in stems of shrubs and herbaceous plants during autumn. Eggs overwinter and hatch in May. Nymphs start to feed and protect themselves from desiccation by forming froth from a liquid excreted from the anus. Adults mature by late July and feed on plants until autumn before laying overwintering eggs and dying.

Treatment. Froth and nymphs can be removed from infested plants quite simply by spraying forcibly with water from a garden hose or pressurised sprayer. If insecticidal treatment is considered necessary, spray with malathion, nicotine or pyrethroids.

LEAFHOPPERS

(Plate 2)

Medium-sized sap-feeding insects (Hemiptera: Cicadellidae = Jassidae), up to 5 mm long. Similar to froghoppers but generally less robust. Many different species are widespread in Britain and northern Europe on wild and cultivated plants. Adults are often abundant and conspicuous on plants in summer jumping, flying briefly and resettling on leaves. Some species transmit pathogens, especially mycoplasmas (p. 277).

GLASSHOUSE LEAFHOPPER

Hauptidia maroccana (=Zygina pallidifrons) **Pl. 2**

Symptoms. Coarse white mottling of upper leaf surfaces on glasshouse and house plants (Pl. 2). Young and adult leafhoppers and cast skins are usually present on undersides of damaged leaves; leaves completely blanched in severe attacks. Primulas, especially *Primula malacoides* and *P. obconica*, are most susceptible but tomatoes, calceolarias, fuchsias, gloxinias, pelargoniums, verbenas and many other plants are commonly affected. Some other leafhopper species cause similar symptoms.

Biology. First introduced into Britain about 1918 and now well established in glasshouses. Females live on plants for 2–3 months and lay about 50 eggs, inserting them singly into leaf veins. Eggs hatch after about a week in summer or a month or more in winter. Nymphs feed on undersides of leaves, moulting five times and maturing to winged adults in 1–2 months. Breeding continues throughout the year in heated glasshouses and in houses but slows down during winter.

Treatment. Remove older affected leaves to reduce numbers of eggs and nymphs, then protect new growth by spraying or dusting with a contact insecticide, such as malathion, nicotine or pyrethroids on two or three occasions at fortnightly intervals.

RHODODENDRON LEAFHOPPER *Graphocephala fennahi*

Formerly incorrectly referred to as *Graphocephala coccinea.*

Adults have striking red longitudinal bands on wing cases and are present on plants in late summer/early autumn. They sit on leaves but jump and fly briefly when disturbed. They do not cause any direct damage but may facilitate the spread of bud blast disease (see p. 232).

ROSE LEAFHOPPER

Edwardsiana rosae (= Typhlocyba rosae) **Pl. 2**

Symptoms. Fine white mottling on upper leaf surfaces (Pl. 2), especially on climbing roses on walls. Adults, nymphs and cast skins are usually present on undersides of leaves (Pl. 2). Severe attacks may develop in dry summers and can cause premature leaf-fall. Damage generally restricted to roses but this species also occurs on apple leaves in summer.

Biology. Eggs laid by females in shoots in autumn overwinter and hatch from May onwards. Nymphs of first generation mature by July and females lay eggs in leaf tissues. These eggs hatch in August and September, producing a second generation of adults which later lay the overwintering eggs.

Treatment. Systemic insecticides, such as dimethoate and formothion, used against aphids, also check leafhoppers. Spray against the first generation in May and June and repeat later in the season, if necessary. Non-persistent contact insecticides, such as pyrethroids, malathion or nicotine, may also be used.

Many different species of leafhopper occur in gardens and may damage plants directly by feeding or indirectly by transmitting diseases. Apple, strawberry, raspberry, blackberry, loganberry and potatoes may be affected, and leafhoppers may also be particularly abundant on hornbeam and beech hedges. Biology and treatment are essentially as for rose leafhopper (see above).

PSYLLIDS
(Plate 2)

Small sap-feeding insects (Hemiptera: Psyllidae), about 2–3 mm long. Nymphs, commonly known as 'suckers', have wide, flattened bodies, prominent eyes and conspicuous wing buds. Adults have two pairs of wings and can jump and fly. Both nymphs and adults feed by extracting sap from leaves, stems and other parts of wild and cultivated plants. Young buds and shoots are damaged and plants are often fouled with sticky honeydew and sooty moulds. Many species are widespread and often abundant in Britain and northern Europe.

APPLE SUCKER *Psylla mali* **Pl. 2**
Symptoms. Blossom trusses and leaf buds of apple trees are damaged as they open in April and May. Affected blossom is discoloured and distorted (Pl. 2) and may fail to develop at all if attack is severe. This damage is sometimes wrongly attributed to late frost but close examination will usually reveal psyllid nymphs which are orange–brown or green, with bright red eyes.
Biology. Females lay pale yellow, elongate oval eggs (Pl. 2) near leaf scars and buds on fruit spurs in September. Eggs overwinter on trees and hatch in March and April. Young nymphs immediately crawl into opening buds and start to feed. They mature from May onwards and adults live on trees until autumn, when overwintering eggs are laid and adults die out. There is only one adult generation each year.
Treatment. Overwintering eggs are easily killed by a 5% tar oil wash applied in December or January, when the trees are dormant. This treatment is also used against overwintering aphid eggs (p. 104) but does not control fruit tree red spider mites and can lead to an increase of this pest (p. 172). It may therefore be better to wait until the green cluster stage of bud development and then apply a systemic insecticide, such as dimethoate or heptenophos, as for aphids (p. 104). If apple sucker attack is severe, spray with HCH as it gives a better kill.

PEAR SUCKER *Psylla pyricola*
Symptoms. Leaf and blossom buds are damaged in spring, as with apple sucker (see above) but damage may continue through the summer as populations increase. This often causes extensive fouling of foliage and fruit with sticky honeydew and black sooty moulds. Fruit buds forming in late summer for the following season may also be damaged, with resultant loss of crop potential, and severe infestations may cause premature leaf-fall.
Biology. Pear sucker overwinters as adults, not as eggs. Adults remain on twigs and branches of pear trees and on other trees and shrubs in gardens

and hedgerows. In late March females lay eggs on spurs and shoots of pear trees and these eggs hatch within a few weeks. Young nymphs feed in buds and on young growth and mature by early June. Breeding and feeding then continues until winter sets in. Three generations of adults develop, with population peaks in June, July and October, but there is much variation in different places and seasons.

Treatment. Spraying with tar oil in winter is not effective against this pest as adults survive in sufficient numbers to re-invade treated trees in spring. Best control is given by spraying with dimethoate, heptenophos or malathion three weeks after petal fall to kill nymphs of the first generation. If spring infestations are particularly severe, apply this spray immediately after petal fall and repeat three weeks later and if summer populations are high, spray again after harvest to reduce damage to next year's buds.

BAY SUCKER *Trioza alacris*

Symptoms. Leaves of bay laurel (*Laurus nobilis*) are attacked in late spring and early summer. Leaf edges thicken and curl over and sucker nymphs are present under curled leaves. Nymphs secrete tufts of conspicuous white woolly wax and also excrete sticky honeydew which fouls foliage and encourages growth of sooty moulds. Young plants, up to about five years old, are most susceptible and, when heavily infested, leaves shrivel and fall prematurely and shoots die.

Biology. Bay sucker occurs in Europe and parts of North America. It was introduced to Britain in the early 1920's and is now well established. Adults overwinter in curled leaves, amongst dense foliage, in leaf litter and in similar situations. On warm sunny days in spring they assemble on young bay shoots and feed on the leaves. Leaves then curl and females lay clusters of about six eggs under the edge of each curled leaf. Flat, oval, yellow-brown nymphs hatch from May onwards and feed until mid-October, when they become adult.

Treatment. Prune off and burn severely affected shoots and clear accumulations of leaf litter under plants. Spray with malathion in April–May to kill females before they have laid eggs. Control is more difficult after eggs have hatched as nymphs are protected from insecticides both by the wax that they secrete and by the curled leaves. Systemic insecticides, such as dimethoate or heptenophos, may therefore give better control of established infestations.

BOX SUCKER *Psylla buxi*

Symptoms. Leaves at tips of infested box shoots curve inwards and form tight clusters, like miniature cabbages. Severe infestations make box hedges look unsightly and may check growth.

Biology. Females lay eggs in slits in leaf axils and twigs in August. Eggs overwinter and hatch in following April, just as new leaf buds start to develop. Psyllid nymphs then feed in malformed shoots until August, when they become adult.

Treatment. Cut out affected shoots and burn them, preferably before April, to reduce numbers of overwintering eggs. Spray thoroughly with a contact insecticide, such as malathion or HCH, or with a systemic insecticide, such as dimethoate or heptenophos, in May and June to kill nymphs.

WHITEFLIES

(Plate 2)

Small sap-feeding insects (Hemiptera: Aleyrodidae), up to 2 mm long. Pure white adults have two pairs of wings folded over back of abdomen when at rest. Young nymphs crawl over plants but soon settle to feed and become immobile scales. Many species occur in Britain and northern Europe on wild and cultivated plants. Most are very similar in appearance and biology.

GLASSHOUSE WHITEFLY *Trialeurodes vaporariorum* **Pl. 2**

Symptoms. Adults, eggs and scales are present on undersides of leaves (Pl. 2) and upper leaf surfaces are often fouled with sticky honeydew and sooty moulds (p. 209). Tomatoes and cucumbers are often severely infested but this pest also attacks many other glasshouse plants and house plants, especially abutilons, begonias, calceolarias, chrysanthemums, cinerarias, coleus, dahlias, freesias, fuchsias, gerberas, heliotropes, hibiscus, pelargoniums, poinsettias, primulas, salvias, verbenas and zantedeschias. Sometimes occurs on outdoor plants and weeds in summer but may be confused with other species. Persistent infestations reduce plant vigour and sooty moulds make infested plants look unsightly. Leaves of some plants develop yellow spots and other discolourations where whiteflies have fed.

Biology. Originally a tropical and sub-tropical species accidentally introduced to glasshouses in Britain and northern Europe and now widely established. Adults live for a month or more and each female lays up to 200 eggs on undersides of leaves, often in neat circles. Eggs darken soon after laying and hatch about ten days later. Young nymphs crawl over plants for a few hours then settle to feed. Legs and antennae degenerate and nymphs then become immobile scales which feed for about two weeks before entering a non-feeding pupal stage from which adults emerge. Development from egg to adult takes three weeks at 21°C (70°F); four weeks at 15°C (60°F), and much longer at lower temperatures. Breeding continues throughout the year in heated glasshouses and is mainly parthenogenetic. Outdoor populations on weeds and other plants are killed by severe winters but some hibernating adults may survive mild winters.

Treatment. Prevent serious damage by examining plants regularly. If adult or immature whiteflies are seen, spray thoroughly with an appropriate contact insecticide, such as malathion, HCH, pyrethrum, permethrin or bioresmethrin, or with a systemic insecticide, such as dimethoate or heptenophos, and repeat on two or three occasions at about weekly intervals. Fumigants, such as HCH or dichlorvos, may also be used to kill adult whiteflies but may have to be used repeatedly at weekly intervals as they have little effect on nymphs, pupae or eggs. In southern England, and probably elsewhere, populations of glasshouse whitefly are now resistant to organochlorine and organophosphorus insecticides and control with these chemicals may fail. If so, pyrethrum, resmethrin, permethrin or bioresmethrin may still be effective.

Biological control by introduction of a small parasitic hymenopteran,

Encarsia formosa, gives good results at temperatures above 21°C (70°F) and has been used in commercial horticulture. *Encarsia* females lay eggs in whitefly scales and parasitised scales turn black. Adults emerge through holes in the tops of parasitised scales and are almost all females, since reproduction is parthenogenetic.

Encarsia has been widely distributed in Britain and elsewhere during the past sixty years and is likely to be present in established glasshouses. Where it does not occur, it can be established quite easily by introducing a few leaves bearing parasitised scales. Supplies of these can be bought from commercial suppliers and from some other organisations, but may only be available for a restricted period. Enquire about supplies well in advance of intended use as it may be difficult to obtain stocks of the parasite at short notice. Use of insecticides must be kept to a minimum once *Encarsia* has been introduced and persistent insecticides, such as HCH, should not be used.

CABBAGE WHITEFLY *Aleyrodes proletella* **Pl. 2**

Symptoms. Adults and scales infest undersides of leaves of cabbages, Brussels sprouts and other brassicas (Pl. 2). Leaves are fouled with sticky honeydew and sooty moulds. Infestations are often severe on allotments in southern England where brassica plants at different stages of growth maintain breeding populations throughout most of the year. In such situations adults may be found at any time and may even be seen flying on sunny, frosty mornings in mid-winter when most other insects are inactive.

Biology. This pest resembles the glasshouse whitefly but is biologically quite distinct since it only attacks brassicas and it can survive severe winter weather. Breeding continues through spring, summer and autumn, but ceases in early winter as temperatures fall. Adults, and possibly some pupae, overwinter on infested plants and breeding starts again when temperatures rise in early spring.

Treatment. Pull up and burn severely infested plants after harvest to reduce numbers of whiteflies surviving to the next season and protect young brassica plants by examining them frequently and spraying as soon as any adult whiteflies are seen on them. Thorough high-volume spraying gives best results and the spray must be directed to the undersides of the leaves as that is where most whiteflies congregate. Non-persistent insecticides, such as bioresmethrin, pyrethrum, malathion or nicotine are safest to use but may have to be applied at weekly or fortnightly intervals. Systemic insecticides, such as dimethoate or heptenophos, give longer protection but should not be applied within a week or so of harvest. Biological control, which works against glasshouse whitefly, is not effective against cabbage whitefly.

Garden plants may be attacked by a number of superficially similar species of whitefly, especially the rhododendron whitefly, *Dialeurodes chittendeni*; the azalea whitefly, *Pealius azaleae*; the honeysuckle whitefly, *Aleyrodes lonicerae*, and the viburnum whitefly, *Aleurotrachelus jelinekii*. Symptoms, biology and treatment are essentially the same as for the two species dealt with above.

APHIDS

(Plate 3)

Small sap-feeding insects (Homoptera: Aphididae) generally 1–5 mm long with soft bodies, relatively long legs and antennae and usually a conspicuous pair of tube-like structures, the siphunculi, at the end of the abdomen. Body colour varies between species and sometimes within species and ranges from white through various shades of red, yellow, orange, green, brown and blue to black. Aphid colonies often consist of winged and wingless individuals and the winged aphids have two pairs of broad, transparent wings with conspicuous dark veins. They are weak fliers but can be carried in thermals and air currents for hundreds of miles and this is how many species disperse and migrate to new host plants. Aphid mouth-parts contain very fine stylets which are inserted into plant tissues so that plant sap can flow up minute canals in the stylets and so enter the aphid's digestive system. Both young and adult aphids feed almost continuously and colonies are commonly found on leaves, buds, stems, roots and flowers (Pl. 3). Large volumes of sap are ingested by most species and excess sugars and water are excreted as drops of a sticky substance, commonly known as honeydew. This usually falls from the aphids or is flicked away by the hind legs but some aphid species are tended by ants which feed on honeydew and give the aphid colonies some protection from predators and parasites.

More than 500 aphid species occur in Britain and northern Europe. Many of these are common pests of fruits, vegetables and ornamental plants growing outdoors and some are particularly troublesome on glasshouse and house plants. Some species are restricted to one plant species or to a few closely related species or genera but others, such as the peach-potato aphid (p. 109) attack hundreds of different plant hosts, many of which may not be closely related botanically.

Aphids are one of the most important groups of pests attacking garden plants and are well known to gardeners. They are often referred to as blackfly, greenfly or blight and other common names are used locally in different countries and regions. Primary damage to plants results from the effects of colonies feeding on young tissues, which weakens and distorts new growth. Secondary effects, which are often more important, result from fouling of leaves and stems with honeydew, which encourages the growth of sooty moulds (see p. 209), and from the transmission of viruses (p. 277) which are carried from diseased plants to healthy plants on the stylets and in the saliva.

Aphid reproduction is mainly asexual and most aphids seen on plants are parthenogenetic females which are capable of giving birth to live young. At summer temperatures, young aphids mature in about a week and populations can therefore increase very rapidly to make maximum use of their plant hosts while conditions are favourable. The reproductive potential of many common species is so great that a single aphid would give rise to about ten million tons of aphids by the end of 100 days of summer breeding. This theoretical maximum is never achieved since many factors operate to control populations.

The seasonal biology of some aphids is complicated by alternation of sexual and asexual periods of development, combined with migrations from one set of host plants to another. This type of seasonal biology is exemplified by the black bean aphid (p. 112) and by some of the apple aphids (p. 106). Other species, such as the mottled arum aphid (p. 118) may never reproduce sexually and simply continue to breed asexually on the same host plant so long as conditions are suitable.

The symptoms and biology of the main pest species are detailed in the following section and for convenience they are grouped under fruits, vegetables and ornamentals. It should however be realised that the same species may be an important pest on all three groups of plants, as in the case of the peach-potato aphid which attacks peaches, potatoes, lettuces, tomatoes, chrysanthemums, roses, China asters and many other plants.

General methods of treating aphid infestations are summarised below and detailed recommendations are given in the entries for each of the main pest species.

General treatment. The aphids that attack garden plants are mostly mobile species and serious infestations often develop after plants have been colonised by a few airborne winged females. These may have come from many miles away, possibly from hundreds of miles away, but they soon become established and breed rapidly when conditions favour them. The main danger period on outdoor plants is from March to October but in glasshouses, houses and other protected situations infestations may develop at any time of year. Non-chemical methods of control are seldom effective in these circumstances. It may be theoretically possible to limit aphid infestations on some plants by reducing the use of nitrogenous fertilisers so that young growths are less attractive to these pests but this is hardly practicable in most gardens. Greater reliance must therefore be placed on chemical control if plants are to be adequately protected.

Many different insecticides may be used to control aphids but to be really effective they must be applied before damaging populations have built up. This calls for frequent and careful examination of plants so that the first signs of attack can be noticed and prompt action can be taken. If this is not done, insecticides may be applied too late, after plants have been seriously damaged and often at the point where aphid populations are in any case about to be dramatically reduced by predators, parasites and other natural control factors. The full impact of the insecticides may then fall on predators and parasites and this may result in a subsequent increase in aphid numbers, rather than the expected reduction.

The chemicals that are used against aphids fall into three main categories: winter washes, non-systemic insecticides and systemic insecticides.

Winter washes based on tar oil are used only on fully dormant woody deciduous plants, such as apples, pears, cherries, currants, birch and willow, during December and January. They are sprayed or brushed onto plants to kill overwintering eggs of aphids and also control some other pests, especially psyllids, scale insects, mealybugs and some moth eggs. Winter washes must be applied very carefully as they may irritate skin and eyes and will kill any green plant tissues that they contact. On old apple trees this latter effect may prove beneficial as they will kill off growths of mosses and lichens on trunks and branches.

Non-systemic insecticides are used on growing plants and they kill aphids mainly by direct contact. They are mostly formulated as water-based sprays or as aerosol packs. Non-persistent insecticides, such as derris, malathion, nicotine, pyrethrum and the newer synthetic pyrethroids, bioresmethrin, permethrin and resmethrin, may be used on edible and ornamental plants at any time when aphids are present. Residues do not persist for more than one or two days and phytotoxic side effects are less likely than with more persistent insecticides. Application to outdoor plants is usually by conventional sprayer but glasshouse and house plants may be treated with aerosols. None of these non-persistent insecticides will protect plants from subsequent reinvasion by aphids and frequent applications may be necessary if plants are to be kept clean.

More persistent non-systemic insecticides, such as diazinon, fenitrothion, HCH, pirimicarb and pirimiphos-methyl give longer protection, usually of one to two weeks after application. Pirimicarb is especially useful since it is a highly selective insecticide which kills aphids rapidly but does not affect beneficial predators and parasites. When these persistent non-systemic insecticides are used on edible plants the label instructions should be observed to ensure that the required minimum period of one or two weeks elapses before harvest and to avoid possible phytotoxic side effects.

Systemic insecticides, such as dimethoate and heptenophos, give best control of aphids feeding in protected situations in rolled and curled leaves, in galls, and on higher branches of trees, as they are absorbed into plant tissues and poison the sap on which aphids feed. These chemicals may be applied either as water-based sprays or as soil drenches of spray-strength solutions watered into the roots. They protect plants for two to three weeks after treatment and minimum periods between application and harvest of edible crops must be observed. Because of their systemic activity these insecticides tend to be phytotoxic to some plants and must be used cautiously.

Aphids on glasshouse plants can be controlled by fumigating with HCH, nicotine or dichlorvos and dichlorvos may also be used to fumigate house plants by sealing them in large plastic bags with dichlorvos resin strips for one to two hours.

APPLE APHIDS Pl. 3

Five different species commonly infest apples in Britain and northern Europe. Four of these have similar seasonal cycles and are therefore dealt with together while the fifth species, the woolly aphid, is dealt with separately.

ROSY APPLE APHID *Dysaphis plantaginea*

Infests leaves and blossom in early spring and may cause considerable stunting of fruits. The aphids are pink to grey and are covered with a white wax powder.

ROSY LEAF-CURLING APHID *Dysaphis devecta*

Infested leaves curl tightly and curled areas turn bright red or yellow. The aphids are bluish grey with a mealy wax covering and mostly occur within the curled leaves. This pest is usually restricted to older trees, especially those with rough bark, and tends to recur on the same trees every year.

APPLE-GRASS APHID *Rhopalosiphum insertum*

Also known as the oat-apple aphid. Attacks rosette leaves of blossom trusses on apple and may also attack medlar, rowan and hawthorn. Damaged leaves curl and yellow but the effect is only serious when substantial infestations develop. The aphids are yellow-green, rather plump, with short siphunculi.

GREEN APPLE APHID *Aphis pomi*

Colonies develop in late spring and early summer on young extension growths of fruiting and ornamental apples and pears and on cotoneasters, hawthorn, pyracanthas, rowan and quinces. This is a bright green to yellow-green aphid with contrasting dark brown siphunculi. It is mainly a pest of young plants.

Biology. All four species overwinter as eggs laid on apple and other woody hosts in summer and autumn. Adults do not normally survive the winter. The eggs are black, about 0.5 mm long, and can be seen quite easily on twigs and branches during the winter months (Pl. 3). They hatch from mid-March onwards and young aphids quickly move into opening buds to feed on new leaves and blossom trusses. Peak populations develop by mid-June and most damage is done in the spring months. Rosy apple aphids migrate to plantains and apple-grass aphids migrate to oats, grasses and reeds during the summer but the other two species do not migrate from their main hosts. Overwintering eggs of the rosy leaf-curling aphid are laid under flakes of bark and in crevices as early as mid-June but the sexual egg-laying generations of the other three species do not normally develop until the autumn and most eggs are laid in September, October and early November. Reproduction at all other times is parthenogenetic and viviparous.

Treatment. Most apple trees are attacked by aphids every year and spring infestations of buds, blossom and young shoots may affect growth and yield. Valuable trees should therefore be treated by spraying thoroughly in the pre-blossom period with a systemic insecticide, such as dimethoate, or with contact insecticides, such as pirimicarb, pyrethroids or malathion. Trees should be sprayed when they have reached the 'green cluster' stage of development since most of the overwintering eggs will have hatched by then. Dwarf pyramid trees, cordons, espaliers and fans are easily treated with hand sprayers but larger trees require power equipment and should only be sprayed if it can be done efficiently, since inefficient spraying may do more harm than good by killing predators and parasites without killing the aphids.

Aphids on apple and on other deciduous woody trees and shrubs may also be controlled by applying a tar oil winter wash in late December or in January, while the plants are fully dormant. Some gardeners favour this treatment as it cleans up trunks and branches by killing growths of moss, lichen and algae, but it will also scorch evergreen herbaceous plants and must be applied carefully. It may also favour increases in fruit tree red spider mites by killing off some of the predators that normally keep populations of this pest at a low level.

WOOLLY APHID *Eriosoma lanigerum* Pl. 3

Symptoms. Colonies of small brown aphids, covered by conspicuous tufts of white woolly wax, infest stems and branches of apple trees, ornamental crab apples, cotoneasters, hawthorn, pyracanthas, sorbus and some other plants. Colonies are most conspicuous in late spring and early summer but are present throughout the year. Infested plants develop irregular swellings on twigs and branches (Pl. 3) and these may later crack open and provide foci of infection by pathogens that cause canker and dieback.

Biology. Accidentally introduced into Europe, possibly from North America, and was first reported from London by Sir Joseph Banks in 1787. Now well established but is still sometimes referred to as 'American blight'.

Young aphids overwinter in cracks in bark and in galls. From March onwards they feed on twigs and branches, especially in leaf axils, on spurs and in wounds. Successive generations of wingless aphids develop during the summer. Some winged aphids develop and fly off to other host plants but this species does not spread so widely or rapidly as other aphids and colonies tend to persist on the same trees or shrubs year after year. Breeding stops in the autumn and immature aphids seek sheltered overwintering sites. No overwintering eggs are laid by this species in Europe.

Treatment. Localised infestations on trunks and branches can be dealt with by applying a spray-strength solution of malathion or pirimicarb with a brush but if infestations are too extensive the affected plants should be sprayed thoroughly after flowering. Systemic insecticides, such as dimethoate or heptenophos, are most effective but contact insecticides, such as malathion or pirimicarb, will give good results if applied thoroughly. Severely galled branches of apple and of cotoneasters, pyracanthas and other ornamentals should be pruned out and burned before the plants are sprayed as they will never recover and will make complete chemical control more difficult.

Biological control of woolly aphid in southern England was attempted about 1924 by introduction of a small parasitic hymenopteran, *Aphelinus mali*, from North America. This parasite lays eggs in the bodies of live woolly aphids and the parasitic larvae feed within the aphids and eventually kill them. They then pupate within the dead aphids and adult parasites emerge through small holes that they cut in the bodies. *Aphelinus* is now well established throughout southern England and parasitised aphids can usually be found in woolly aphid colonies. If the parasite is known to be active in a garden it should be conserved by limiting the use of persistent insecticides.

PEAR-BEDSTRAW APHID *Dysaphis pyri*

This is the commonest species affecting pears although some other species may also occur on this host.

Symptoms. Colonies of relatively large pink or pink-brown aphids, covered with white mealy wax, infest young growths in early spring and cause severe leaf-curl and discolouration. Colonies may persist on pears into July and at times these aphids are so numerous that they swarm over trunks and branches of infested trees.

Biology. Overwintering eggs are laid in autumn, mainly on the swollen sections of fruiting spurs. They hatch in early spring and aphids breed on pear trees before migrating to bedstraws from late spring onwards. There is a return migration of aphids to pear trees in the autumn.

Treatment. Prune out and burn old fruiting spurs during the winter to reduce the numbers of overwintering eggs. Apply winter washes and spring and summer sprays as for apple aphids (see p. 106).

PEACH-POTATO APHID *Myzus persicae*

Symptoms. This aphid attacks more host plants than any other species and is the most important aphid vector of plant virus diseases (p. 277). Colonies feeding on young growths of peaches and nectarines in spring cause severe leaf-curl. On other host plants dense colonies seldom form and the aphids are generally dispersed over the undersides of the leaves. This may cause some distortion of young growths as well as contaminating the upper surfaces of older leaves with sticky honeydew, sooty moulds, and the white moult skins. Glasshouse and house plants may be infested at any time of year but outdoor plants are mainly attacked in spring and summer. Tomatoes, lettuces and potatoes are commonly affected as well as many ornamentals, including antirrhinums, aubrietias, begonias, calceolarias, carnations, China asters, chrysanthemums, cinerarias, hibiscus, hyacinths, lilies, myosotis, nasturtiums, orchids, palms, phlox, primulas, roses, tulips and sweet peas. Among the important viruses transmitted by this pest are bean yellow mosaic, cauliflower mosaic, cucumber mosaic, dahlia mosaic, lettuce mosaic, pea leaf roll, plum pox, potato leaf roll, tomato aspermy and tulip breaking virus.

Biology. Peaches and nectarines are the primary woody hosts of this species and it overwinters on them as eggs. It also survives the winter as actively breeding populations in heated glasshouses and houses and in some protected situations outdoors. Development from nymph to adult is greatly influenced by temperature, taking over a month at an average of 6°C (43°F) but only a week at 24°C (75°F). Winged aphids appear from May onwards and migrate to other hosts and it is at this time that most virus diseases are spread.

The colour of peach-potato aphids varies from green to pale yellow and pink and individuals of different colours may be present together in the same colony.

Treatment. Overwintering eggs on peaches and nectarines may be killed by spraying with a tar oil winter wash, as for apple aphids (p. 106) but this must be done by the end of December as peaches and nectarines break dormancy earlier than apples, especially under glass, or control may be delayed until the spring when systemics, such as dimethoate, applied as soon as flowering has finished, will give best results. Systemics or non-systemics may be used on vegetables and ornamentals providing minimum periods to harvest are observed and phytotoxic effects are avoided.

Some populations of the peach-potato aphid are now resistant to organophosphorus and other insecticides, especially on chrysanthemums and other commercially-grown plants which have been intensively treated with chemicals. Because of the danger of selecting resistant strains, insecticides should only be applied when really necessary and it is best to use a number of unrelated materials rather than rely on continuous use of any one insecticide.

Resistant aphids on commercial chrysanthemums have been controlled biologically by rearing and releasing the small hymenopterous parasite *Aphidius matricariae*. This technique might be adapted for garden use but it requires considerable skill.

PLUM APHIDS

Three species are important pests of plums and damsons and also attack some ornamental plants:

LEAF-CURLING PLUM APHID *Brachycaudus helichrysi*

Dense colonies of small yellow-green aphids with pale siphunculi infest young shoots of plums and damsons causing severe leaf-curl during spring and early summer. From May onwards winged aphids migrate onto China asters, chrysanthemums, cinerarias, myosotis and other herbaceous ornamentals and aphid colonies stunt and distort growth of young plants. Aphids migrate back to plum and damson in the autumn and overwintering eggs are laid on twigs, especially at the bases of buds. They hatch early in the following year, usually by mid-January, and the first generation of aphids develops on the dormant buds. This pest is therefore already well established by the time the buds open.

MEALY PLUM APHID *Hyalopterus pruni* **Pl. 3**

Tightly packed colonies of green, narrow-bodied aphids with a slightly blue tinge and powdery white wax covering develop on the undersides of plum and damson leaves. Infested leaves are not deformed and the most obvious symptom of attack is the extensive growth of sooty mould on the upper leaf surfaces. Large quantities of honeydew are excreted by this pest and the sooty moulds growing on it often form a thick coating. This affects growth and contaminates fruit.

Eggs overwinter on plums and damsons but do not hatch until April so that colonies seldom build up to damaging levels before mid-summer. Colonies may persist on plum trees until August but winged aphids migrate to reeds from June onwards and there is a return migration to plums and damsons in the autumn.

DAMSON-HOP APHID *Phorodon humuli*

Colonies of shiny yellow-green aphids with dark green longitudinal stripes develop on young growths. Most troublesome on damsons in gardens but is also an important pest of commercial hops. Eggs overwinter on damsons, plums and blackthorn and hatch in February and March. Colonies increase until May when winged aphids migrate to hops. This species has become resistant to many insecticides.

Treatment. Plum aphids may be checked by spraying with tar oil between mid-December and mid-January but the buds of some cultivars, especially 'Belle de Louvain', 'Victoria', 'Yellow Egg' and the gages may be damaged, especially if they are sprayed during frosty or wet weather, and myrobalan is so susceptible to damage that it should not be sprayed with tar oil at all.

Spraying in the spring with systemic insecticides, such as dimethoate, or with contact insecticides, such as fenitrothion, malathion, pyrethroids or nicotine, will generally give equally good results if done thoroughly in

March, just before flowering, with a second treatment in May or June if mealy plum aphid is troublesome. By the end of June most aphid colonies on plum will contain coccinellid beetles (ladybirds) and their larvae, hover-fly larvae, anthocorid bugs, hymenopterous parasites and other natural enemies. These reduce aphid populations only after the main damage has been done but they may restrict aphid populations in late summer and autumn and so reduce the numbers of overwintering eggs laid. Use of insecticides on plums and damsons should therefore be limited to spring and early summer.

Plum aphid infestations on ornamental plants may be treated with systemic or non-systemic insecticides (see p. 105) and pirimicarb will give particularly good control of aphids, with little or no effect on natural enemies and hardly any danger of phytotoxicity.

CHERRY BLACKFLY *Myzus cerasi*

Symptoms. Colonies of black aphids infest young leaves and shoots of fruiting and ornamental cherries in spring. Leaves are distorted, growth is checked, and foliage is fouled with sticky honeydew and sooty moulds. *Prunus avium* and *Prunus cerasus* are especially susceptible; *Prunus serrulata* and *Prunus yedoensis* are less susceptible, and *Prunus sargentii* and *Prunus subhirtella* are usually unaffected.

Biology. Eggs laid near buds in October overwinter and hatch in March. Young aphids feed on leaves and shoots and colonies increase until July when winged aphids migrate from cherry trees to bedstraws (*Galium* spp.) and some other wild plants. Colonies on cherries are usually eliminated by parasites and predators towards the end of July but winged aphids migrate back to cherry trees from summer hosts in autumn and lay overwintering eggs before dying out.

Treatment. Tar oil winter wash, applied in late December or early January, will kill overwintering eggs and reduce initial infestations of young growths. Alternatively, wait until early April and spray with a systemic or non-systemic insecticide to kill young aphids (see p. 105).

CURRANT APHIDS

At least seven different species of aphid infest black, red and white currants in Britain and northern Europe. One of these, the gooseberry aphid, *Aphis grossulariae*, is dealt with on p. 112 and the other main pest species are the currant-sowthistle aphid, *Hyperomyzus lactucae*, which mainly infests young leaves of black currants in early spring; the red currant blister aphid, *Cryptomyzus ribis*, which causes characteristic red blistering on leaves of red and white currants and similar yellow blistering on leaves of black currants, and the black currant aphid, *Cryptomyzus galeopsidis*, which forms dense colonies on the undersides of black currant leaves.

Biology. All three species overwinter as eggs laid near buds in the previous autumn. Eggs hatch as soon as buds open in spring and young aphids quickly infest young leaves. Colonies breed until early summer when winged aphids migrate to various weeds which are the summer hosts. In early autumn winged aphids return to currants and the sexual generation produces the overwintering eggs.

Treatment. Apply a tar oil winter wash in January to kill overwintering eggs and spray with a systemic or non-systemic insecticide immediately before flowering and, if necessary, after flowering to kill any aphids that survive the winter treatment (see p. 105).

GOOSEBERRY APHID *Aphis grossulariae*

Symptoms. Dense colonies of small grey-green aphids infest tips of gooseberry shoots in spring, causing slight leaf-curl.

Biology. Eggs overwinter on gooseberries and hatch in early spring. Colonies develop on young growths and may persist throughout the season but some winged aphids migrate to willow herbs during the summer.

Treatment. As for currant aphids (see above).

RASPBERRY, LOGANBERRY and BLACKBERRY APHIDS

Two species, the large raspberry aphid, *Amphorophora idaei*, and the small raspberry aphid, *Aphis idaei*, occur commonly on raspberries in Britain and northern Europe and both are important vectors of virus diseases. The same or similar species also attack loganberries and blackberries.

Biology and Treatment. Similar to currant aphids. Use winter washes against overwintering eggs and systemic or non-systemic insecticides before flowering, with repeat applications after flowering, if necessary. The various viruses inducing raspberry mosaic can be spread by quite small populations of aphids and it is difficult to obtain complete control of aphids in gardens so some virus transmission may occur despite the use of routine chemical control.

STRAWBERRY APHID *Chaetosiphon fragaefolii* (=*Pentatrichopus fragaefolii*)

This is the main species on strawberries in Britain and northern Europe although some other species also occur on these plants.

Symptoms. Pale green or yellow aphids with long siphunculi infest the undersides of strawberry leaves. Infestations are most severe on young growth in spring, especially on strawberries grown in glasshouses and houses and under glass or polythene protection outdoors. Aphids may also be present at other times of year and are potentially damaging on runner beds as they transmit several different viruses, especially those associated with yellow edge disease.

Biology. This species lives on strawberry plants throughout the year. Populations are low during the winter but increase as temperatures rise.

Treatment. Spray with systemic or non-systemic insecticides, when necessary, outside the flowering and fruiting period. Do not rely entirely on any one insecticide as that may encourage the development of resistant strains of glasshouse red spider mites and strawberry mites.

BLACK BEAN APHID *Aphis fabae* **Pl. 3**

One of the best known aphids in gardens. Common and widespread in Britain and northern Europe.

Symptoms. Conspicuous dense colonies of small black aphids (Pl. 3) develop on young shoots of broad, French and runner beans in May, June and July and on dahlias, poppies, nasturtiums (*Tropaeolum*) and some other ornamentals later in the summer. Infested shoots are often stunted, leaves are curled and distorted, and growth is checked. Similar infestations develop on *Euonymus*, *Viburnum opulus* and *Philadelphus* in early spring.

Many other black aphids occur on cultivated and wild plants so all black aphids seen in gardens are not necessarily *Aphis fabae*.

Biology. Females of the sexual generation developing in the autumn lay many small black shiny eggs near buds of the winter hosts, which are mainly *Euonymus europaeus* and *Viburnum opulus*. Adults usually die out in the winter but in milder southern areas wingless females may overwinter on plants. Eggs start to hatch in April, just as the buds of the winter hosts are opening, and colonies develop on young leaves and shoots. Winged females migrate to beans and other summer hosts from May onwards and as summer temperatures rise the rate of reproduction increases so that in June and July each successive generation may mature in about a week. Most damage is done at this time, especially on beans, but colonies persist on the summer hosts until autumn when winged females migrate to the winter hosts and the sexual generation develops. This aphid is also an important vector of bean yellow mosaic virus.

Treatment. Serious infestations of black bean aphids tend to occur every other year so trouble can be anticipated by observing the relative severity of attacks on the summer hosts each year and by looking for eggs on the winter hosts, especially on *Euonymus europaeus*, in late winter and early spring.

Infestations on broad beans can be checked by pinching out infested shoots in May and early June but in most cases of moderate to severe infestation chemical control is easier and more effective. Low-persistence contact insecticides, such as malathion or pirimicarb, sprayed in the pre-flowering period will give good control if applied thoroughly but longer lasting protection will be given by systemic insecticides, such as dimethoate or heptenophos, either sprayed onto plants or watered into the roots. Do not apply insecticides to beans in flower as they may kill bees and other pollinating insects.

Infestations on ornamentals may be treated with systemic or non-systemic insecticides, providing phytotoxic effects are avoided by choosing the correct insecticides for the plants to be treated.

CABBAGE APHID *Brevicoryne brassicae* Pl. 3

Symptoms. Dense colonies of grey-green aphids covered with a powdering of white mealy wax develop on leaves of many brassicas, especially cabbages (Pl. 3), Brussels sprouts, broccoli, cauliflowers and swedes. Leaves are discoloured and distorted where aphids are feeding and severe infestations check growth and may kill young and weak plants. Infestations build up from July onwards and usually reach a peak in September and October.

Biology. This species remains on cultivated and wild brassicas throughout the year. A sexual generation develops in autumn and overwintering eggs are laid on stems and leaves of brassicas but asexual females may also survive the winter in milder areas. Eggs hatch in April and young aphids feed on leaves and, later in the season, flower buds and flower stalks are infested. During May, June and July winged aphids fly off old brassica plants and establish new colonies on younger plants. Parthenogenetic reproduction of wingless females then continues until autumn when the next sexual generation matures. This aphid is an important vector of cauliflower and turnip mosaic viruses.

Treatment. Limit the carry-over of eggs from one season to the next by pulling up old brassicas as soon as cropping is over and destroying them by burning or burying. If this can be done by mid-April local sources of re-infestation will be reduced but plants will still be open to invasion by winged aphids from more distant sources. This risk is often greatest on allotments where brassicas at different stages of growth are present most of the time. All young plants should therefore be examined regularly from June until September and should be sprayed thoroughly with a suitable insecticide as soon as any cabbage aphids are seen. Malathion or nicotine give good short-term control and systemics give longer protection. Give particular attention to brassica seed-beds and, if necessary, dip transplants in a spray-strength solution of malathion or nicotine just before planting out. Wear water-proof gloves when doing this to prevent contact of the insecticide with the skin.

LETTUCE ROOT APHID *Pemphigus bursarius* **Pl. 3**

Symptoms. Colonies of yellow-white wingless aphids develop on roots of lettuces in summer (Pl. 3). Severe infestations kill plants, especially during dry weather.

This aphid also attacks Lombardy poplars (*Populus nigra* var. *italica*), where it lives in pouch-like galls on the leaf stalks. A related species, *Pemphigus spirothecae*, produces spiral pouch-galls on Lombardy poplars.

Biology. Eggs overwinter on Lombardy poplars and hatch in early spring. Wingless females feed on young leaf stalks and galls develop. Dense colonies of aphids then build up inside the galls and when these dry and split in June winged aphids migrate to the roots of lettuces and sowthistles where colonies feed and breed throughout the summer. Winged aphids return to Lombardy poplars in the autumn and lay overwintering eggs but summer colonies on lettuces may persist well into the winter and can survive in the soil until the following season.

Treatment. Some lettuces, such as 'Avoncrisp' and 'Avondefiance', are resistant to this pest but most of the varieties commonly grown in gardens are highly susceptible. Root systems of infested lettuces may be treated by applying a spray-strength solution of malathion or nicotine as a soil drench, and damage can be prevented by applying diazinon or chlorpyrifos granules to the soil before planting. Adequate watering during dry weather, good hygiene, rotation of crops and thorough cultivation all help to prevent serious attacks. If plants are severely damaged, dig up and destroy by burning or burying; cultivate the affected area thoroughly and do not grow lettuces on the same site in the following season.

Lombardy poplars are not normally treated since they are usually too large to spray and they are not appreciably affected by this pest.

WILLOW-CARROT APHID *Cavariella aegopodii*

Symptoms. Medium-sized green aphids with swollen siphunculi infest carrot leaves in late spring and early summer. Colonies are generally inconspicuous but conspicuous secondary symptoms are produced by the viruses that induce carrot motley dwarf disease (p. 277), which are transmitted by this pest.

Biology. Eggs overwinter on willows, mainly *Salix fragilis* and *Salix alba*, and winged aphids migrate to carrots in May and June. Colonies breed on carrots and related plants throughout the summer and there is a return migration to willows in the autumn.

Treatment. Early control of this aphid on carrots by spraying with systemic or non-systemic insecticides may prevent or check spread of motley dwarf disease but this treatment is only necessary if the disease is expected to be troublesome.

PEA APHID *Acyrthosiphon pisum*

Symptoms. Large pale green, pink or yellow aphids with long body, long legs and cauda, and very long siphunculi form smothering colonies on young growths of culinary and ornamental peas and on many other leguminous plants. In addition to direct damage caused by colonies feeding, this pest transmits a number of viruses, including bean yellow mosaic and pea leaf-roll.

Biology. Eggs and some adults overwinter on clovers, lucerne, trefoils and sainfoin and winged aphids spread to peas, beans and other leguminous plants from May onwards.

Treatment. Systemic or non-systemic insecticides applied in late May or in June, before plants come into flower, should give adequate protection to pea crops.

MELON AND COTTON APHID *Aphis gossypii*

Symptoms. Colonies of relatively small aphids, usually dark green but sometimes yellow or black, infest shoots and leaves of cucumbers and melons in glasshouses and may also attack these and other plants outdoors. Growth is checked, distorted and fouled with honeydew and sooty moulds and this species also transmits cucumber mosaic and other viruses.

Biology. This species can breed continuously on glasshouse plants throughout the year. Reproduction is mainly parthenogenetic and sexual forms of this aphid seldom occur. Development is slow during the winter but colonies increase to damaging levels quite rapidly as soon as temperatures start to rise in the spring. At summer temperatures aphids mature in about three weeks. Winged aphids spread infestations but there is no regular migration to and from winter hosts, as in many other aphid species.

Treatment. Spray thoroughly with systemic or non-systemic insecticides as soon as infestations are detected, but do not use HCH on cucumbers, melons and related plants as it is toxic to them.

POTATO APHID *Macrosiphum euphorbiae*

Symptoms. Colonies of large, long-bodied aphids with long legs, antennae and siphunculi develop on young shoots. Individual aphids are either green or pink and are rather restless. Potatoes are commonly affected but many other cultivated plants are attacked, both outdoors and in glasshouses and houses. It is often troublesome on tomatoes, lettuces, strawberries, aquilegias, carnations, cinerarias, China asters, chrysanthemums, dahlias, gladioli, hollyhocks, irises, roses, sweet peas, tulips, zantedeschias and zinnias. Because of its restless behaviour this pest is an important virus vector, transmitting narcissus yellow stripe, tulip breaking virus and others.

Biology. This is probably a north American species. It first appeared in Europe about 1917 and is now widely established. Parthenogenetic females overwinter on various plants in glasshouses and in protected situations outdoors and eggs overwinter on roses. Colonies increase from early spring and winged aphids spread infestations.

Treatment. Use appropriate systemic or non-systemic insecticides as soon as infestations are detected (see p. 105).

GLASSHOUSE AND POTATO APHID *Aulacorthum solani*

Symptoms. Medium-sized shiny green-yellow aphid with cylindrical tapering siphunculi, each with a dark green pigmented area at the base, infest young leaves, causing some distortion and discolouration. Many different plants are attacked, both outdoors and in glasshouses and houses, and infestations are most troublesome on potatoes, including sprouting tubers, lettuces, tomatoes, anemones, calceolarias, campanulas, carnations, chrysanthemums, dahlias, foxgloves, gloxinias, hyacinths, nasturtiums (*Tropaeolum*), pelargoniums, salvias and zantedeschias.

Biology. Parthenogenetic colonies overwinter in glasshouses and other protected situations. They increase in spring and early summer and winged aphids disperse from June onwards. This species seems to be mainly parthenogenetic in Britain and northern Europe but may occasionally overwinter as eggs produced by a sexual generation in the autumn.

Treatment. As for potato aphid (see above).

ROSE APHIDS

At least seven different species attack roses in Britain and northern Europe. One of these, the potato aphid, is dealt with above and some of the others are noted below.

The rose aphid, *Macrosiphum rosae*, is widespread and is the commonest species infesting buds, shoots and leaves (Pl. 3). It is usually most abundant in spring and early summer but colonies may persist on plants throughout the year. Other species include the lesser rose aphid, *Myzaphis rosarum*, which lives mainly in young folded leaves; the rose-grain aphid, *Metopolophium dirhodum*, which is an important pest of cereals and infests roses in spring and autumn; the small green rose aphid, *Chaetosiphon tetrarhodus*, which may cause severe damage to climbing roses; and the rose root aphid, *Maculolachnus submacula*, which produces colonies on roots and stem bases.

Treatment. Aphid populations tend to increase most rapidly on soft sappy growths in spring and early summer. Restricted use of nitrogenous fertilisers may limit such growths and so check aphids but cultural methods such as this are of doubtful value and the only certain way of keeping roses free from aphids is to use insecticides. Systemic insecticides, such as dimethoate or heptenophos, give good results, applied either as sprays or as soil drenches. Rates of application of soil drenches must be varied according to the size of plant and extent of root system. A litre of spray-strength solution may be sufficient to treat a small floribunda but larger shrub roses and climbers will need much more than this.

Many non-systemics give good control if applied thoroughly. Pirimicarb is one of the best and other effective insecticides include HCH, malathion, nicotine and pyrethroids. Soapy water may also be effective, if applied with sufficient force.

Chemical control is most necessary in April, May and June and two or three applications of insecticide made at this time before the plants come into full bloom may give adequate control of aphid colonies on new growths. Later in the season natural enemies will limit the increase of any surviving aphids so that further spraying may not be necessary but roses growing in glasshouses may need additional protection at other times of year.

CHRYSANTHEMUM APHIDS

Chrysanthemums growing outdoors or under glass in Britain and northern Europe may be attacked by at least four different species of aphid. Three of these, peach-potato aphid (p. 109), mottled arum aphid and leaf-curling plum aphid (p. 110) have extensive host ranges and are not restricted to chrysanthemums. The fourth species is the chrysanthemum aphid which is dealt with below.

CHRYSANTHEMUM APHID *Macrosiphoniella sanborni*

Glossy brown or green-black aphids with short stout siphunculi form dense colonies on stems and buds and may also affect flowers. Restricted to chrysanthemums.

Treatment. Many different insecticides have been developed for aphid control on chrysanthemums and plants can be kept relatively clean by spraying or fumigating whenever aphids are seen on them. Stools and cuttings growing in glasshouses in winter may be attacked by aphids moving off other glasshouse plants and plants growing outdoors in spring, summer and autumn will be colonised by winged migrants. Fumigation of glasshouses with permethrin or HCH gives good control at temperatures above 16°C (60°F). Systemic insecticides should not be used on chrysanthemums as they may harm some cultivars but non-systemics can be used. Pirimicarb gives good control and can be used on plants in bloom. Spray formulations of malathion, HCH, nicotine or pyrethroids are also suitable. Resistance to organophosphorus and carbamate insecticides has developed in strains of some of the aphids that attack chrysanthemums and it is therefore best not to rely on any one insecticide for control.

Biological control of chrysanthemum aphids has been developed on commercial crops by rearing a small parasitic hymenopteran, *Aphidius matricariae*, for release on cuttings before distribution. This ensures that the parasite will be present on young plants and will help to eliminate aphids that may have survived chemical treatments. This technique could possibly be used in gardens but requires more expertise than the use of chemicals.

MOTTLED ARUM APHID *Aulacorthum circumflexum* Pl. 3

Common and widespread on glasshouse and house plants.

Symptoms. Colonies of shiny yellow or green aphids with dark U-shaped marks on older individuals infest buds, leaves, flowers and stems (Pl. 3). Plants may be distorted and fouled with honeydew and sooty mould and, in

addition to this primary damage, this pest is an important virus vector, transmitting at least 30 different plant virus diseases. Zantedeschias and pot cyclamen are especially susceptible to infestation by this species but many other plants are attacked, including anemones, anthuriums, ornamental asparagus, azaleas, begonias, calceolarias, chrysanthemums, cinerarias, dahlias, freesias, irises, lilies, primulas, roses, saxifrages, schizanthus, tulips and violets.
Biology. Eggs and sexual forms are unknown and breeding is entirely parthenogenetic. Colonies breed throughout the year in glasshouses and houses and generally increase most rapidly between February and May. Populations can reach damaging levels at other times of year if conditions favour them. Winged aphids spread infestations but there are no regular migrations as in some other species.
Treatment. Appropriate systemic or non-systemic insecticides may be used as sprays or fumigants (see p. 105) but HCH is not particularly effective. This seems to be a case of natural resistance or tolerance rather than acquired resistance through over-use of insecticides.

TULIP BULB APHID *Dysaphis tulipae*
Symptoms. Light brown or yellow aphids infest bulbs and corms of tulips, gladioli, irises, crocuses and some other plants. Colonies establish on young shoots and may check growth. Mainly a pest on stored bulbs and corms in winter and early spring but may continue to affect growth after planting.
Biology. Breeds parthenogenetically throughout the year and survives the winter either underground or indoors.
Treatment. Easily controlled by spraying or fumigating as soon as aphids are noticed (see p. 105). Small quantities of bulbs or corms can be treated by enclosing them with dichlorvos strips in polythene bags for 1–2 hours.

HONEYSUCKLE APHID *Hyadaphis foeniculi*
Symptoms. Colonies of dark blue-green aphids with long black inflated siphunculi infest the undersides of honeysuckle leaves in spring and summer. Severe infestations cause extensive fouling of foliage with sticky honeydew and sooty moulds and check new growth, sometimes preventing normal development of the flowers.
Biology. Colonies build up on honeysuckle early in the year and die out during the summer when winged females migrate to umbelliferous wild plants, especially hemlock.
Treatment. Spray thoroughly as soon as aphids are seen. Systemics or pirimicarb give best control and systemics may be applied as a soil drench if overall spraying is not possible (see p. 105).

PRIVET APHID *Myzus ligustri*
Symptoms. Colonies develop on young privet leaves in spring and early summer. Affected leaves roll up tightly and, if opened carefully, aphids may be found inside. Extensive infestations make hedges look unsightly and persistent infestations weaken growth and may cause premature leaf-fall.
Biology. This species has not been studied in detail although it is often common in suburban areas. Presumably it overwinters on privet and

populations build up on young leaves. Hedge clipping probably encourages this pest by stimulating new growth.

Treatment. Spray thoroughly with a systemic or non-systemic insecticide in spring, if necessary (see p. 105).

SYCAMORE APHID *Drepanosiphum platanoidis*

Symptoms. Large green aphids with long swollen siphunculi infest buds and undersides of leaves of sycamores and other species of *Acer* in spring and summer. Large quantities of honeydew are produced and foliage is extensively fouled, becoming shiny and sticky in dry weather and with secondary development of sooty moulds. Plants, garden furniture and cars under infested trees are affected.

Biology. Eggs overwinter on trees and hatch from March onwards. Populations increase until July or August and during this period all adults are winged and viviparous. In autumn wingless sexual forms develop and females lay overwintering eggs in November and December.

Treatment. It is usually quite impossible to control this aphid on large trees but small trees can be protected by applying a tar oil winter wash in early January to kill overwintering eggs. Aphids appearing later in the year may be controlled by spraying with systemic or non-systemic insecticides (see p. 105), if feasible.

BEECH APHID *Phyllaphis fagi* **Pl. 3**

Symptoms. Colonies of yellow or green aphids, covered by tufts of white woolly wax, infest the undersides of beech leaves from April onwards. Foliage is fouled with sticky honeydew and sooty moulds and growth may be checked. This pest is particularly troublesome on beech hedges.

Biology. Restricted to beeches. Eggs laid in autumn overwinter on twigs and hatch in April. Young aphids feed on leaves and colonies increase during late spring and early summer. Winged aphids disperse to other beeches and colonies decline in late summer. Sexual forms develop in autumn and lay overwintering eggs.

Treatment. Apply tar-oil in December or early January and use systemics or non-systemics in spring and early summer, if feasible (see p. 105).

LARGE WILLOW APHID *Tuberolachnus salignus* **Pl. 3**

Many different aphid species feed on leaves and shoots of willows but this species is particularly conspicuous because of its size.

Symptoms. Colonies of large aphids, 4–5 mm long, dark brown and covered with fine grey hairs, feed on woody stems and branches of willows. Infestations first appear in late June and populations increase until autumn, often causing extensive fouling of foliage with honeydew and sooty moulds. Honeydew attracts flies and wasps.

Biology. The seasonal biology of this conspicuous and common aphid is not fully known. Colonies die out in winter and no sexual forms or overwintering eggs are produced. Small numbers of parthenogenetic females may survive on willows in protected situations and winged migrants may move north from warmer southern areas in early summer.

Treatment. Spray colonies and infested plants with systemic or non-systemic insecticides as soon as they are detected (see p. 105).

GREEN SPRUCE APHID *Elatobium abietinum*

Symptoms. Small green aphids with distinctive bright red eyes feed on leaves of spruces. At first feeding causes localised yellow discolouration of the leaves but this yellow mottling may be followed by general discolouration and premature shedding of leaves. This is most likely on Sitka spruce, *Picea sitchensis*, and on blue spruce, *Picea pungens* 'Glauca', but most species of *Picea* are attacked. Symptoms develop in early spring, especially after mild winters, and infestations tend to be worst on trees that are waterlogged, dry, exposed, or growing in other unfavourable conditions.
Biology. This species is active on spruces throughout the year. Wingless females overwinter on the undersides of leaves and can be found quite easily in winter and early spring. They continue to reproduce in mild winters and even after severe winters colonies may start to increase as early as March. Peak populations are usually reached in summer and winged aphids spread infestations.
Treatment. Spray thoroughly with malathion or pyrethroids in March–April or at other times when the pest is active.

ROOT APHIDS Pl. 3

Symptoms. Colonies of white or light-coloured aphids, sometimes covered in white powdery wax, infest roots of some glasshouse, house and outdoor plants (Pl. 3). Severe infestations check growth and plants may wilt. Pot plants are often attacked and root aphid colonies may be discovered when plants are being re-potted. Lettuces, auriculas, primulas, carnations and pinks are especially susceptible but many other plants may be attacked.
Biology. Various aphid species attack plant roots. Sometimes they do this only during one phase of their annual migratory cycle, as in the cases of the lettuce root aphid (p. 114), but other species, notably the artichoke tuber aphid, *Trama troglodytes*, live on roots continuously. They reproduce parthenogenetically and winged asexual females disperse to new host plants.
Treatment. Treat infested plants with a spray-strength solution of malathion or nicotine applied as a soil-drench in sufficient quantity to permeate the roots. Pot plants may be treated by washing the roots and then dipping them in spray-strength malathion or nicotine before re-potting. Diazinon or chlorpyrifos granules worked into the soil around affected plants may also check infestations.

ADELGIDS

(Plate 4)

Small sap-feeding insects (Hemiptera: Adelgidae), about 1–2 mm long, usually dark brown or black but covered by white wax wool. Closely related to aphids but with shorter antennae, fewer wing veins, and no siphunculi. Restricted to conifers, with many species widely distributed in Northern Hemisphere. Some species cause galls and the biology of many species is complex.

SPRUCE GALL ADELGIDS

Adelges abietis, Adelges viridis **Pl. 4**

Symptoms. Small galls, resembling miniature pineapples, develop at tips of branches of Norway spruce, (*Picea abies*), and of some other species of *Picea* (Pl. 4). Galls first appear in spring but old galls may persist for years. Galls interfere with normal growth and spoil the shape of young trees. Damage tends to be worst on light soils in cold, dry districts and is particularly severe on Christmas trees.

Biology. Young nymphs of *Adelges abietis* overwinter on spruce trees and mature in early spring. Females then lay batches of about 50 eggs, covered by tufts of white woolly wax, and young adelgids hatch within a few weeks. From May onwards they feed at the bases of young leaves at the tips of young shoots. The leaf bases then become abnormally enlarged and form the pineapple-like galls which house the adelgid colonies throughout the summer (Pl. 4). In August and September the galls break open and winged adelgids emerge. Some of these may migrate to other *Picea* trees but there is no migration to other host genera. The biology of *Adelges viridis* is similar but in autumn the winged forms migrate to larches. Wingless nymphs overwinter on larches and in early spring winged forms migrate to spruces.

Treatment. Protect young trees by spraying thoroughly with HCH or malathion during mild weather between November and April to kill off overwintering females before they lay eggs. Remove and burn any galls developing during the summer.

LARCH ADELGIDS *Adelges laricis, Adelges viridis* and other species

Symptoms. Leaves and shoots are infested by wingless adelgids covered in tufts of white woolly wax and foliage may be contaminated with sticky honeydew and sooty moulds. Most conspicuous in summer but adelgids are also present on leaves and on bark during winter. Severe summer infestations develop on European larch, (*Larix decidua*), and other species of *Larix* may also be affected. Adelgids are sometimes associated with die-back but may not be the cause of it.

Biology. Young nymphs of *Adelges laricis* overwinter near buds and mature in April. Females then lay clusters of small grey or orange eggs from which nymphs soon hatch to feed on young leaves. Colonies increase throughout the summer and some winged adelgids may migrate onto spruces. *Adelges viridis* overwinters on larch but does not cause appreciable summer infestations.

Treatment. Spray thoroughly with HCH or malathion as soon as infestations are apparent in early spring. Treat summer infestations by spraying thoroughly with malathion, repeating applications at about weekly intervals, if necessary.

SILVER FIR ADELGIDS *Adelges nordmannianae, Adelges piceae*

Symptoms. Colonies of adelgids develop on young shoots, on leaves and on stems and buds. *Adelges nordmannianae* is a serious pest of common silver fir, (*Abies alba*), and may kill young trees. It also attacks Caucasian fir, (*Abies nordmanniana*), and some other species of *Abies*. Colonies form on young shoots and feed on leaves, causing distortion and dieback.

Adelges piceae, which is known in North America as the balsam woolly aphid, infests stems and shoots of giant fir (*Abies grandis*), noble fir (*Abies procera*) and common silver fir (*Abies alba*). Infested shoots are stunted and distorted, sometimes with swellings on woody stems and branches.

Biology. Young nymphs of *Adelges nordmannianae* hibernate at the bases of leaves on trees. They start to feed in March and mature females lay eggs on shoots from early April. Eggs hatch as buds open in April/May and young adelgids then feed on new leaves. During summer some winged adelgids leave *Abies* and may occasionally establish colonies on *Picea orientalis*, which is an alternative host.

Adelges piceae also overwinters as nymphs and breeds during spring and summer. It seldom produces winged forms in Britain and nothern Europe and is only found on species of *Abies*.

Treatment. Spray infested trees with HCH in March/April. Repeat applications two or three times at about fortnightly intervals if infestations are severe.

DOUGLAS FIR ADELGID *Adelges cooleyi* **Pl. 4**

Symptoms. Small tufts of white woolly wax appear on undersides of leaves and branches of Douglas fir, (*Pseudotsuga menziesii*) during summer (Pl. 4). The tufts conceal small, dark, wingless adelgids. Affected foliage yellows and is fouled by sooty moulds. Growth of young trees may be checked by persistent infestations but older trees are not greatly affected.

Biology. Adelgid nymphs overwinter on leaves of Douglas fir and mature in spring. Females lay eggs from which young adelgids hatch to feed on new leaves as they emerge from the buds. Winged forms are produced from June onwards and these migrate to establish new colonies on Sitka spruce, (*Picea sitchensis*), which is the alternative host, but wingless adelgids continue to feed and breed on Douglas fir throughout the summer.

Treatment. *Adelges cooleyi* is not a serious pest. If necessary, it can be controlled on young trees by spraying thoroughly with HCH or malathion on two or three occasions in April/May.

SCOTS PINE ADELGID *Pineus pini*

Symptoms. Adelgid colonies infest leaves, shoots and bark of Scots pine, (*Pinus sylvestris*), throughout the year. Often conspicuous tufts of white woolly wax develop. Young trees are most susceptible. Foliage may be discoloured but damage is slight. Other pines are sometimes infested and Weymouth pine, (*Pinus strobus*), is attacked by a related adelgid, *Pineus strobi*.

Biology. Adelgid nymphs overwinter on pine trees and mature in March. Eggs are laid on stems in March/April and adelgids hatching from them crawl onto new leaves to feed. Some winged forms are produced during the summer and fly off to colonise spruces but wingless adelgids continue to feed and breed on pines.

Treatment. This pest causes little damage but does make trees look unsightly. Infestations on small trees may be treated by spraying thoroughly with HCH or malathion on two or three occasions in March/April or at other times when the pest is seen to be active.

PHYLLOXERIDS

Small or very small insects (Hemiptera: Phylloxeridae), up to 3–4 mm long. Similar to aphids but lacking siphunculi and adults have wings folding flat over body. Life-cycles are complex, with many different forms of each species.

VINE PHYLLOXERA *Daktulosphaira vitifoliae (=Viteus vitifoliae)*

A north American species introduced into Europe about 1863. It ravaged European vineyards in the second half of the nineteenth century but was eventually checked by grafting all commercial European grape vines onto resistant rootstocks derived from north American vine species and hybrids. Still present in western Europe but not now a serious pest. Very rare in Britain.

Symptoms. European grape vines growing on their own roots show marked red discolouration of leaves, followed by rapid collapse and death. Colonies of small yellow phylloxerids are generally present on roots of affected plants. Leaf galls may develop on some vines.

Biology. In the full life-cycle on American vines five different types of egg and a dozen different forms of individual phylloxerid develop on roots and leaves. On European vines the life-cycle is restricted and reproduction is entirely parthenogenetic and subterranean.

Treatment. Notify local agricultural or horticultural officials if suspected phylloxerid infestations develop on grape vines.

OAK PHYLLOXERIDS *Phylloxera glabra* and other species

Symptoms. Yellow and brown spots appear on oak leaves in summer and small yellow phylloxerids and eggs can usually be seen on the undersides of affected leaves. Severe infestations cause extensive browning of foliage and premature leaf-fall.

Biology. Oak phylloxerids probably overwinter mainly as eggs in crevices in bark. Females appear in spring and colonise young leaves. Asexual reproduction then continues until autumn when very small sexual forms develop.

Treatment. Phylloxerids have little effect on older trees but repeated infestations may weaken young trees. They can be protected, if necessary, by spraying, preferably with a systemic insecticide, such as dimethoate or formothion. This is best done in spring to kill off initial colonies before they become established. Contact insecticides, such as HCH, malathion or pirimicarb may also be effective if applied thoroughly.

SCALE INSECTS

(Plate 4)

Small sap-feeding insects (Hemiptera: Coccoidea). Nymphs and mature females produce characteristic white, yellow or brown wax scales up to about 5 mm long covering their relatively featureless bodies. Scales generally remain static on plants and feed by inserting fine stylets into plant tissues but may occasionally move to new feeding sites. Males are 1–2 mm long, with a single pair of wings but are absent or rare in parthenogenetic species. Many species of scale insect are common and widespread in Britain and northern Europe. They are especially troublesome in glasshouses, where introduced tropical and sub-tropical species are widely established, but many indigenous European species attack outdoor plants. Females usually lay hundreds of eggs under wax scales, under coverings of woolly wax or under their bodies. Young nymphs, known as crawlers, hatch some weeks or months later and disperse over plants before settling to feed.

Symptoms. Colonies of nymphs and mature females infest leaves, stems or fruits (Pl. 4). All stages feed on sap and most species excrete honeydew, which makes plants sticky and encourages growth of sooty moulds (p. 209). The extent of this contamination often seems out of all proportion to the number of scales present and a few young nymphs on the undersides of the upper leaves can cause extensive fouling of the older foliage. Persistent infestations weaken growth as well as making plants unsightly. Some fruits are attacked, especially peaches, nectarines and grape vines, but scale insects are mainly pests of ornamental plants. Vegetables are seldom affected.

The most widespread and troublesome pest species are noted below and details of treatment are given on p. 126.

SOFT SCALE *Coccus hesperidum* Pl. 4

Scales are elongate oval and flat, up to 5 mm long. Colour and shape varies but the outer edge of the scale is usually light brown and the centre is darker. Widespread and troublesome on glasshouse and house plants and also infests outdoor plants, especially in warmer southern areas and in warm situations against walls and buildings. Scales are usually on undersides of leaves, lying alongside veins. Main ornamental plants attacked are abutilons, bay laurel (*Laurus nobilis*), camellias, citrus, clematis, escallonias, ferns, ficus, geraniums, hibiscus, hippeastrums, hollies, ivies, oleanders, poinsettias and stephanotis but many others may also be infested. Females live about three months and produce about 1,000 live nymphs (crawlers) which crawl over plants for 2–3 days before settling to feed. At 18–25°C development to maturity takes about two months. Breeding is almost entirely parthenogenetic and continues throughout the year if conditions are favourable.

HEMISPHERICAL SCALE *Saissetia coffeae* Pl. 4

Scales are almost perfectly hemispherical up to 3 mm long and dark brown when mature. Size and shape is influenced by host plants and may be markedly restricted on hosts with narrow stems and leaves. This species is common in heated glasshouses, especially at higher temperatures. It often attacks asparagus ferns, begonias, carnations, clerodendrums, codiaeums, cycads, ferns, ficus, oleanders, orchids and stephanotis but may also infest many other ornamental plants. Breeding is almost entirely parthenogenetic and continues throughout the year if temperatures are high enough. Each female lays up to 2,000 eggs under the dome-shaped scale and then dies. Crawlers hatch some weeks or months later and disperse over plants before settling to feed.

BROWN SCALE *Parthenolecanium corni*

Also known as peach scale as it is an important pest of peaches and nectarines under glass and outdoors. Similar to hemispherical scale but normally occurs in unheated glasshouses and on outdoor plants. Colonies develop on woody stems as well as on shoots and leaves and mature female scales may be more than 5 mm long. Peaches, nectarines, currants and grape vines are the main fruits affected but this pest has been recorded from more than 300 different ornamental plants, including acacias, brooms, ceanothus, chaenomeles, clematis, cotoneasters, flowering currants (*Ribes*), escallonias, honeysuckle, laurel, magnolias, oleander, ornamental cherries, pyracanthas, roses, spiraeas and wistarias. It also attacks hazel and may affect nut production. Males are very rare and females reproduce parthenogenetically, laying up to 2,000 eggs each under the scale in May–July. Eggs hatch within a month and crawlers disperse and settle to feed on undersides of leaves. In autumn the small nymphs move from leaves to stems and branches where they hibernate. They feed again in spring and mature from April to July. There is only one generation a year and this species is therefore easier to control than species that breed continuously.

A closely related species, *Parthenolecanium pomeranicum*, attacks yew.

OLEANDER SCALE *Aspidiotus nerii*

Scales look like miniature fried eggs up to 2 mm diameter. Colonies develop on undersides of leaves of many glasshouse and house plants, especially on acacias, ornamental asparagus, aucubas, azaleas, pot cyclamen, dracaenas, ericas, fatsias, ficus, laurels, oleanders and palms. Occurs outdoors in warmer southerly areas.

WOOLLY CURRANT SCALE *Pulvinaria ribesiae*
WOOLLY VINE SCALE *Pulvinaria vitis* **Pl. 4**

Scales feed mainly on stems and females produce conspicuous egg sacs of white wax wool in May and June. Currants and grape vines are the main fruits attacked and some ornamental plants, especially alder, birch, hawthorn, cotoneasters and willows, are also susceptible. Generally only attacks outdoor plants. Breeding is parthenogenetic with a single generation a year.

HORSE-CHESTNUT SCALE *Pulvinaria regalis*

Closely related to the woolly currant scale but only established in southern England and north-west France since about 1960. Dense colonies form on branches and trunks of horse chestnut trees and on limes, elms, sycamores, magnolias, maples, cornus and some other ornamental plants. Little apparent damage is done, despite the presence of large colonies. Eggs hatch in June–July and nymphs feed on leaves until autumn when they move onto branches and trunks to overwinter. Females mature in spring and reproduce parthenogenetically.

BEECH SCALE *Cryptococcus fagisuga* (*=Cryptococcus fagi*) **Pl. 4**

Mature females are only about 1 mm long but colonies containing females, eggs and nymphs form conspicuous areas of white wax powder on trunks and branches of beech trees. Reproduction is parthenogenetic and most eggs are laid between June and October. Eggs overwinter and colonies may persist on the same tree for many years. This pest predisposes trees to infection by fungi of the genus *Nectria* which cause a serious and widespread condition known as beech bark disease.

MUSSEL SCALE *Lepidosaphes ulmi* **Pl. 4**

Small mussel-shaped brown scales, up to 3 mm long, form dense encrusting colonies on woody stems and branches of ceanothus, cotoneasters, ornamental and fruiting apples and pears, roses and various other trees and shrubs. Infestations are most severe on old plants lacking vigour and the scales are often so densely packed that they look like a normal feature of the bark. Eggs laid under the scales in late summer overwinter and hatch in the following May–June.

A closely related species, *Lepidosaphes machili*, infests stems and leaves of cymbidiums in glasshouses.

WILLOW SCALE *Chionaspis salicis*

Similar to scurfy scale but female scales are whiter and more irregular, often covering woody stems so densely that they look as if they have been whitewashed. Attacks alder, ash, brooms, ceanothus' elms, lilacs, privet, willows and some other ornamental shrubs and trees.

Treatment. Scale insects are relatively immobile pests. Crawlers move about to a limited extent and may occasionally be blown around by wind or transported on flying insects or on birds but most scales found in gardens will have been introduced on plants. All newly acquired plants should therefore be examined very carefully and should be treated, if necessary, before establishing them in the garden, glasshouse or house.

Some glasshouse and house plants can be treated quite effectively by wiping scales off leaves and stems with a soft rag, sponge, or brush dipped into soapy water. Aspidistras, ornamental citrus, codiaeums, dracaenas, ficus, ivies, orchids, sansevierias and other plants with relatively robust leaves may be treated in this way.

Chemical treatments are most effective when applied to kill young crawlers before they have settled and started to form their protective scale. They are easily killed by thorough application of non-persistent contact insecticides, such as pyrethroids, diazinon, malathion or nicotine, but timing is critical. The main period of crawler activity on outdoor plants is in late spring and early summer but in heated glasshouses and in houses crawlers may hatch at almost any time. By using a magnifying glass or hand lens crawlers can be seen quite easily. Infested plants should be treated with one of the above insecticides when crawlers are active and, since some of them will escape treatment, a second application of insecticide should be made about two weeks after the first.

If insecticide treatment cannot be timed to coincide with egg hatch and crawler activity, systemic insecticides, such as dimethoate or formothion, may be used to kill maturing females but these chemicals may have harmful phytotoxic effects on some ornamental plants.

Fully dormant deciduous woody plants may be sprayed or brushed with tar oil in December or January to kill overwintering scales and eggs and this is a particularly useful treatment against scale insects on grape vines, currants and apples and against beech scale on beech tree trunks and branches. Tar oil must be applied carefully to avoid damage to other garden plants.

MEALYBUGS

(Plate 4)

Small sap-feeding insects (Hemiptera: Pseudococcidae), up to about 4 mm long. Males winged but relatively uncommon. Females wingless, with soft, rounded bodies covered by white wax powder and filaments (Pl. 4). Many different species on wild and cultivated plants but usually most troublesome on glasshouse and house plants.

GLASSHOUSE MEALYBUGS — Pl. 4

Pseudococcus obscurus is the commonest species in glasshouses in Britain. *Planococcus citri*, *Pseudococcus longispinus* and *Pseudococcus calceolariae* are also common and many other species may occur locally. The four main pest species are tropical and sub-tropical and have been accidentally introduced to glasshouses in Britain and northern Europe. They are restricted to glasshouse plants in colder northern climates but will infest outdoor plants in the warmer areas of southern Britain and Europe. All species are very similar in appearance and biology and in the effects that they have on garden plants.

Symptoms. Mealybug colonies (Pl. 4) develop on leaves, stems, buds, flowers, fruits and other aerial parts of plants. Roots are sometimes infested by root mealybugs (see below). Colonies contain young and mature mealybugs clustered together and protected by white wax powder and filaments, which often completely cover the insects, especially when they congregate in leaf axils, in the necks of bulbs and on the spines of cacti. Persistent infestations weaken plants, especially when growing points are attacked, and foul plant surfaces with honeydew and sooty moulds. Many different host plants are attacked and the following are particularly susceptible: vines, currants, sprouting potatoes, abutilons, anthuriums, asparagus fern, begonias, cacti, ceanothus, chrysanthemums, codiaeums, coleus, crassulas, dracaenas, eucharis, ferns, ficus, fuchsias, gardenias, hippeastrums, hoyas, jasmines, laburnums, musas, oleanders, orchids, pelargoniums, robinias, saintpaulias and palms.

Biology. Each female lays about five batches of 100–150 eggs and each batch is protected by a covering of woolly wax. At relatively high temperatures, eggs hatch in a few days and young mealybug nymphs then crawl over plants for a few hours before settling to feed. They are immobile for long periods when feeding but can withdraw their feeding stylets from plant tissues to move during their development. At 28°C (82°F) development from egg to adult takes about a month. Breeding can continue throughout the year in heated glasshouses and in houses but most mealybugs mature in summer and populations are generally highest in autumn and early winter. Winged males develop from delicate white cocoons and may appear in large numbers at times but females can reproduce parthenogenetically when males are not present and some species are almost entirely parthenogenetic.

Treatment. Mealybugs are often difficult to control as they tend to live in inaccessible situations on plants and they are well protected from insecticides by their wax coverings. To eradicate established infestations, first remove as many colonies as possible by cutting out and burning infested shoots and branches, by washing plants with powerful jets of water or by removing mealybugs with a household paint brush. This latter treatment can be made more effective by dipping the brush in a spray-strength solution of malathion or nicotine. Methylated or surgical spirit may also be used. Brushing is often the only way of removing mealybugs from cacti and is also a useful way of treating dormant grape vines.

Once the main colonies have been cleared up, spray plants with malathion, nicotine, or one of the systemic insecticides, such as dimethoate. The systemics may also be applied as soil drenches to be taken up by the roots and translocated within the plant to the sites where mealybugs are feeding. This is often the best way to control infestations on cacti, succulents and bulbs but may cause phytotoxic side-effects on some plants.

Avoid introducing mealybugs into clean collections of plants by examining all new introductions carefully and by keeping them in quarantine for a month or so, if possible. Treat if any sign of mealybug infestation is observed and repeat the treatment on two or three occasions at about fortnightly intervals to make sure that the pests are eradicated.

A predaceous ladybird beetle, *Cryptolaemus montrouzieri*, which was originally introduced from Australia to California to control mealybugs on citrus trees, is now available from specialist suppliers in Britain for use against mealybugs in glasshouses but needs relatively high temperatures to develop successfully.

ROOT MEALYBUGS Pl. 4

Very similar to glasshouse mealybugs described above but they mainly feed on roots. A number of species of the genus *Rhizoecus* occur in Britain and northern Europe. *Rhizoecus falcifer* is the most widespread and troublesome pest species on glasshouse and house plants and other species affect outdoor garden plants.

Symptoms. Colonies of root mealybugs develop on roots (Pl. 4) and on bases of stems of many different plants. Root mealybugs may be confused with root aphids (p. 120) and with springtails (p. 94). Severe root mealybug infestations interfere with normal root function and plants do not grow well and may wilt, especially if they are growing in pots. Damage is generally worst when plants are growing in dry potting composts or in dry borders. Abutilons, acacias, cacti and succulents, cassias, correas, dianthus, dracaenas, gardenias, grevilleas, olearias, pelargoniums, saintpaulias and stephanotis are particularly susceptible.

Biology. The biology of root mealybugs, so far as it is known, resembles that of the glasshouse mealybugs (see above).

Treatment. Water plants regularly to keep the root zone moist and so limit root mealybug populations by creating unfavourable conditions. Drench infested pot plants with a spray-strength solution of a contact insecticide, such as malathion or nicotine, or a systemic insecticide, such as dimethoate, but take care to avoid phytotoxic effects. If root mealybugs are discovered when re-potting plants, wash the infested roots in soapy water or in a spray-strength solution of insecticide. Then re-pot in sterile compost.

THRIPS

(Plate 4)

Small, elongate, cylindrical insects (Thysanoptera), up to 3–4 mm long. Adults, commonly known as 'thunder flies', have two pairs of very narrow wings fringed with long, fine hairs. Colour varies with species from white through shades of yellow to brown and black. Larvae resemble adults but lack wings and are generally lighter coloured. More than 150 species occur on plants in Britain and northern Europe. Many species are abundant and widespread and some are cosmopolitan. Larvae and adults of most species feed on plants, especially on flowers and buds, but some prey on mites, aphids and other small invertebrates. Mouth-parts of larvae and adults are adapted to pierce plant or animal tissues superficially and to extract cell contents. Direct damage to garden plants is caused by large numbers of thrips feeding on leaves, flowers and buds, producing characteristic light mottling and silvering (Pl. 4) and some distortion. Some species may cause indirect damage by transmitting tomato spotted wilt virus disease although this is now less serious than it once was.

Females live for about a month and lay 60–80 eggs which are either inserted into plant tissues with a saw-like ovipositor or are simply deposited on plants. Eggs soon hatch at summer temperatures and larvae feed for a few weeks before passing through quiescent, non-feeding prepupal and pupal stages. Winged adults emerge about a week after pupation and are often carried long distances in thermals and air currents before settling on plants. Development from egg to adult takes about a month at 20°C (68°F) but lasts much longer at lower temperatures. Development is usually sexual but some species are parthenogenetic. Adults and immature stages overwinter in soil, leaf litter and similar situations.

The main species attacking garden plants are noted below and general methods of treatment are summarised on p. 131.

ONION THRIPS *Thrips tabaci*

A cosmopolitan species that attacks many different plants. Mainly a pest of glasshouse and house plants in Britain and northern Europe but also damages some outdoor plants.

Symptoms. Characteristic fine, light flecking and silvering of leaves, buds and flowers, with numerous yellow or brown larvae and adults usually present. Onions, brassicas and tomatoes are the most susceptible vegetables and begonias, carnations, chrysanthemums, cinerarias, cyclamen, dahlias, gerberas, gloxinias, orchids, pelargoniums, sweet peas and zantedeschias are often attacked. Transmits tomato spotted wilt virus.

Biology. Males are rare and breeding is almost entirely parthenogenetic. Females lay eggs in plant tissues and larvae feed for 2–3 weeks before pupating in the soil. There are usually only two adult generations a year outdoors but breeding may continue during most of the year in glasshouses and other protected situations.

Treatment. See p. 131

PEA THRIPS *Kakothrips pisivorus (=Kakothrips robustus)* Pl. 4

Symptoms. Flowers, leaves and pods of peas and broad beans misshapen, discoloured, and usually with characteristic silver sheen. Yellow larvae and yellow-brown adults are present on affected plants in May–July, especially during hot, dry weather.

Biology. Adults emerge from pupae in soil during late spring and early summer and fly up onto plants. Females lay eggs in flower stamens and larvae hatch after a week or so, feed for 2–3 weeks and then descend to the soil to overwinter. There is only one adult generation a year and populations reach a peak between mid-June and the end of July.

Treatment. See p. 131.

GLADIOLUS THRIPS

Thrips simplex (=Taeniothrips simplex) **Pl. 4**

A serious pest of gladioli, first introduced into Britain about 1950 and now well established.

Symptoms. Leaves and flowers of gladioli and related plants show characteristic light flecking where thrips have fed. Yellow larvae and darker adults are usually present, especially under leaf bases, in flowers and in flower buds. Severe attacks ruin flowers which wilt, brown and die (Pl. 4). Most severe attacks develop on growing plants during July and August but corms may be attacked in store during winter and early spring by thrips feeding on the scales.

Biology. Thrips overwinter on corms in store and some may also survive mild winters outdoors in soil and leaf litter. When temperatures rise above 10°C (50°F), females lay eggs in plant tissues and larvae soon hatch. Breeding continues so long as conditions are favourable and damaging populations build up rapidly in summer.

Treatment. Control is relatively easy and effective since the annual cycle can be broken by dusting corms with gamma HCH before they are stored and before they are planted out in spring. HCH may also be applied to growing plants if thrips are present or a less persistent contact insecticide, such as malathion, or nicotine may be used to check early infestations on susceptible plants.

ROSE THRIPS *Thrips fuscipennis*

Symptoms. Flowers of roses and of some other plants are flecked with numerous light spots and streaks, which later darken and rot. Leaves may also show silver flecking and brown thrips are usually present on plants. Roses grown under glass may be severely damaged by infestations developing early in the season.

Biology. Adults overwinter in cracks in brickwork, woodwork, canes, stakes and similar situations and some thrips may continue to breed through the winter in protected situations. Females lay eggs from February onwards in young petals and other soft tissues and breeding continues until autumn.

Treatment. See below.

CARNATION THRIPS *Taeniothrips atratus*

Produces typical thrips symptoms on carnations in glasshouses and also attacks many other plants outdoors.

GLASSHOUSE THRIPS *Heliothrips haemorrhoidalis*

Generally not as common in glasshouses as the onion thrips (see p. 130). Adults have dark brown bodies with light yellow tips to the abdomen and attack azaleas, citrus, ferns, fuchsias, orchids, zantedeschias and many other plants growing in glasshouses and houses. Infested plants are marked with small red and brown globules of liquid that are deposited by feeding thrips.

PRIVET THRIPS *Dendrothrips ornatus*

Yellow larvae and dark-bodied adults, with alternating dark and light bands on wings attack privet and lilac, causing characteristic silvering of leaves. Established plants are not appreciably damaged but young plants may be checked by severe infestations causing premature leaf-fall.

General Treatment. Severe thrips attacks on glasshouse and house plants are often associated with poor growing conditions resulting from underwatering and overheating. Regular watering and maintenance of a cooler, more humid atmosphere can therefore help to prevent infestations. Similarly, infestations on outdoor plants are usually worst during hot dry periods and thrips populations are reduced in cool, wet weather.

Most species are easily controlled with contact insecticides, if necessary, and HCH, malathion or nicotine are generally effective. These are usually applied as sprays, but dusts or fumigants may be used when appropriate. If insecticides are used, they should be applied as soon as thrips or symptoms are seen, with a repeat application after 2–3 weeks if damage continues.

CATERPILLARS

(Plate 5)

Caterpillars are larvae of moths and butterflies (Lepidoptera) and all have a generally similar structure which resembles that of some sawfly larvae (see p. 154). The head is well developed and has a pair of strong mandibles which are used to bite and chew plant tissues; the thorax is three-segmented, usually with a pair of jointed legs on each segment, and the abdomen consists of ten segments bearing up to five pairs of fleshy, non-jointed legs (prolegs).

Size (5–100 mm) and colour pattern vary with species and more than 2,500 species are recorded from Britain and northern Europe. Caterpillars of most species feed on wild plants but at least fifty species are widespread pests of garden plants.

Biology is varied but relatively uncomplicated. Adults feed only on nectar and other sugary fluids or do not feed at all. Reproduction is normally sexual and, after mating, females lay a few hundred eggs on or near plants, either singly or in batches. Caterpillars generally hatch within a few weeks and feed for 1–2 months before pupating on plants, in soil and plant debris or on fences, buildings and other structures. Adults usually emerge from pupae after a few weeks. They fly during daytime (most butterflies) or at night (most moths) and some species migrate over long distances, often reaching Britain by non-stop flights from northern Africa or central Europe.

Many important families of Lepidoptera have similar habits and are known by their family names (pyralids, tortricids, tineids, noctuids, geometrids, hepialids, pierids, etc.). Larval habitats include all parts of plants (leaves, stems, buds, flowers, fruits and roots) and symptoms are correspondingly varied. Most caterpillars feed openly on leaves, buds and shoots but some produce silk webbing which they use to draw leaves together into protective tent-like coverings. Some caterpillars live in soil and a few are able to tunnel in woody branches and trunks of trees.

The symptoms and biology of the main pest species are detailed in the following section and for convenience they are grouped under fruits, vegetables and ornamentals. To some extent this is an artificial division since many species commonly attack all of these groups of plants.

General methods of treating caterpillar pests are summarised below and specific recommendations are given under the main pest entries.

General Treatment. Non-chemical methods of control can be used against some caterpillars, especially when they occur in small numbers on a few plants. The simplest and most effective method is to examine plants regularly and crush eggs and caterpillars whenever they are seen. This technique may seem crude and cruel but it kills eggs and caterpillars more certainly and swiftly than insecticides. Species that overwinter as caterpillars or pupae in the soil or in plant debris may be partly controlled by good hygiene and thorough cultivation during autumn and early spring and species that overwinter as conspicuous egg batches can be restricted by pruning out and destroying the eggs in winter. Grease-banding is a special non-chemical technique that is only effective against the winter moth group and sack-banding is occasionally used against codling moth (see p. 134).

Contact insecticides are widely used against caterpillars, generally as sprays but sometimes as dusts. Their effectiveness is enhanced if they have some residual activity so that they act as internal poisons when ingested on treated plant tissues, but this is not essential. Systemic insecticides, which are so effective against aphids and other sap-feeding insects, are not equally effective against caterpillars although some of them do have sufficient contact activity to be of use.

Non-persistent contact insecticides, such as derris, bioresmethrin, resmethrin or malathion, are quite adequate for treatment of caterpillars feeding in exposed situations on plants and can be used safely on vegetables and fruits within a few days of harvest. More persistent insecticides, such as HCH, permethrin, carbaryl or trichlorphon, may give better control of caterpillars feeding in protected situations on plants and in soil. A bacterial spray containing *Bacillus thuringiensis* is available from specialist suppliers and can be used to give safe and effective control of caterpillars without harming beneficial insects.

WINTER MOTHS Pl. 5

Three main species are grouped under this heading: the winter moth, *Operophtera brumata*; the March moth, *Alsophila aescularia*, and the mottled umber moth, *Erannis defoliaria*. All are widespread, important pests of fruit trees and ornamental plants in Britain and Northern Europe.

Symptoms. Leaves, buds and young shoots are eaten during spring and early summer by green, yellow-green or brown 'looper' caterpillars (Pl. 5). Characteristic irregular holes are eaten in leaves, often before they have expanded from the buds, and these symptoms persist throughout the growing season (Pl. 5). Extensive damage to fruit blossom and foliage may affect cropping and leaf damage on ornamental trees, shrubs and hedges makes them look unsightly. Persistent attacks weaken plants and facilitate the development of bacterial and other diseases. Apples, pears, plums and cherries are the main fruit trees attacked and many ornamentals, especially beech, flowering cherries, cotoneasters, crab-apples, dogwoods, elms, hawthorns, hazels, hornbeams, limes, rhododendrons, roses, sycamores and willows, are commonly affected.

Biology. Wingless female moths emerge from pupae in soil during winter or early spring, mate with winged males, and then crawl up trunks and stems of trees and shrubs to lay about 200 eggs each. Winter moths emerge in October–December; mottled umbers emerge in October–March and March moths emerge from January to April. Winter moth and mottled umber females lay eggs singly or in small clusters near buds and in crevices in bark and March moths lay distinctive bands of eggs around twigs. Eggs hatch from March onwards and caterpillars feed on buds and young leaves as they develop. Caterpillars of all three species are similar in structure but differ in colour. Winter moth caterpillars are usually green with three yellow longitudinal stripes; mottled umber caterpillars are dark brown with yellow lateral longitudinal bands (Pl. 5) and March moth caterpillars are green with light stripes. All grow to a length of about 30 mm and most finish feeding from mid-May to the end of June. They then go to the soil to pupate and are often seen at this time of year hanging from trees and shrubs on long silken threads. There is only one adult generation a year and pupae remain dormant in the soil until the next adults emerge in the following winter and spring.

Treatment. Protect valuable fruit and ornamental trees by applying grease bands to the trunks in October to stop females crawling up to lay eggs. Use specially formulated grease (*not* car grease) applied either direct to the bark or onto strips of paper to form a band about 100 mm wide about 1–2 metres above soil level. (Ready-made grease bands can be bought from gardening shops.) Tie bands tightly onto trunks after removing any loose or rough bark and make sure that female moths cannot by-pass the bands by crawling under them or by crawling over them on dead leaves or other plant debris. Inspect regularly and renew if necessary.

Where grease bands cannot be used effectively, as on shrubs and hedges, use insecticides. Tar oil winter washes applied to control aphids (p. 105) will give some protection by killing overwintering eggs but contact insecticides such as trichlorphon, fenitrothion, malathion, permethrin, or derris, applied as soon as buds have opened in spring, will give better control, especially on fruit trees.

CODLING MOTH *Cydia pomonella*

(=Laspeyresia pomonella) **Pl. 5**

A common and world-wide pest of apples. The closely related plum fruit moth, *Cydia funebrana*, causes similar damage to plums.

Symptoms. Caterpillars eat into flesh of maturing apples, making them inedible (Pl. 5). Pears and some other fruits are occasionally attacked but apples are the main host plants. Tortrix caterpillars (p. 142) and apple sawfly larvae (p. 154) produce similar symptoms but do not tunnel so extensively within the mature fruit.

Biology. Adults are active on warm nights in June/July but are small and inconspicuous. Females lay flat, translucent eggs singly on fruits and leaves and caterpillars hatch from them after about two weeks. They immediately tunnel into developing fruits, often entering through the eye (calyx) so that there is no apparent entry hole. Caterpillars feed within fruits for a month or more, eating down through the flesh to the core, and when they have finished feeding they leave the damaged fruits and spin cocoons under loose bark, under tree ties, and in similar situations. Most caterpillars remain in cocoons until the following season but some pupate in August to produce a second adult generation in September.

Treatment. Chemical control is difficult since timing must be sufficiently accurate to ensure that young caterpillars are killed before they can enter fruits and thorough spraying may only be possible on smaller trees. If possible, spray apple trees with fenitrothion or permethrin after blossoming, first about mid-June with a second application three weeks later.

Sacking or corrugated cardboard tied around branches and tree trunks by mid-July can be used to trap caterpillars seeking sites in which they can form cocoons but is of doubtful value since the fruits will have been damaged before the caterpillars are trapped. Trapping is also unlikely to reduce numbers of egg-laying females in the following season since they can easily fly into gardens from adjacent untreated trees.

FRUIT TORTRIX MOTHS

Three species of tortrix caterpillar attack fruits: the fruitlet mining tortrix, *Pammene rhediella*; the summer fruit tortrix, *Adoxophyes orana*, and the fruit tree tortrix, *Archips podana*. All three produce similar symptoms.

Symptoms. Attacked fruits show various types of superficial scarring, distortion and tunnelling. Ripening apples are commonly affected but fruits of pears, plums and cherries may also be attacked. Green caterpillars, up to 25 mm long, may be found feeding on damaged fruits and on leaves and buds. They spin silk to draw leaves into protective covers and if these are opened carefully caterpillars will characteristically wriggle backwards as they are disturbed.

Biology. Small, inconspicuous adult moths fly at night during the summer. Females lay eggs singly or in small batches on leaves and caterpillars feed for about a month before spinning cocoons and pupating. A second generation of adults emerges in autumn and the young caterpillars hatching from eggs laid by females of this generation hibernate in cocoons on infested plants. They become active again in the following spring and feed on young buds and leaves before pupating.

Treatment. Damage is often slight and tortrix activity is generally too unpredictable for chemical controls to be used effectively. Sprays applied to control winter moths (p. 133) will give some incidental control of tortrix moths and, if tortrix moths are known to be particularly troublesome, a post-blossom fenitrothion spray applied in mid-June, with a second application a fortnight later, will limit damage to fruits.

MAGPIE MOTH *Abraxas grossulariata*

Symptoms. Black, white and yellow 'looper' caterpillars, up to 40 mm long, eat leaves of many plants in April/June. Gooseberries and currants may be stripped of leaves and other plants, especially apricots, cherries, crab apples, euonymus, hawthorns, hazels, laurels and plums are similarly affected. Gooseberry sawfly (p. 156) produces similar symptoms on gooseberries and currants.

Biology. Adult moths are active at night in July/August and females lay eggs singly or in small batches on undersides of leaves. Caterpillars hatch about a fortnight later and feed on leaves until autumn. The caterpillars, which are still small, overwinter in cracked bark, leaf litter and similar situations and start to feed again in the following spring, from about April onwards. After feeding voraciously for a month or so, conspicuous black and yellow banded pupae develop in thin cocoons attached to leaves and twigs of host plants or to fences, walls and other structures. Adults emerge from these in July/August to complete the cycle.

Treatment. Look for caterpillars on susceptible host plants in early spring, paying special attention to the centres of gooseberry and currant bushes, where attacks often develop. Remove caterpillars by hand or spray with non-persistent contact insecticides. Spraying with tar oil (p. 134) may help to limit infestations by killing some of the overwintering caterpillars.

LEOPARD MOTH *Zeuzera pyrina* Pl. 5

Symptoms. Terminal leaves on branches of young trees suddenly wilt and die when caterpillars tunnel in wood (Pl. 5). Holes and frass on the surface of branches indicate the presence of caterpillars within. Attacks are local and sporadic but can cause serious damage to young apple, pear and cherry trees and to many ornamental trees and shrubs, especially ash, birch, cotoneasters, elms, hawthorns, horse chestnuts, lilacs, maples, sycamores and rhododendrons.

Biology. Adult moths are large (wing-span up to 60 mm) but fly at night and are seldom seen. Females lay eggs in bark during June/July and caterpillars spend their first autumn and winter feeding just beneath the bark. In the following spring they tunnel into the wood and each caterpillar eats out a gallery up to 20 cm long. Caterpillars feed for up to three years before pupating in galleries and when adults emerge the empty pupal cases are often left protruding from the exit holes.

Treatment. This pest is so sporadic and local that it is difficult to prevent attacks but if symptoms are recognised soon enough it may be possible to save branches by killing caterpillars. First locate holes, clear them with a stick or wire and introduce an insecticide, such as HCH, and seal the holes with plasticine or putty. Branches that have been seriously damaged will not recover and should be pruned out and burned.

CUTWORMS Pl. 5

Caterpillars of various noctuid moths live in the upper few centimetres of the soil and feed at the surface, mainly at night. They attack young plants at ground level, often eating right through the stems, and are therefore commonly known as cutworms. Most species are widespread and abundant. The main pest species found in gardens are the large yellow underwing, *Noctua pronuba*, the turnip moth, *Agrotis segetum*, and the heart and dart moth, *Agrotis exclamationis*.

Symptoms. Stems of young plants are eaten at ground level and are often completely severed. Damaged plants wilt and die. Young vegetable plants, especially lettuces and brassicas, are especially susceptible and small numbers of cutworms can cause considerable damage by working along rows. Roots, tubers, corms and leaves are also eaten. Carrots, celery, beet and potatoes are often attacked but strawberries are usually the only fruit plants likely to be damaged. Many ornamental plants are attacked, especially China asters, chrysanthemums, dahlias, marigolds, primulas, zinnias, and young trees and shrubs in nurseries. Plants may be damaged at almost any time of year and attacks are often severe on light soils during dry summers. Drab cutworm caterpillars (Pl. 5) may be found by searching the soil near damaged plants and adult moths are sometimes disturbed from leaf litter and other plant debris.

Biology. Most species have similar life-cycles. Adults emerge from pupae in the soil in June/July and females lay eggs in batches of 30–50 on leaves and stems of cultivated plants and weeds and on dead leaves and other plant debris. Each female lays up to 1,000 eggs over a period of 1–2 weeks and eggs hatch about two weeks after laying. During summer the caterpillars feed for 1–2 months before pupating and a second adult generation emerges in August/September. Caterpillars that develop later in the season overwinter in the soil, feeding whenever the weather is favourable, and finally pupate in the following spring. There is considerable variation in the time taken for development from egg to adult.

Treatment. Cultivate soil thoroughly in winter to expose cutworm caterpillars to weather and to birds and other predators. Keep plots free from weeds as they encourage egg-laying. Protect susceptible young plants during the early stages of growth by applying bromophos, chlorpyrifos or other insecticides to the soil around the stems. On a small scale it may be possible to locate and destroy caterpillars by hand, especially in small nursery beds and in frames.

SWIFT MOTHS

Pl. 5

Various species of hepialid moth, especially the garden swift moth, *Hepialus lupulinus*, and the ghost swift moth, *Hepialus humuli*, are widespread pests of garden plants. Symptoms, biology and treatment are essentially the same for all species.

Symptoms. White caterpillars, up to 65 mm long, with shiny brown heads (Pl. 5) live in soil and feed on roots, tubers, bulbs, corms and rhizomes of many plants. Unlike cutworms, swift moth caterpillars feed almost entirely below ground. Strawberries and lettuces may be seriously damaged by caterpillars eating up into stems from below and many ornamentals are susceptible to attack, especially anemones, perennial asters, auriculas, chrysanthemums, colchicums, convallarias, daffodils, dahlias, delphiniums, gladioli, irises, lilies, paeonies and perennial phlox. Damage may occur at almost any time of year and caterpillars are often seen when old herbaceous borders, old strawberry beds, grassland and weedy or uncultivated areas are being dug in winter.

Biology. Adult moths fly at dusk during June–August and hover over borders, beds, lawns and patches of weeds. Females release eggs while in flight and each female may lay up to 700 eggs. These fall to the soil and hatch about a fortnight later. Young caterpillars then burrow into the soil and start to feed on fine roots of cultivated plants and weeds. They continue to feed throughout autumn and winter, attacking major root systems, bulbs, corms, tubers and other underground parts of plants, and either pupate in the following spring or continue to feed for a further year before pupating.

Treatment. Female swift moths are attracted to overgrown weedy areas to lay eggs and do not normally lay over bare soil. Good weed control and regular cultivation can therefore prevent attacks by limiting egg-laying. Cultivation also exposes caterpillars to predators and weather and thorough winter digging is particularly effective since young caterpillars die as a direct result of exposure or indirectly as a result of infection by disease-causing fungi. Perennial plants, such as strawberries and herbaceous ornamentals, should be lifted and replanted regularly and, if necessary, susceptible plants may be protected by applying HCH, bromophos, or other insecticides to the soil around them, preferably in autumn to kill young caterpillars. Newly cultivated land is always likely to contain caterpillars and should therefore be thoroughly cleaned and cultivated before planting.

CABBAGE CATERPILLARS Pl. 5

Caterpillars of four different species of Lepidoptera are widespread and common pests of cabbages and other brassicas and some other species also occasionally attack these plants.

Symptoms. Caterpillars eat holes in leaves and tunnel into hearts. Damage encourages secondary rotting and plants are often fouled with excreta produced by caterpillars. Caterpillars of some species feed in exposed positions on leaves (Pl. 5) but others feed under silken webbing or in cavities eaten in heart leaves. Plants may be attacked at almost any time of year but the most serious damage is generally that done to mature plants in summer, autumn and early winter.

The main pest species are:

LARGE WHITE BUTTERFLY *Pieris brassicae* Pl. 5

Also known as the cabbage white. Adults emerge from overwintered pupae in April/May and each female lays a few hundred yellow, conical eggs in batches of 10–20 on leaves of brassicas and of garden nasturtiums (*Tropaeolum*). Eggs hatch about a fortnight after laying and yellow and black, hairy caterpillars (Pl. 5), up to 50 mm long, feed on plants for a month or more. Fully-fed caterpillars then leave plants to pupate in sheltered situations on fences, walls and buildings. A second generation of adults emerges in July/August and caterpillars developing from eggs laid by females of this generation are often abundant in August/September. A further adult generation may develop in September/October but most pupae developing in autumn overwinter to produce the first adult generation of the following year. Adult large white butterflies migrate and local populations are often augmented by invasions of adults from distant sources, which may be hundreds of miles away.

SMALL WHITE BUTTERFLY *Pieris rapae* Pl. 5

Biology and host range are similar to those of the large white but eggs are laid singly and caterpillars are smaller and velvety-green (Pl. 5). Adults emerge from overwintered pupae in February/April; a second generation of adults appears in June/July, and peak populations of caterpillars develop in August/September, often outnumbering large white caterpillars.

Another closely related species, the green-veined white, *Pieris napi*, is similar but does not attack garden plants to the same extent.

CABBAGE MOTH *Mamestra brassicae*

This is a noctuid moth, related to the cutworms (p. 136), but caterpillars behave quite differently. Adults emerge in May/June from pupae that have overwintered in the soil and females lay batches of 20–100 hemispherical eggs on the undersides of leaves of cabbages and other brassicas and also on lettuces, onions, sweet corn, tomatoes and various ornamental plants. Small, green caterpillars hatch about a fortnight later and feed on leaves for a month or more. Full-grown caterpillars are up to 50 mm long and their colour varies from light green, through brown to black. They pupate in the soil and some adults emerge in August/September to produce a second generation of caterpillars. The remaining pupae, together with pupae of this second generation, overwinter and these pupae may be seen in the soil during winter digging.

DIAMOND-BACK MOTH *Plutella xylostella*

This species has a world-wide distribution but tends to be a local and sporadic pest with severe attacks suddenly developing after long-range migrations by adult moths. It is much smaller than the other species described above and the inconspicuous adults are generally active at night from May onwards. Small, green caterpillars, up to 12 mm long, feed for about a month under silk webbing on the undersides of leaves and then pupate in cocoons under this webbing. Two or three generations of adults develop during the growing season and the species probably overwinters mainly as cocoons on plants.

General Treatment. Inspect susceptible plants weekly throughout their growth and crush any eggs or caterpillars seen. If necessary, dust plants with carbaryl or spray with fenitrothion, pyrethroids or trichlorphon. Apply insecticides thoroughly so that they make good contact with caterpillars on both sides of leaves and in growing points and try to eliminate all caterpillars from cabbages before the plants start to heart up.

PEA MOTH *Cydia nigricana (=Laspeyresia nigricana)* Pl. 5

Symptoms. Small caterpillars, up to 6 mm long, with pale yellow bodies and black heads, feed on peas inside ripening pods (Pl. 5). Damage is usually most severe in July/August.

Biology. Small, inconspicuous moths emerge from cocoons in soil from early June onwards and females fly to pea plants to lay small flat eggs singly or in clusters on leaves and stipules. Adults are most active during warm, sunny weather in July. Eggs hatch about a week after laying and caterpillars eat into young pods to feed on developing peas for about a month. Caterpillars then eat their way out of pods and descend to the soil where they overwinter in cocoons. There is only one adult generation a year.

Treatment. Since egg-laying is mainly restricted to June/July, serious infestations can be avoided by sowing early or late, so that peas are not in flower and pod during this critical period. If possible, do not sow peas in March/April for June/July cropping but sow earlier and later than this. If crops are in flower during June/July they may be protected by chemicals but correct timing is essential since the young caterpillars must be killed before they enter the pods. Apply fenitrothion or permethrin spray about a week after first flowering, and make a repeat application about a fortnight later. Thorough winter cultivation may also help to check this pest by exposing overwintering caterpillars to weather and predators.

SILVER Y MOTH *Autographa gamma* Pl. 5

Symptoms. Leaves of beans, cabbages, lettuces, potatoes and many ornamental plants are eaten by bright green to dark olive caterpillars, up to 40 mm long (Pl. 5). Infested plants may be extensively defoliated and large pellets of frass, deposited on leaves, often indicate the presence of caterpillars, which hide during the day and feed mainly at night. This pest is often troublesome in glasshouses where it feeds on many ornamentals, especially pot azaleas, chrysanthemums, coleus, daturas and pelargoniums.

Biology. The silver y moth is a migrant species and is unable to survive northern winters, although some caterpillars may overwinter in heated glasshouses. In May/June adult moths migrate north and west from per-

manent breeding areas around the Mediterranean and sometimes reach as far north as Iceland and Finland. They are relatively small, with a wing-span of 35–45 mm, and the dark fore-wings are marked with a distinctive small white Y. Females lay up to 500 eggs each, either singly or in small batches, on leaves of host plants. Caterpillars hatch about ten days later and feed for about a month before pupating in loose cocoons on infested plants. Populations of adults often reach a peak in autumn when dozens of moths may be seen feeding at dusk on buddleias, sedums and other flowers. By late autumn many of these adults will have migrated south to the Mediterranean and north Africa where breeding continues.
Treatment. Watch glasshouse and house plants carefully at all times and locate and destroy caterpillars if symptoms appear. Apply contact insecticides (see p. 132), if necessary, to indoor and outdoor plants.

TOMATO MOTH *Lacanobia oleracea*

Symptoms. Holes are eaten in leaves and fruits of tomatoes during summer and autumn by yellow-green to brown caterpillars, up to 40 mm long, with yellow bands and white spiracles. Caterpillars mainly attack tomatoes and some other plants, especially carnations and cucumbers, growing in glasshouses but will occasionally attack brassicas growing outdoors.
Biology. Adults emerge from overwintered pupae in May/June outdoors and earlier in glasshouses. Females lay up to 1,000 eggs each in batches of 60–300 on the undersides of leaves. Caterpillars hatch about ten days later and at first feed in groups, eating away the surfaces of leaves. Later they disperse and feed voraciously on the leaves, often eating them down to a skeleton of veins. Full-grown caterpillars pupate in cocoons on walls, woodwork and plant debris and a second generation of adults emerges about 2–3 weeks later. During July–September long-term pupae develop and these remain dormant until the following season.
Treatment. Remove and destroy egg masses and caterpillars whenever they are seen and use contact insecticides (see p. 132), if necessary.

ANGLE SHADES MOTH *Phlogophora meticulosa* Pl. 5

Symptoms. Leaves, buds and flowers of outdoor and indoor plants are eaten by caterpillars feeding at night. Caterpillars are soft and plump, green to brown, minutely spotted with white, with a light band along the back and grey V-shaped markings on the sides (Pl. 5), and they grow to a length of 40–50 mm. Adults are sometimes seen in plant debris and on sides of glasshouses and are marked with a characteristic camouflage pattern of fawn, green and pink.
Biology. Adults are active from May to October outdoors and longer in heated glasshouses. Females lay clusters of 50–100 eggs on leaves and caterpillars hatch about ten days later. They feed on leaves, buds and flowers for 1–2 months and then pupate in cocoons in the soil. Two generations of adults develop outdoors, usually in May/June and September/October, but breeding may continue throughout the year in heated glasshouses.
Treatment. Inspect plants regularly and destroy egg batches and caterpillars. Apply contact insecticides (see p. 132), if necessary.

VAPOURER MOTH *Orgyia antiqua* **Pl. 5**

Symptoms. Leaves of many outdoor plants are eaten in summer by conspicuous hairy caterpillars, up to 25 mm long, marked with red and yellow dots and lines (Pl. 5). Roses, rhododendrons, flowering cherries, crab apples, hawthorns, pyracanthas, ceanothus, buddleias and heathers are particularly susceptible and this pest tends to be most troublesome in urban and suburban gardens. Outbreaks are usually local and damage is seldom severe, but caterpillars have urticating hairs which may cause skin irritations.

Biology. Eggs overwinter on cocoons attached to twigs and branches and hatch sporadically from May onwards. Caterpillars feed until July/August and then construct cocoons and pupate. Wingless female moths emerge in August/September and, after mating with winged males, lay 200–300 eggs each on or near their cocoons. Adults die out in autumn and eggs overwinter.

Treatment. Remove and destroy cocoons and eggs in winter and apply contact insecticides (see p. 132) in spring and summer, if necessary. Wear gloves when handling caterpillars and cocoons to avoid contact with urticating hairs.

BUFF-TIP MOTH *Phalera bucephala*

Symptoms. Leaves of oaks, limes, elms, hazels, willows, roses and other trees and shrubs are eaten in August/September by groups of a dozen or so yellow and black caterpillars, up to 50 mm long. These caterpillars feed voraciously and strip leaves but damage is usually restricted to one or two branches and the overall effect on plants is slight.

Biology. Adult moths emerge from overwintered pupae in July/August. They are nocturnal but may sometimes be seen resting on trees or in plant debris, where they look like small pieces of broken stick. Females lay eggs in small batches on the undersides of leaves and caterpillars hatch about a week later. They then feed for about a month before going to the soil to pupate. Pupae overwinter in the soil and adults emerge in the following summer.

Treatment. Remove caterpillars by hand and destroy them or transfer them to wild host plants. Use contact insecticides (see p. 132), if necessary.

GARDEN TIGER MOTH *Arctia caja*

Symptoms. Very hairy large, dark brown caterpillars, commonly known as 'woolly bears', feed on leaves of many cultivated plants and on various weeds, especially during May/June. Caterpillars are 60–80 mm long when fully fed and are often seen wandering over paths, walls and lawns in June.

Biology. Caterpillars hatch in August/September and feed for a few weeks before seeking suitable hibernation sites on plants, in plant debris, and in walls, fences and other structures. They emerge in early spring and feed for about a month before pupating in cocoons in June. Adults emerge in July/August and lay eggs on plants.

Treatment. Remove caterpillars from plants by hand and use contact insecticides (see p. 132), if necessary. Caterpillars have urticating hairs which may irritate skin and gloves should be worn when handling them.

HAWK MOTHS

Caterpillars of some species of hawk moth occasionally attack garden plants and cause consternation because of their large size (up to 10 cm long) and strange appearance. They can consume large quantities of leaves quite quickly but seldom occur in any numbers and are not important pests. The main species likely to be found in gardens are the privet hawk moth, *Sphinx ligustri*, on privet and lilacs; the elephant hawk moth, *Deilephila elpenor* on fuchsias and impatiens, both outdoors and in glasshouses and houses, and the eyed hawk moth, *Smerinthus ocellata*, on apples, willows and poplars.
Treatment. Remove caterpillars by hand and transfer them to suitable wild hosts to complete their development. The use of insecticides against hawk moth caterpillars is seldom, if ever, justified.

TORTRIX MOTHS

Many species of tortrix moth attack ornamental plants and some species damage fruit (see p. 135). The carnation tortrix and the green oak tortrix, which are dealt with below, are typical of most of the species that occur in gardens.

CARNATION TORTRIX MOTH

Cacoecimorpha pronubana **Pl. 5**

This is the commonest and most troublesome species attacking glasshouse and house plants but some other species produce similar symptoms.
Symptoms. Small yellow or green caterpillars, up to 20 mm long, feed in leaf axils, in the tips of young shoots, in buds and in flowers and characteristically draw the affected parts together with silk webbing to form a protective covering enclosing the caterpillars (Pl. 5). Caterpillars can usually be found by pulling this webbing apart. They wriggle backwards when disturbed and drop from plants on silk threads. Plants are damaged directly by caterpillars eating leaves and other tissues and are also affected indirectly by the webbing, which restricts young growths. Many glasshouse and house plants are attacked, especially acacias, carnations, cytisus, daphnes, grevilleas, and hypericums. Outdoor plants may also be damaged, particularly euonymus, ivies, laurel and privet.
Biology. This species is native to southern Europe but is now well established in glasshouses and outdoors in Britain and northern Europe. Small, inconspicuous adult moths have grey-brown fore-wings and copper-orange hind-wings. They are active at night and each female lays about eight batches of 10–200 flat, oval, overlapping eggs, protected by a mucilaginous covering. Eggs hatch after 2–3 weeks and young caterpillars wander over plants to find suitable feeding sites. They then spin silk webbing to protect themselves and start to feed on plant tissues. After feeding for 1–2 months, caterpillars pupate under webbing on plants and adults emerge about a month later. There are usually two adult generations a year but the length of larval development is so variable that there is no distinct gap between them. Caterpillars overwinter and may be present in heated glasshouses at all times of year.
Treatment. Examine glasshouse and house plants regularly and crush caterpillars by hand. This is much more effective than using contact insecticides but sprays and fumigants may be used against adults and young caterpillars (see p. 132).

GREEN OAK TORTRIX MOTH *Tortrix viridana*

Symptoms. Small grey-green caterpillars, up to 20 mm long, draw young leaves of oak trees together with silk webbing and feed on them from May onwards. In some seasons mature oaks are extensively defoliated and many caterpillars may be seen hanging from branches on long silk threads. The pedunculate oak (*Quercus robur*), is generally more severely damaged than the sessile oak (*Quercus petraea*), possibly because the latter has hairy leaves and bud scales and comes into leaf earlier, so that leaves are tougher and less attractive to young caterpillars. Many other plants are also attacked.

Biology. Eggs overwinter on twigs and branches and hatch in April–June, as buds open. Caterpillars feed on young leaves for about a month and then pupate in webbing on damaged trees. Adults emerge about 2–3 weeks later and females lay eggs which remain on the trees until the following spring.

Treatment. Various parasites and predators feed on the caterpillars when they are abundant and, as a result, years when serious damage occurs are usually followed by years when this pest is relatively scarce. Young trees may be protected by applying contact insecticides (see p. 132), if necessary, but larger trees cannot be sprayed adequately with normal garden spraying equipment.

LACKEY MOTH *Malacasoma neustria*

Symptoms. Groups of blue-grey caterpillars, up to 50 mm long, with longitudinal white and orange stripes feed on leaves and twigs of outdoor plants in summer and spin protective silk webbing over affected parts to form 'tents'. Similar webbing is also produced by caterpillars of the brown-tail moth and by the hawthorn webber and ermine moths. Lackey caterpillars attack many different ornamental plants, especially alders, birch, cotoneasters, elms, eucryphias, hawthorn, lilacs, roses, pyracanthas and willows, and occasionally attack apple and other fruit trees.

Biology. Bands of 100–200 eggs, laid on twigs and branches in the previous season, hatch in April/May. Caterpillars feed for 1–2 months and gradually construct communal 'tents', which may be up to 30 cm long. Caterpillars pupate in cocoons on bark and between leaves and adults emerge from July to September. Females lay overwintering eggs and adults die out in autumn.

Treatment. Cut out and destroy egg bands in winter and spray thoroughly with contact insecticides (see p. 132) in spring and early summer, if necessary. Cut out and burn large communal tents found in late summer as insecticides cannot penetrate them effectively.

HAWTHORN WEBBER MOTH *Scythropia crataegella*

Symptoms. Colonies of small red or yellow-brown caterpillars, up to 15 mm long, feed on leaves of hawthorn and cotoneasters from May onwards and spin silk webbing over infested branches. Outbreaks are local and are most likely in southern areas.

Biology. Female moths lay eggs on plants in July/August and young caterpillars eat out mines in leaves in autumn. Mined leaves remain attached to plants and caterpillars overwinter in them. From March onwards caterpillars spin protective webbing and feed on leaves, eventually pupating in cocoons on webbing in June/July.

Treatment. Remove mined leaves from plants in winter and destroy them and spray with contact insecticides (see p. 132) in spring to kill young caterpillars.

SMALL ERMINE MOTHS *Yponomeuta* spp.

At least four different species of *Yponomeuta* attack garden plants. They are all very similar in appearance and biology but have preferences for different host plants.

Symptoms. Small grey-green caterpillars, up to 20 mm long, feed in colonies on leaves of many garden plants and spin silk webbing which is similar to that produced by caterpillars of the lackey moth (p. 143) and hawthorn webber (above). Apples, euonymus, hawthorns, willows and bird cherries are particularly susceptible but some other garden plants may also be attacked.

Biology. Caterpillars hatch in August/September but remain under egg scales until the following April/May. They then become active and feed on leaves and flowers until June when they pupate in cocoons on infested plants. Small, pure white moths with black spots on their wings emerge in July/August and females lay batches of flat eggs covered by a hard coat which protects the overwintering young caterpillars.

Treatment. Cut out and burn webbing and caterpillars, if possible, or spray forcibly with contact insecticides (see p. 132), if necessary.

LEAF MINERS

Some species of caterpillar tunnel in leaf tissues, producing leaf mines which resemble leaf mines produced by some fly maggots (see p. 145). Three of the most damaging species are dealt with below but there are many others that may occur in gardens, such as the apple leaf mining moth, *Lyonetia clerkella*, which produces numerous and conspicuous mines but causes no appreciable damage.

LILAC LEAF MINER *Caloptilia syringella*

Symptoms. Large brown blistered areas appear on leaves of lilac and privet from June onwards. Each blister contains one or more small white or green legless caterpillars. Later in the season some leaves are rolled and tied with silk by caterpillars that have left their mines.

Biology. Caterpillars overwinter in cocoons at the bases of lilac trees, privet hedges, fences and other structures. Small silvery-white moths emerge in May/June and females lay batches of eggs on undersides of young leaves. Caterpillars hatch about a week later and feed inside leaves to make blister mines. When they have almost finished feeding, they come out of the mines, roll and tie leaves with silk threads, and then continue to feed within the protection of the rolled leaves. They then pupate in cocoons in leaf axils, and on branches and stems, and a second generation of adult moths emerges in July/August. Caterpillars developing from eggs of this generation are fully fed by September/October and then form overwintering cocoons.

Treatment. Remove and destroy affected leaves, if possible, or spray with HCH, nicotine or trichlorphon in May/June and again later in the season if new mines appear.

LABURNUM LEAF MINER *Leucoptera laburnella*

Symptoms. Unsightly spiral and blotch mines appear on laburnum leaves from June onwards. Each mine contains a single small green-white caterpillar but more than one mine may develop on each leaf. Severely damaged leaves turn brown and shrivel.

Biology. Pupae overwinter in cocoons on stems and branches and in leaf litter under plants. Inconspicuous adult moths emerge in May/June and females lay eggs on the undersides of young leaves. Caterpillars soon hatch and eat through the bottom of the egg into the leaf tissues where they eat out spiral mines. As the caterpillars grow they make more extensive blotch mines which obliterate the original spiral mines. Fully-fed caterpillars spin cocoons on damaged leaves and a second generation of adults emerges from them in August. More mines develop and caterpillars leave them in September/October to spin overwintering cocoons.

Treatment. Remove and destroy affected leaves, if possible, and spray with insecticides, if necessary, as for lilac leaf miner (p. 144).

FLIES

(Plate 6)

Adult flies (Diptera) have only one pair of functional wings, the hind wings being reduced to a pair of club-shaped balancing organs (halteres). This clearly distinguishes them from whiteflies, greenflies, butterflies and other groups of insects which, despite their common names, are not true flies. Size of adult flies varies from very small (1–2 mm long) to large (3–4 cm long) and detailed structure also varies considerably. The head is prominent, with large eyes, a pair of antennae, and mouth-parts modified for piercing and sucking rather than biting and chewing. More than 5,000 species occur in Britain and northern Europe. Some of these feed on blood (mosquitoes, clegs, biting midges); others prey on insects and other invertebrates (hover-flies, robber-flies) or are parasites (tachinid flies) and many feed on decaying animal and vegetable matter (house-flies, flesh-flies, moth-flies). In most cases the larva is the main feeding stage and adults only feed casually on fluids, such as nectar, exudations of sap, animal secretions and similar materials. Larvae always lack legs and are mostly colourless, relatively featureless maggots. Sexual reproduction is usual and females generally lay eggs on or near suitable food for the larvae. Larvae feed for a few weeks or months and then pupate, often inside a characteristic hard, dark puparium (Pl. 6). The larvae of some species feed directly on living plant tissues and may be important pests of cultivated and wild plants. The main species attacking garden plants in Britain and northern Europe are dealt with in detail in the following section.

PEAR MIDGE *Contarinia pyrivora* **Pl. 6**

This gall midge (Cecidomyiidae) is one of two species that occasionally attack pears in Britain and northern Europe. The other species is the pear leaf midge, *Dasineura pyri*, which causes characteristic leaf-rolling on young shoots but is not an important pest.

Symptoms. Young pear fruitlets that have been attacked by pear midge larvae swell rapidly and then fail to develop normally. Many small yellow-white larvae, up to 4 mm long, may be present inside cavities in blackened, distorted fruitlets (Pl. 6) and affected fruitlets fall prematurely in May/June. Attacks are usually local, often affecting one particular tree every year, and severe attacks reduce yields by limiting the numbers of fruits developing. Pears flowering in mid-season are most susceptible to attack and varieties flowering early or late often escape the main period of midge activity.

Biology. Larvae overwinter in small silk cocoons in soil under pear trees and pupate in spring. Small, inconspicuous adult midges, up to 4 mm long, emerge in March/April and females fly up onto pear blossom to lay eggs in unopened flowers. Eggs hatch about a week later and larvae enter young fruitlets to feed for about a month. Fully-fed larvae either leave fruitlets while they are still on the tree or fall with them to the ground. They then enter the soil, spin cocoons, and remain dormant until the following spring.

Treatment. Reduce the numbers of larvae entering the soil by picking off affected fruitlets as soon as they are seen and by collecting fallen fruitlets. Destroy them immediately, preferably by burning. In addition, cultivate the soil under infested trees in summer and apply HCH dust to the soil in spring. Spraying with fenitrothion in spring to kill emerging adults may check attacks but timing must be correct if the females are to be killed before they lay eggs. Best results are usually given by spraying just before the blossom opens.

BLACK CURRANT LEAF MIDGE *Dasineura tetensi*

Symptoms. The youngest terminal leaves on black currant shoots fail to open and remain folded and twisted. Small white or orange larvae, up to 3 mm long, may be found by carefully unrolling affected leaves. Plants are attacked from April to August and persistent infestations check growth and may encourage the development of lateral shoots. 'Goliath', 'Seabrook's Black', 'Baldwin' and 'Wellington XXX' are more susceptible to attack than other cultivars.

Biology. Larvae overwinter in cocoons in soil and pupate in spring. Inconspicuous adult midges, up to 3 mm long, emerge from April onwards and females fly to the tips of young shoots to lay eggs on the youngest unopened leaves. Eggs hatch after about a week and larvae feed for about a month before going to the soil to pupate. Three or four generations develop during the growing season and increasing numbers of larvae form cocoons in the soil and remain dormant until the following spring.

Treatment. Spray the tips of shoots with dimethoate as soon as symptoms are seen but do not spray during the flowering period when pollinating insects will be visiting the plants.

RASPBERRY CANE MIDGE *Resseliella theobaldi*
(= Thomasiniana theobaldi)

Symptoms. Small pink or red larvae, up to 4 mm long, feed in cracks and under raised bark of raspberry canes in summer and autumn. Affected areas of bark peel away and cane blight, due to a fungal infection (see p. 219) may develop, causing die-back of shoots. 'Bath's Perfection', 'Malling Enterprise', 'Malling Jewel' and 'Malling Promise' are particularly susceptible to attack.

Biology. Larvae overwinter in cocoons in soil near raspberry canes and pupate in the spring. Adults emerge in May/June and females lay eggs in cracks in bark and in wounds. Larvae hatch about a week later and feed under the bark for about a month before going to the soil to pupate. A further three or four generations develop between July and September and increasing numbers of larvae go to the soil to overwinter.

Treatment. Spray canes with fenitrothion during the first week in May and repeat about a fortnight later. In addition, cultivate the surface layers of the soil in winter to expose overwintering larvae to weather and predators.

LEATHERJACKETS **Pl. 6**

Leatherjackets are the larvae of crane-flies (Tipulidae), also known as daddy-long-legs. Many species occur in grassland and the commonest are *Tipula paludosa*, *Tipula oleracea* and *Nephrotoma maculata*. They are mainly pests in newly cultivated land and in lawns.

Symptoms. Grey-brown larvae, up to 5 cm long (Pl. 6), live in soil and feed on roots and stems of many different plants. Most damage is done to young plants in spring but attacks may develop at other times during the growing season. Affected plants turn yellow, wilt and may die and symptoms often resemble those produced by cutworms (p. 136) and certain root-infecting fungi. Young cabbages and other brassicas, lettuces, strawberries and various ornamental plants are susceptible to attack and a few leatherjackets can cause considerable losses of seedlings and young plants. They are occasionally introduced into seed boxes and pots in unsterilised potting composts. High populations of leatherjackets in lawns produce yellow patches during dry weather and affected lawns may be further damaged by starlings and other birds that probe and loosen the turf to extract leatherjackets from the soil.

Biology. Adult crane-flies emerge from pupae in soil during August/September and, after mating, females lay up to 300 eggs each in soil near plants. Eggs hatch about a fortnight later and larvae feed during the autumn and again in the following spring and summer before pupating. There is usually only one generation a year. High populations of leatherjackets develop after prolonged damp, warm weather in summer and early autumn and are mainly found in old meadow land and in poorly maintained lawns.

Treatment. Leatherjackets are usually only troublesome during the first few years after new areas of garden have been brought into cultivation. Thorough and regular digging and hoeing and a summer fallow period should be used to reduce populations of larvae before plants are grown. Susceptible plants can be protected by working a little HCH dust into the soil around them but over-use of this insecticide should be avoided, especially on vegetable plots where root crops may be tainted. Applications of bromophos, diazinon or chlorpyrifos granules to the soil around plants may give some protection and the use of methiocarb pellets against slugs may also help to check leatherjackets. Affected areas of lawn can sometimes be treated by thoroughly soaking them with water and then placing a tarpaulin or black polythene sheet on the affected area overnight. Leatherjackets will then work to the surface by the following morning and may then be swept up and killed.

SCIARID FLIES

Also known as mushroom flies. Larvae of many different species feed in larger fungi and also feed on fungal mycelium in soil, in decaying plant tissues and in similar situations. Most species are of no importance as pests but a few do occasionally attack garden plants and some may damage cultivated and wild mushrooms.

Symptoms. White larvae, up to 25 mm long, with distinct black or brown heads live in soil and in potting and rooting media where they may feed on root-hairs and roots of seedlings, in the bases of cuttings and in the stalks and caps of mushrooms. Carnation, chrysanthemum and pelargonium cuttings and seedlings and young plants of cucumbers, sweet peas, orchids, primulas and freesias are especially susceptible to attack. Adult sciarids are small, dark, midge-like flies, up to 5 mm long, with relatively long, narrow antennae and they are often seen in glasshouses and on pot plants in houses as they swarm over the surfaces of moist soil and potting media, characteristically running rapidly with wings vibrating.

Biology. Adults are attracted to soil and potting media, especially if the organic content is high. Females deposit about 100 eggs each and these hatch after about a week. Larvae feed for about a month before pupating in the soil and adults emerge after a further week or so. Breeding continues throughout the season. Populations are often highest in heated glasshouses, where high temperatures favour rapid and continuous breeding, but adults and larvae are also abundant outdoors when conditions are favourable.

Treatment. The presence of sciarid adults or larvae near plants does not necessarily mean that the plants will be damaged, since many of the harmless species will be attracted to potting media, manures and plant debris. If established plants do show signs of attack, water a spray-strength solution of malathion or nicotine around them but first note possible phytotoxic effects on some plants. Seeds, seedlings and cuttings of susceptible plants may be protected by a light dusting with HCH or malathion dust and adult flies in glasshouses can be killed by fumigating with HCH, nicotine or dichlorvos. Correct watering of seedlings, cuttings and pot plants may also help to limit attacks since sciarid larvae tend to thrive on plants that are under or over-watered.

FRIT FLY *Oscinella frit*

This is mainly a pest of oats and other cereal crops but it also attacks sweet corn in gardens.

Symptoms. Light yellow longitudinal stripes appear on young leaves of sweet corn plants and affected leaves later disintegrate into frayed strips. Infested plants are often stunted and this early check in growth, which usually occurs in June/July, may reduce the number of cobs produced later in the season. In severe attacks the growing point is killed and plants die. Close examination of damaged plants may reveal small white larvae, up to 5 mm long, feeding in the stems and at the bases of leaves.

Biology. Larvae overwinter on grasses and winter cereals and pupate in the spring. The small, inconspicuous adults emerge in May/June and females lay eggs on or near the bases of young sweet corn and other host plants. Eggs hatch about a week later and larvae enter the young shoots to feed for 2–3 weeks. They pupate in late June/early July, either within damaged plants or in the soil, and a second generation of adults emerges in July/August. Females of this generation mainly lay eggs in developing

seed-heads of oats and wheat. In autumn a third generation of adults emerges and females lay eggs on grasses and winter cereals. Larvae hatch and then develop slowly on these hosts during the winter and pupate in the following spring.
Treatment. Protect sweet corn seedlings during June/July by dusting with HCH. In addition, provide good growing conditions so that plants can become established rapidly.

BEET LEAF MINER *Pegomya hyoscyami (=P. betae)*

This pest is also known as the beet fly or the mangold fly.
Symptoms. White larvae, up to 10 mm long, tunnel in leaves of beetroot and spinach beet and occasionally attack some other vegetables, making extensive blotch mines. Severe attacks on young plants may check growth but older plants are only slightly affected. Most damage is done in early summer but attacks may continue into the autumn.
Biology. Pupae overwinter in the soil and adults emerge in April/May. Females lay batches of eggs on the undersides of leaves and larvae hatch about a week later. They soon eat into the leaves and feed for 2–3 weeks before dropping to the soil to pupate. Two or three generations develop during the growing season and puparia overwinter.
Treatment. Cultivate thoroughly in winter to reduce the numbers of overwintering puparia and grow susceptible plants under favourable conditions in well-prepared soil so that they can establish themselves quickly. If necessary, spray plants thoroughly with dimethoate or trichlorphon as soon as mines appear, repeating later in the season if attacks persist.

CELERY FLY *Euleia heraclei (=Philophylla heraclei)* **Pl. 6**

This pest is also known as the celery leaf miner. Symptoms resemble those of the beet leaf miner (see above) but these two pests are not closely related and they affect different plants.
Symptoms. White larvae, up to 7 mm long, tunnel in leaves of celery and parsnips, producing conspicuous yellow-brown blotch mines (Pl. 6). Symptoms first appear in May but attacks may continue throughout the growing season, often with peak activity in summer and early autumn. Severe attacks check plant growth.
Biology. Pupae overwinter in the soil and adults emerge during April–June. They are small, up to 5 mm long, and have conspicuous dark markings on the wings. Females lay about 100 eggs each in leaves and eggs hatch about a week after laying. Larvae then eat into leaves and feed for about a month before pupating either within the leaf mines or in the soil. A second generation of adults emerges in late summer and a third generation may develop in autumn.
Treatment. Protect young plants by spraying with malathion, trichlorphon or dimethoate as soon as symptoms appear or as soon as females are seen on plants. Light attacks on established plants can be checked by crushing larvae and pupae within the mines.

CARROT FLY *Psila rosae* **Pl. 6**

Symptoms. Cream-white larvae, up to 10 mm long, feed on roots of carrots and also attack parsnips, celery and parsley. In early summer the finer roots are attacked and this causes reddening of the leaves and some stunting of growth, which resembles symptoms produced by the willow-carrot aphid (p. 114) and by motley dwarf disease (p. 277). Later in the growing season carrot fly larvae tunnel into the main roots and eat out irregular, discoloured galleries (Pl. 6). Light infestations may have little effect on well-grown crops but serious attacks may make roots unusable.

Biology. Pupae and some larvae overwinter in soil and in roots left in the ground and the small, shining-black adults emerge in May/June. Females lay clusters of small white eggs in soil near carrots and other host plants and eggs hatch after about a week. Larvae feed for about a month before pupating in the soil. A second generation of adults emerges in August/September and larvae from this generation continue to feed well into the winter before pupating.

Treatment. This pest is common in most gardens where carrots and related plants are grown regularly and it may prove difficult to control. Low levels of injury may be tolerated, since it is relatively easy to cut away affected parts when roots are being prepared for cooking, but persistent infestations should be checked by a combination of chemical and non-chemical methods. Clean and dig vegetable plots thoroughly during the winter to reduce populations of overwintering pupae and larvae and clear overgrown adjoining areas, especially nettle beds, which may provide cover for adult flies in spring and summer. If possible, avoid the first generation attack by delaying sowing until late May or early June and sow thinly to limit the need for hand thinning later. If thinning is necessary, remove thinnings immediately, consolidate the soil around the plants and water thoroughly to disperse the odour of crushed plants which may attract egg-laying females. Lift roots as soon as they are ready and store them rather than leaving them in the soil. Applications of bromophos, chlorpyrifos or diazinon granules to seed drills may give some protection against early attacks and a spray-strength solution of pirimiphos-methyl watered in as a soil drench on two or three occasions in August/September may limit damage on established plants.

CABBAGE ROOT FLY *Delia radicum* (*= Erioischia brassicae*) **Pl. 6**

This is a serious pest of cultivated brassicas throughout Europe and N. America.

Symptoms. White larvae, up to 8 mm long, feed on roots of cabbages, cauliflowers, Brussels sprouts, calabrese, radishes, turnips, swedes and some ornamental plants, especially wallflowers. Severe attacks during April–July kill young plants and transplanted brassicas are especially susceptible (Pl. 6). The first signs of attack often show on outer leaves which wilt and develop a blue-red tinge but similar symptoms are caused by club root (p. 223) and other types of root damage. Established plants can usually survive slight to moderate infestations by cabbage root fly but growth may be checked and yields reduced. Larvae feeding in the main roots of radishes, swedes and turnips and inside Brussels sprouts make them inedible. The most severe damage is usually done in late spring and early summer but this pest remains active throughout the growing season and can continue to damage plants well into the autumn.

Biology. Pupae overwinter in the soil and adult flies emerge in late April/early May. Adults resemble small house-flies and are relatively inconspicuous. Females lay eggs in soil near host plants and occasionally lay some eggs actually on host plants. Eggs hatch about a week after laying and larvae feed for about a month before pupating in the soil. A second generation of adults emerges in June/July and a third generation develops in autumn.

Treatment. Thorough winter cultivation and good hygiene will reduce numbers of overwintering pupae but adult flies are mobile and may move into gardens from adjoining areas. Calomel dust, which is sometimes used to combat clubroot disease (p. 223) may give partial control of cabbage root fly and on a small scale it may be possible to protect young brassica plants by cutting felt, cardboard or plastic discs to fit around the bases of stems to stop females laying eggs. If serious attacks are expected, protect susceptible plants by incorporating granules of bromophos, chlorpyrifos or diazinon in the soil at each planting position just before the plants are set out. This is especially advisable in spring when the main period of egg-laying usually coincides with the flowering of hedge parsley (*Anthriscus sylvestris*). If attacks develop on established plants, water a spray-strength solution of pirimiphos-methyl into the soil to drench the roots. Cabbage root flies are resistant to certain insecticides in some areas and expert advice should be obtained if the above treatments fail to give satisfactory results.

ONION FLY *Delia antiqua* **Pl. 6**

Symptoms. White maggots, up to 8 mm long, feed in stems and bulbs of onions and may also attack shallots and leeks. Young plants wilt and die (Pl. 6) and tissues of older plants soften and rot. Most damage is done in June/July but plants may also be attacked at other times during the growing season. Identical symptoms are produced by the bean seed fly (see below) and similar symptoms are caused by stem eelworm (p. 84) and by white rot disease (p. 245).

Biology. Pupae overwinter in soil and adults emerge in May. Females lay eggs on young leaves and stems or in the soil near them and larvae hatch 3–4 days later. They then feed in plants for 2–3 weeks before leaving them to pupate in the soil. Two or three further generations may develop during summer and early autumn but increasing numbers of pupae remain dormant in the soil until the following spring.

Treatment. Cultivate thoroughly during the winter to disturb overwintering pupae and apply chlorpyrifos or diazinon granules to the soil before planting or sowing during spring and summer, and protect onions sown in late summer and early autumn by applying granules of one of these insecticides along the rows during the following May/June.

BEAN SEED FLY *Delia platura (=Delia cilicrura)* **Pl. 6**

This pest is very similar to the onion fly. It occasionally attacks onions but is more important as a pest of peas and beans. Larvae attack germinating seeds and seedlings early in the season and losses may be considerable, especially if germination is slowed by cold weather. Protect seeds with a combined HCH/captan seed-dressing or apply bromophos, diazinon or chlorpyrifos granules to the soil just before sowing.

VIOLET LEAF MIDGE *Dasineura affinis*

Symptoms. Leaves of cultivated and wild violets thicken abnormally and roll upward and inward. Young leaves are attacked throughout the growing season and persistent infestations check growth and limit flowering. If thickened leaves are unrolled carefully, many small white to orange larvae, up to 4 mm long, and clusters of white silk cocoons may be found inside.
Biology. Larvae overwinter in cocoons inside galled leaves or in the soil. Adults emerge from April onwards and females lay eggs on the youngest leaves. Eggs hatch within a week and larvae feed on the developing leaves, which react by curling and thickening to produce the galls. Larvae feed inside galls for 2–3 weeks before pupating and adults emerge about two weeks later to repeat the cycle. Four or five generations develop during the growing season and larvae of the last generation overwinter.
Treatment. Pick off affected leaves and destroy them, preferably by burning. If necessary, spray with HCH, fenitrothion or dimethoate.

YEW GALL MIDGE *Taxomyia taxi* Pl. 6

Symptoms. Characteristic leafy galls, resembling miniature young globe artichokes, develop at the tips of young shoots of yews (Pl. 6). Galls persist on affected yews for two or more years and are often so common that they may be mistaken for a normal feature of the plants. The overall effect is not particularly harmful but infested hedges and specimen trees look unsightly and persistent infestations interfere with normal growth.
Biology. Almost the entire life-cycle of this pest is spent within the galls. Inconspicuous adults, up to 4 mm long, emerge from galls in May/June and females lay eggs in the tips of young shoots. Larvae soon hatch and galls develop around them as they feed. Each gall contains a single larva but there may be many galls on one plant. Larvae mostly remain within galls until the following season when they pupate and give rise to the next generation of adults.
Treatment. Chemicals are unlikely to be effective against this pest except during the brief period in May/June when the adults are active. Spraying with HCH, fenitrothion, or other contact insecticide during this period may check infestations and slight attacks may be dealt with by picking off and destroying galls as soon as they develop.

LARGE NARCISSUS FLY *Merodon equestris* Pl. 6

Symptoms. Narcissus, hyacinth and some other bulbs produce narrow, yellow, distorted leaves in spring and fail to flower. If affected bulbs are lifted and opened, single, large, dirty grey-brown, fleshy larvae, up to 20 mm long, may be found inside rotting tissues (Pl. 6). Larvae of small narcissus flies (see below) may also be found in rotting bulbs but are smaller and more numerous. The large narcissus fly mainly attacks bulbs growing in open, sunny situations and severe attacks may kill bulbs so that no foliage or flowers are produced in spring. Similar symptoms are produced by stem eelworm (p. 84).
Biology. Adult flies emerge from pupae in the soil during April–June and are active on warm, sunny days. They are about 15 mm long, resemble small bumble bees, and make a distinct humming sound in flight. Females lay about 40 eggs each near the necks of bulbs, often entering the holes left

in soil above bulbs as the leaves die down. Larvae hatch about a week later, crawl to the bases of the bulbs, and tunnel through the base into the interior. Usually only one larva develops in each bulb and it feeds for six months or more before leaving to pupate in the soil in the following spring.
Treatment. This is a difficult pest to control since symptoms do not appear until after the damage has been done. Bulbs bought from reputable suppliers are unlikely to contain narcissus fly larvae since they are killed by commercial hot water and chemical treatments. Bulbs obtained from other sources should be carefully examined before planting and any suspect bulbs should be destroyed, preferably by burning. In areas where this pest is known to be troublesome, healthy stocks of bulbs can be preserved by planting them in shade or by providing artificial shade with muslin rolls or similar materials as the foliage dies down. Egg-laying females can also be discouraged by raking or sifting soil over plants to fill the holes that are left as the leaves die down. HCH dust applied over plants in June/July may also be partially effective.

SMALL NARCISSUS FLIES *Eumerus tuberculatus* and *Eumerus strigatus*

Larvae of these two species feed in rotting narcissus and other bulbs. They are only about half the size of large narcissus fly larvae, are lighter in colour, and usually feed in groups of six or more. They may occasionally cause primary damage to otherwise healthy plants but are much more likely to have invaded plants that have already been damaged by other pests, such as stem eelworm (p. 84), or by diseases. Affected bulbs should be destroyed, preferably by burning, and the initial cause of the trouble should be diagnosed and treated.

CHRYSANTHEMUM LEAF MINER *Phytomyza syngenesiae*

Pl. 6

Symptoms. Sinuous white mines appear in the leaves of chrysanthemums (Pl. 6), cinerarias, calendulas, lettuces and some other cultivated plants and weeds. Attacks generally develop during May/June on plants growing out of doors but occur at most times of year on glasshouse and house plants. In severe attacks leaves are extensively mined and plants may collapse and die. Chrysanthemum cultivars 'Galaxy', 'Vibrant', 'Tuneful', 'Long Island Beauty', 'Ice cap', 'Salmonchip', 'Silverstone', 'Criterion', 'Favourite', 'Corsair', 'Yellow Iceberg', 'Yellow Shasta', 'Dark Delmar', 'Cerise Shoesmith' and 'Delightful' are particularly susceptible.
Biology. Adult chrysanthemum leaf miners are small, inconspicuous, dark flies, about 3 mm long, with a light grey bloom on the thorax. They make short, jerky flights amongst leaves of their host plants and females pierce leaf tissues with their ovipositors to feed on sap that exudes from the wounds. This produces characteristic white spots, which are the first indication of the presence of this pest on plants. Each female lays up to 100 eggs in similar incisions and larvae hatch about a week later. They then tunnel into the leaves and as the larvae grow, the mines get wider and meander towards the mid-rib. Larvae feed for 2–3 weeks and then pupate within the mines, where they can be seen as small, dark bumps. At 16–21°C

(60–70°F) adults emerge from pupae after 9–12 days but at lower temperatures the pupal stage lasts much longer. In heated glasshouses and in houses breeding continues through most of the year but out of doors it is restricted to the summer months.
Treatment. Examine susceptible plants regularly and treat them as soon as feeding punctures or mines are seen. If only a few leaves are attacked, pick them off and destroy them by burning. If necessary, spray plants with HCH or pirimiphos-methyl to kill eggs and young larvae, repeating after two weeks if attacks persist. Control weeds, especially groundsel and sowthistle, as these may support populations of this pest.
Note: Another species, the American serpentine leaf miner, *Liriomyza trifolii*, has been introduced into Britain and northern Europe in recent years, especially on chrysanthemums, and may become established as a pest.

HOLLY LEAF MINER *Phytomyza ilicis* Pl. 6

Symptoms. Blotch mines develop in leaves of wild and cultivated hollies (Pl. 6). Few hollies are ever completely free from this pest.
Biology. The small, inconspicuous adult flies emerge from pupae from May onwards and lay eggs on the undersides of the leaves near the mid-rib. Larvae soon hatch and tunnel into the leaves, first making a straight and narrow mine but later eating out a larger blotch mine as they grow. Larvae feed throughout the growing season and remain in the mines until the following spring, when they pupate. Only one generation of adults develops each year.
Treatment. If only a few leaves are affected, pick them off and destroy them, preferably by burning. If necessary, spray with HCH or pirimiphos-methyl once or twice in May/June to kill egg-laying females. Once larvae are inside leaves they are not easily killed but systemic insecticides, such as dimethoate, might be effective.

SAWFLIES

(Plate 7)

Adult sawflies are relatively small, usually up to 10 mm long, and generally inconspicuous insects (Hymenoptera: Tenthredinoidea), with two pairs of wings and usually with dark bodies and legs. They resemble flying ants but can be distinguished by the absence of a distinct waist-like constriction between thorax and abdomen. Females have a saw-like ovipositor which is used to insert eggs in cuts made in soft plant tissues. Larvae resemble caterpillars of moths and butterflies (p. 132) but differ in having at least six pairs of fleshy prolegs on the abdominal segments. Adults feed mainly on pollen but larvae eat leaves and other plant organs. At least 400 different species attack wild and cultivated plants in Britain and northern Europe and some of these are important pests of garden plants. Reproduction is usually sexual, with both males and females being produced, but males are rare in some species and reproduction is then parthenogenetic.

APPLE SAWFLY *Hoplocampa testudinea* Pl. 7

Symptoms. Cream-white larvae, up to 15 mm long, tunnel into developing apple fruitlets in May/June and eat out large cavities, which are filled

with wet red-brown frass (Pl. 7). Similar but distinct symptoms are produced by codling moth caterpillars (p. 134) but they attack later in the season. Many of the fruitlets damaged by sawfly larvae fall prematurely in June/July but some fruits that are only superficially damaged survive until harvest and show characteristic scars and distortions (Pl. 7). 'Worcester Pearmain', 'Charles Ross', 'James Grieve' and 'Ellison's Orange' are generally more susceptible to sawfly attack than other cultivars.
Biology. Larvae overwinter in cocoons in soil and adults emerge in spring. Peak activity generally coincides with the main flowering period of apples in April/May. Females lay about 30 eggs each in the open blossom and eggs hatch about a fortnight later, just as the petals are falling. Young larvae then tunnel into the fruitlets, eventually penetrating to the core and eating the developing seeds. They then leave damaged fruitlets to enter healthy ones and during their feeding period of about a month each larva feeds on 2–3 fruitlets. Fully-fed larvae drop to the soil in June/July and spin cocoons in which they overwinter. Most larvae pupate in the following spring but some may remain dormant in the soil for a further year before completing their development to adults.
Treatment. Spray trees thoroughly with HCH, permethrin, dimethoate or fenitrothion about a week after the petals have fallen. Timing is critical as the young larvae must be killed before they tunnel into the fruitlets. If hive bees are visiting blossom, defer spraying until late evening and use non-persistent insecticides, such as malathion or nicotine.

PLUM SAWFLY *Hoplocampa flava*

This species is closely related to the apple sawfly but only attacks plums and damsons.
Symptoms. Cream-white larvae, up to 15 mm long, eat into developing fruitlets of plums and damsons in spring and early summer. Dark, sticky frass exudes from holes in damaged fruits as larvae tunnel into the flesh. Fruits fall prematurely and severe attacks reduce crops. 'Czar', 'Belle de Louvain' and 'Victoria' plums are generally more susceptible to attack than other cultivars.
Biology. Larvae overwinter in cocoons in soil and adults emerge in spring. Females-lay eggs in blossom during April/May and larvae hatch after about a week. Young larvae tunnel into fruitlets but the initial entry holes are inconspicuous. Larvae move from damaged to healthy fruits during their development, attacking about four fruits each in a month, and it is the older, larger larvae that cause the most obvious damage. Fully-fed larvae leave damaged fruits and go to the soil to overwinter in cocoons.
Treatment. Attacks are sporadic and years of severe attack may be followed by years in which little damage is done. In areas where this pest is known to be troublesome, spray with dimethoate or fenitrothion about a week after petal-fall.

PEAR AND CHERRY SLUGWORM *Caliroa cerasi* Pl. 7

Symptoms. Small, shiny black, slug-like larvae (Pl. 7), up to 15 mm long, feed on upper surfaces of leaves of pears, cherries, apples, almonds, hawthorns and rowans during June–September. Leaf tissues are characteristically eaten away from the upper surfaces, leaving the veins and lower epidermis intact (Pl. 7). These symptoms are sometimes referred to as 'window-paning' or 'skeletonizing'.

Biology. Larvae overwinter in cocoons in soil and small, black adult sawflies emerge in May/June. Females lay eggs in slits in leaves. Eggs hatch about two weeks later and larvae feed on leaves for about a month before going to the soil to pupate. A second generation of adults emerges in July/August and larvae feed until autumn before going to the soil to overwinter in cocoons.

Treatment. This pest is easily controlled by spraying with non-persistent insecticides, such as derris, malathion or pyrethroids, as soon as young larvae are seen on plants.

COMMON GOOSEBERRY SAWFLY *Nematus ribesii* Pl. 7

This is the main species attacking gooseberries but related species also occur on gooseberries and currants.

Symptoms. Leaves of gooseberries are eaten in spring and summer by green larvae, up to 40 mm long, with black heads and black spots (Pl. 7). Magpie moth caterpillars cause similar symptoms but differ in colour and form (p. 132). Leaves attacked by sawfly larvae are often reduced to a skeleton of veins and this type of severe defoliation affects yields.

Biology. Larvae overwinter in cocoons in soil and small black and orange-yellow adults emerge from April onwards. Females lay eggs in slits made alongside the main leaf veins on the undersides of leaves and eggs hatch about a week later. Larvae feed for about a month and then pupate in the soil. A second generation of adults emerges about three weeks later and the cycle is repeated. Three adult generations develop during the growing season and larvae of the third generation overwinter in cocoons in the soil.

Treatment. Inspect gooseberry bushes carefully every week from May onwards, paying particular attention to the centres of bushes, since females generally lay most of their eggs there. If caterpillars are seen, spray immediately with permethrin, derris or fenitrothion, and repeat at intervals of a week or so if damage continues.

ROSE SLUG SAWFLY *Endelomyia aethiops* Pl. 7

This species is also known as the rose slugworm or rose sekeletonizer.

Symptoms. Soft, yellow-green, slug-like larvae, up to 15 mm long, eat away leaf tissues, exposing veins and usually leaving the epidermis intact on one side (Pl. 7). Symptoms may appear at any time between May and September. Plants are seldom severely affected but damaged leaves look unsightly.

Biology. Larvae overwinter in cocoons in soil and pupate in early spring. Females emerge in May/June and lay eggs in the edges of leaves. Eggs hatch about a week later and larvae feed for about a month before going to the soil to pupate. A second generation of females emerges in August/September and larvae from this generation go to the soil to overwinter in cocoons. Males are extremely rare and reproduction is therefore almost entirely parthenogenetic.

Treatment. Winter and early spring cultivation of soil under roses may reduce populations of overwintering larvae by exposing them to weather and predators. If attacks develop in spring and summer, spray thoroughly with a contact insecticide, such as fenitrothion, derris or pyrethroids, as soon as larvae are seen on plants, and repeat treatment after a week or so, if attacks persist.

LEAF-ROLLING ROSE SAWFLY

Blennocampa pusilla **Pl. 7**

Symptoms. Rose leaves roll up tightly, with the edges rolled downwards and inwards along their length (Pl. 7). Symptoms first appear quite suddenly in May. Leaves remain rolled for the rest of the season and, although there is little direct effect on the vitality of infested plants, the rolled leaves look unsightly. This pest is most troublesome in southern areas of Britain and northern Europe and some rose cultivars, especially 'Peace', 'Albertine', 'Frensham', 'Golden Wings', 'Grand'mère Jenny', 'Masquerade', 'Mischief', 'Mme Butterfly', 'New Dawn', 'Queen Elizabeth' and 'Sutter's Gold' are more susceptible to attack than others.

Biology. Larvae overwinter in cocoons in soil and pupate in early spring. Adults emerge in May/June and females probe young leaves with their saw-like ovipositors before laying eggs. They only lay eggs in some of the probed leaves but any leaf that has been probed rolls up within a few hours. Larvae hatch from eggs after about a week and feed on leaf tissues within rolled leaves until July/August, when they go to the soil to overwinter in cocoons.

Treatment. Cultivation of soil under roses in winter and early spring will help to reduce the numbers of overwintering larvae and slight infestations developing on plants in May/June can be easily dealt with by picking off and burning all affected leaves. Insecticides are not particularly effective against this pest but spraying with contact insecticides, such as fenitrothion or permethrin, may check egg-laying females in May/June and systemic insecticides, such as dimethoate or heptenophos, may give some control of larvae later in the season.

WILLOW BEAN-GALL SAWFLY *Pontania proxima* Pl. 7

This is one of many species of *Pontania* that cause various types of leaf galls on willows.

Symptoms. Conspicuous, hard, raised, red or green galls, up to 2 cm long, develop on leaves of willows (Pl. 7) in summer. Sawfly larvae eat out cavities within galls but cause little direct damage to plants, although the galls may sometimes be considered unsightly.

Biology. Galls develop after female sawflies have laid eggs in young leaves during May and they are usually first noticed in June. Larvae feed within galls until July and then leave them to pupate in cocoons on bark or in soil. A second generation of adults emerges in September/October and larvae of this generation overwinter. Males are relatively rare and reproduction is therefore mainly parthenogenetic.

Treatment. Pick off and destroy affected leaves, if necessary and feasible. Chemical control is seldom, if ever, justified.

PINE SAWFLIES

At least twelve different species of sawfly attack pines in Britain and northern Europe. The two commonest are usually *Neodiprion sertifer* and *Diprion pini*.

Symptoms. Yellow-green larvae, up to 25 mm long, feed together in parties of a dozen or more on shoots of pines. Leaves are eaten and shoots may be rapidly defoliated. *Diprion pini* larvae feed on leaves of both the current and the past year's growth but larvae of *Neodiprion sertifer* only attack the older leaves and do not feed on new growth of the current season. *Pinus contorta* is especially susceptible to attack but other pines and some other conifers, such as spruces, are also attacked.

Biology. The seasonal biology of these two species differs quite markedly. *Diprion pini* larvae overwinter in cocoons in the soil and adults emerge in May/June. Females then lay eggs in slits in older leaves. Larvae hatch about two weeks later and feed until July when they spin cocoons and pupate either on the trees or in the soil. A second generation of adults emerges in July/August and the cycle is repeated, with larvae going to the soil in autumn to overwinter. *Neodiprion sertifer* overwinters as eggs which are laid in the leaves in September/October. These hatch in the following May and larvae feed on leaves until June/July before going to the soil to pupate. Adults emerge in autumn and females lay overwintering eggs before dying out.

Treatment. Spray larvae with contact insecticides, such as HCH, pyrethroids or malathion, as soon as they are seen on plants.

SPIRAEA SAWFLY *Nematus spiraeae*

Symptoms. Groups of green-yellow larvae, up to 20 mm long, with pale brown heads, feed on undersides of leaves of *Aruncus sylvester* from May onwards. Leaves are often reduced to a skeleton of veins when larvae are abundant.

Biology. Larvae overwinter in the soil and adults emerge in April/May. Males are very rare and reproduction is normally parthenogenetic. Females lay eggs on the undersides of leaves during May/June and larvae hatch after about a week. They then feed for a month before pupating in the soil. A second generation of adults emerges in July/August and a third generation may develop in September.

Treatment. Apply contact insecticides, such as HCH, pyrethroids or malathion, as soon as larvae are seen on plants.

GALL WASPS

(Plate 7)

Small, inconspicuous insects (Hymenoptera: Cynipidae), up to 8 mm long, with two pairs of wings, long antennae and elongate dark body. Despite their common name, they do not resemble wasps. Females generally lay eggs in young buds, leaves and other plant tissues and larvae develop within characteristic galls that are produced by the host plant. Each gall wasp species induces development of a particular gall or series of galls and many of these are conspicuous and well known. Oaks are especially liable to attack by gall wasps and at least 100 different species have been recorded in Britain and northern Europe. Although the symptoms are often spectacular, galls seldom cause severe damage to plants, but persistent infestations on young plants may check growth. The biology of many gall wasp species is complicated by alternation of sexual and asexual generations which develop in quite distinct galls, often on different parts of the same host plant.

MARBLE GALL WASP *Andricus kollari* **Pl. 7**

Widespread and especially common on young scrubby oaks. Large, spherical, smooth, green or brown woody galls, up to 25 mm across, develop from buds (Pl. 7) after female gall wasps have laid eggs in them in spring. Each gall contains a single small larva which feeds in an internal chamber. Adults emerge through holes in galls in September/October and brown, empty galls remain attached to trees for years.

OAK-APPLE GALL WASP *Biorhiza pallida*

Also common and widespread on oaks and is sometimes confused with the preceding species. Large, pithy, slightly irregular, smooth galls develop from buds in May. At first they are green or yellow but they soon turn red and look like small apples. Each gall contains many small chambers in which larvae feed. Adults emerge in June/July and females crawl down stems and trunks to lay eggs on roots. Root galls then develop and house larvae of the overwintering generation. Adults emerge in spring and move up to the young buds to lay eggs and complete the cycle.

ARTICHOKE GALL WASP *Andricus fecundator*

Oak buds develop into galls that resemble small artichokes. These galls appear in June after females have laid eggs in young buds and they persist for a year or more. Female gall wasps emerge in the following spring and lay eggs in male flower buds. Hairy galls then develop on male catkins and adults of the sexual generation emerge from them in May/June. After mating, the females lay eggs and give rise to the next crop of artichoke galls.

SPANGLE GALL WASPS *Neuroterus* species **Pl. 7**

Four different species of *Neuroterus* induce the development of small, circular, 'spangle' galls, up to 4 mm diameter, on the undersides of oak leaves in late summer and autumn. These are the common spangle gall wasp, *Neuroterus quercusbaccarum*, the silk-button spangle gall wasp, *Neuroterus numismalis*, the cupped spangle gall wasp, *Neuroterus tricolor*, and the smooth spangle gall wasp, *Neuroterus albipes*. Each gall contains a single gall wasp larva in a small chamber. Galls fall off leaves in autumn, often in great numbers which carpet the soil under infested trees. Larvae overwinter in them and adults emerge in the following spring. Parthenogenetic females then lay eggs on catkins or leaves and various specifically distinct pea and blister galls develop before the sexual generation of adults emerges in June/July to give rise to the next crop of spangle galls.

Treatment. Oaks are seldom seriously affected by spangle galls and it is generally unnecessary to try to control them. Young trees may be protected to some extent, if necessary, by applying a contact insecticide, such as HCH, during June/July when adults of the sexual generation are active.

ACORN CUP GALL WASP *Andricus quercuscalicis*

Causes 'knopper' galls on acorns which develop conspicuous irregular green sticky growths. Established in southern England since 1960 and extremely abundant in recent years. Mostly noticed in September–October when galled acorns fall from trees.

PLATE 1 Eelworms, Slugs, Millepedes, Woodlice

Stem Eelworm *Ditylenchus dipsaci* 84

1. Bloated onion plant with swollen, distorted leaves.
2. Live eelworms in water, as seen through a × 10 magnifier.
3. Infested narcissus plant showing damaged flower and weak growth.
4. Narcissus leaves with characteristic raised bumps ('spickels').
5. Infested narcissus bulb cut across to show brown rings of dead tissue.

Chrysanthemum Eelworm *Aphelenchoides ritzemabosi* 86

6. Chrysanthemum plant showing discolouration of upper leaves and collapse of lower leaves.

Root-knot Eelworms *Meloidogyne* spp. 88

7. Root system of infested plant showing characteristic hard irregular swellings (galls).

Yellow Potato Cyst Eelworm *Globodera rostochiensis* 89

8. Cysts on potato roots, as seen through a × 10 magnifier.

Slugs 90

9 .Potato tuber showing tunnels eaten out by subterranean slugs.
10. Garden slug.
11. Slug eggs in soil.

Millepedes 92

12. Black millepede.
13. Spotted millepedes.

Woodlice 93

14. Adult woodlouse on rotting wood.

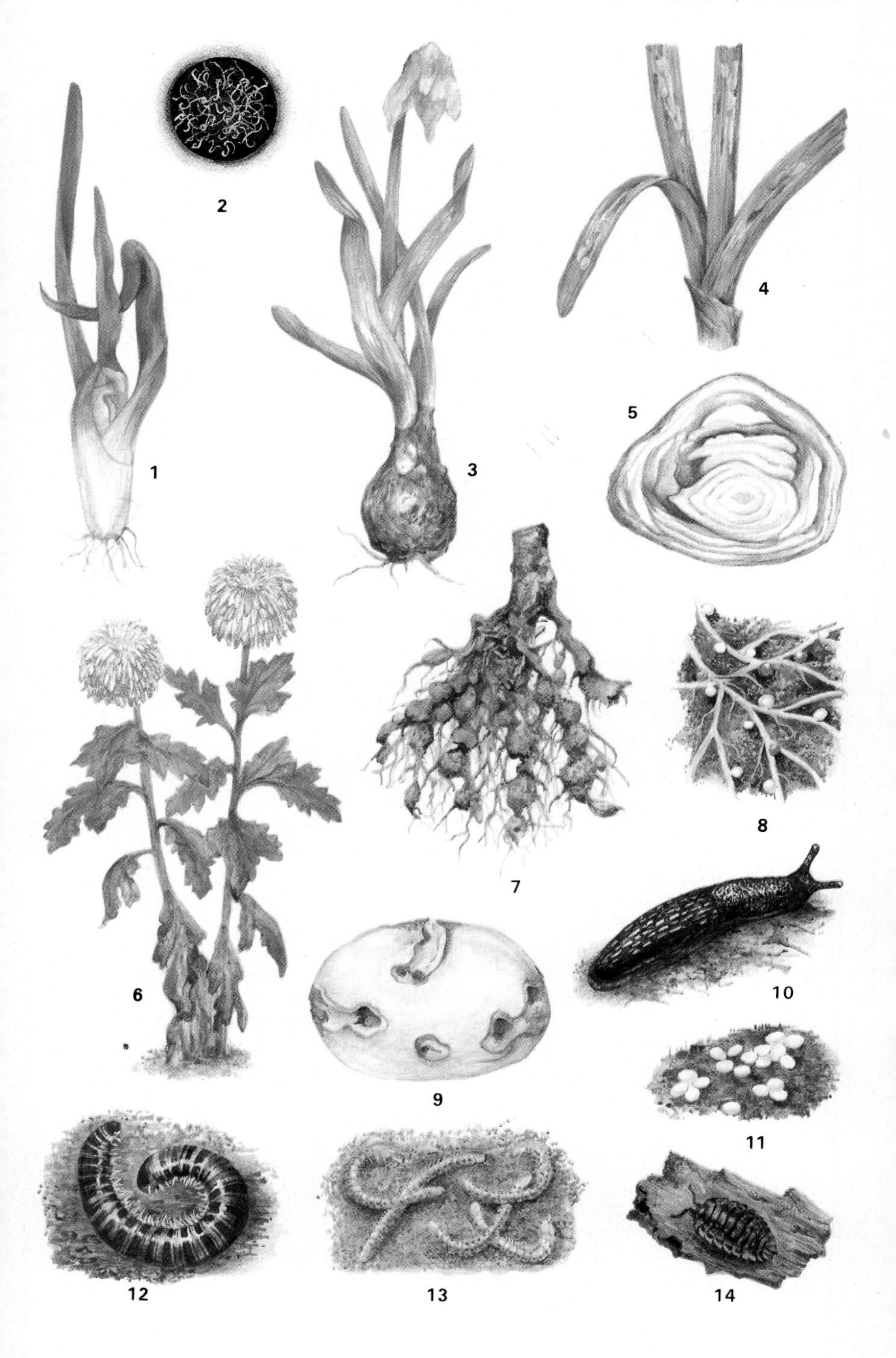
1
2
3
4
5
6
7
8
9
10
11
12
13
14

PLATE 2 Earwigs, Rhododendron Bug, Capsid Bugs, Froghoppers, Leafhoppers, Psyllids, Whiteflies

Earwigs 94

1. Adult earwigs in chrysanthemum flower.

Rhododendron Bug *Stephanitis rhododendri* 96

2. Underside of infested rhododendron leaf showing characteristic brown rust-like discolouration.

Capsid Bugs 97

3. Leaf damage caused by capsid adults and/or nymphs feeding on young tissues at tips of shoots.
4. Apple fruit showing bumps and scarring caused by capsid bugs feeding on young fruitlets.
5. Flowers of perennial chrysanthemum distorted by capsid bugs feeding on flower buds.

Common Froghopper *Philaenus spumarius* 98

6. Froth masses ('cuckoo-spit') covering nymphs on lavender shoots.

Leafhoppers 98

7. Coarse white mottling of upper leaf surface caused by glasshouse leafhopper, *Hauptidia maroccana*, on primulas and other glasshouse and house plants.
8. Severe damage to a rose leaf caused by rose leafhoppers, *Edwardsiana rosae*.
9. Underside of a rose leaflet showing leafhoppers and cast skins.

Psyllids 100

10. Overwintering eggs of apple sucker, *Psylla mali*.
11. Young apple sucker nymphs feeding at the base of developing apple blossom shoot.

Whiteflies 102

12. Eggs, pupae and adults of the glasshouse whitefly, *Trialeurodes vaporariorum*, on the underside of a leaf, as seen through a × 10 magnifier.
13. Larvae, pupae and adults of the cabbage whitefly, *Aleyrodes proletella*, on the underside of a cabbage leaf, as seen through a × 10 magnifier.
14. Adult azalea whiteflies, *Pealius azaleae*, congregating on the undersides of young azalea leaves.
15. White-fringed black scales of the viburnum whitefly, *Aleurotrachelus jelinekii*, on the underside of a leaf of *Viburnum tinus*.

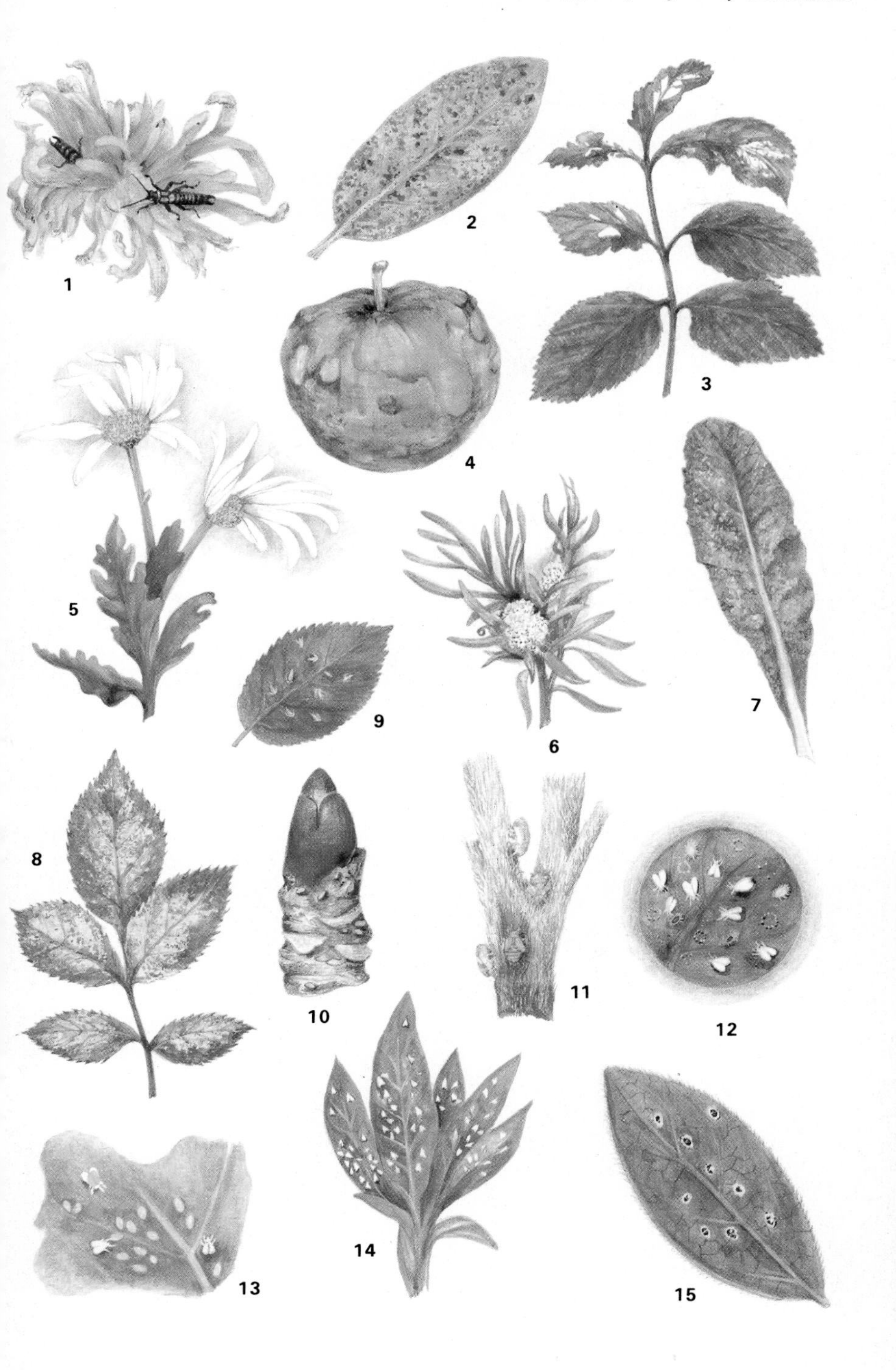
1
2
3
4
5
6
7
8
9
10
11
12
13
14
15

PLATE 3

Aphids

Apple Aphids 106

1. Young aphids hatching in spring from overwintered eggs and invading apple bud as it opens.
2. Misshapen apples resulting from aphid infestation earlier in the season.
3. Woolly aphid, *Eriosoma lanigerum*, colonies on apple twigs in summer. The colonies are covered by white, woolly wax.

Mealy Plum Aphid *Hyalopterus pruni* 110

4. Plum leaf with upper surface thickly contaminated with sooty moulds and cast aphid skins following severe infestation of undersides of leaves by dense aphid colonies.

Black Bean Aphid *Aphis fabae* 112

5. Broad bean plant with stems and leaf bases infested by colonies of aphids.
6. Close-up of part of broad bean stem showing aphids, as seen through a × 10 magnifier.

Cabbage Aphid *Brevicoryne brassicae* 113

7. Colony of wingless aphids on underside of cabbage leaf.

Rose Aphid *Macrosiphum rosae* 116

8. Winged and wingless aphids feeding on flower bud, stem and leaves of rose.

Mottled Arum Aphid *Aulacorthum circumflexum* 117

9. Wingless aphids feeding on dahlia stem.

Beech Aphid *Phyllaphis fagi* 119

10. White waxy secretions covering colonies of aphids on undersides of beech leaves.

Large Willow Aphid *Tuberolachnus salignus* 119

11. Wingless aphids feeding on woody stems of willow. The largest aphids are 5 mm long.

Root Aphids 120

12. Colonies of lettuce root aphid, *Pemphigus bursarius*, feeding on roots of lettuce plant.

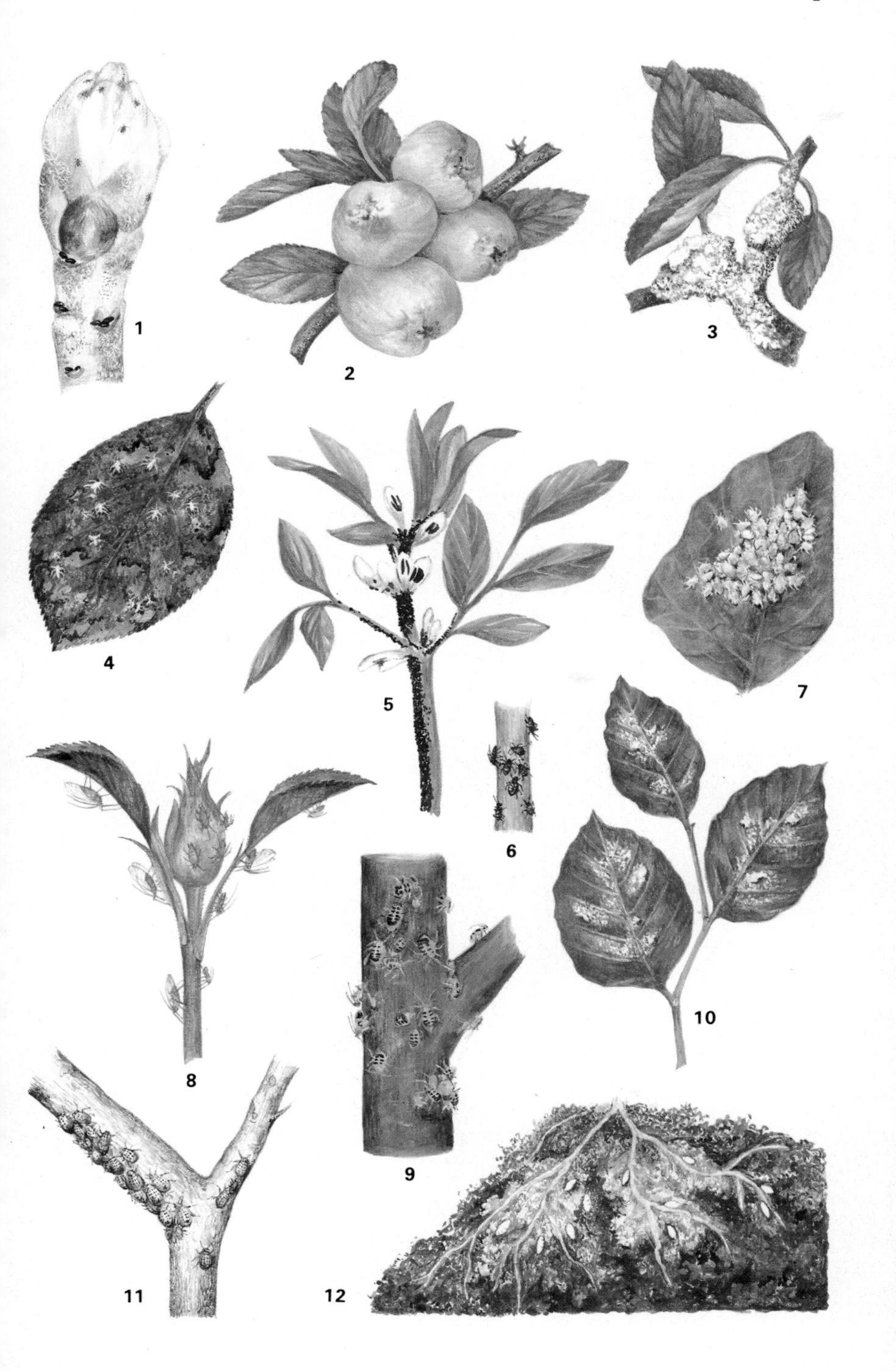
1
2
3
4
5
6
7
8
9
10
11
12

PLATE 4 Adelgids, Scale Insects, Mealybugs, Thrips

Spruce Gall Adelgids 121

1. Gall resembling a miniature pineapple at tip of shoot of Norway spruce. The compartments of the gall are starting to open, revealing the tightly packed adelgids inside.

Douglas Fir Adelgid *Adelges cooleyi* 122

2. Shoot of Douglas fir infested by adelgids with white wax coverings.

Soft Scale *Coccus hesperidum* 124

3. Underside of leaf of bay laurel infested by soft scales.
4. Upperside of leaf from the same plant showing thick encrustation of sooty moulds caused by soft scale infestation.

Woolly Vine Scale *Pulvinaria vitis* 125

5. Two dead female scales on vine stem with conspicuous white woolly wax egg sacs.

Hemispherical Scale *Saissetia coffeae* 124

6. Three mature females on ornamental citrus fruit. Each scale will contain up to 2,000 eggs.

Mussel Scale *Lepidosaphes ulmi* 126

7. Apple fruit infested by mussel-like scales.

Beech Scale *Cryptococcus fagisuga* 126

8. Trunk of beech tree thickly infested by scales which are completely covered by white waxy secretions.

Mealybugs 127

9. Colony of mealybugs feeding on a stem of grape vine.
10. Root mealybugs feeding on root system of pot plant.

Thrips 129

11. Pea pod showing characteristic silvering following attack by pea thrips, *Kakothrips pisivorus*.
12. Gladiolus plant showing severe damage to flowers and leaves caused by gladiolus thrips, *Thrips simplex*.

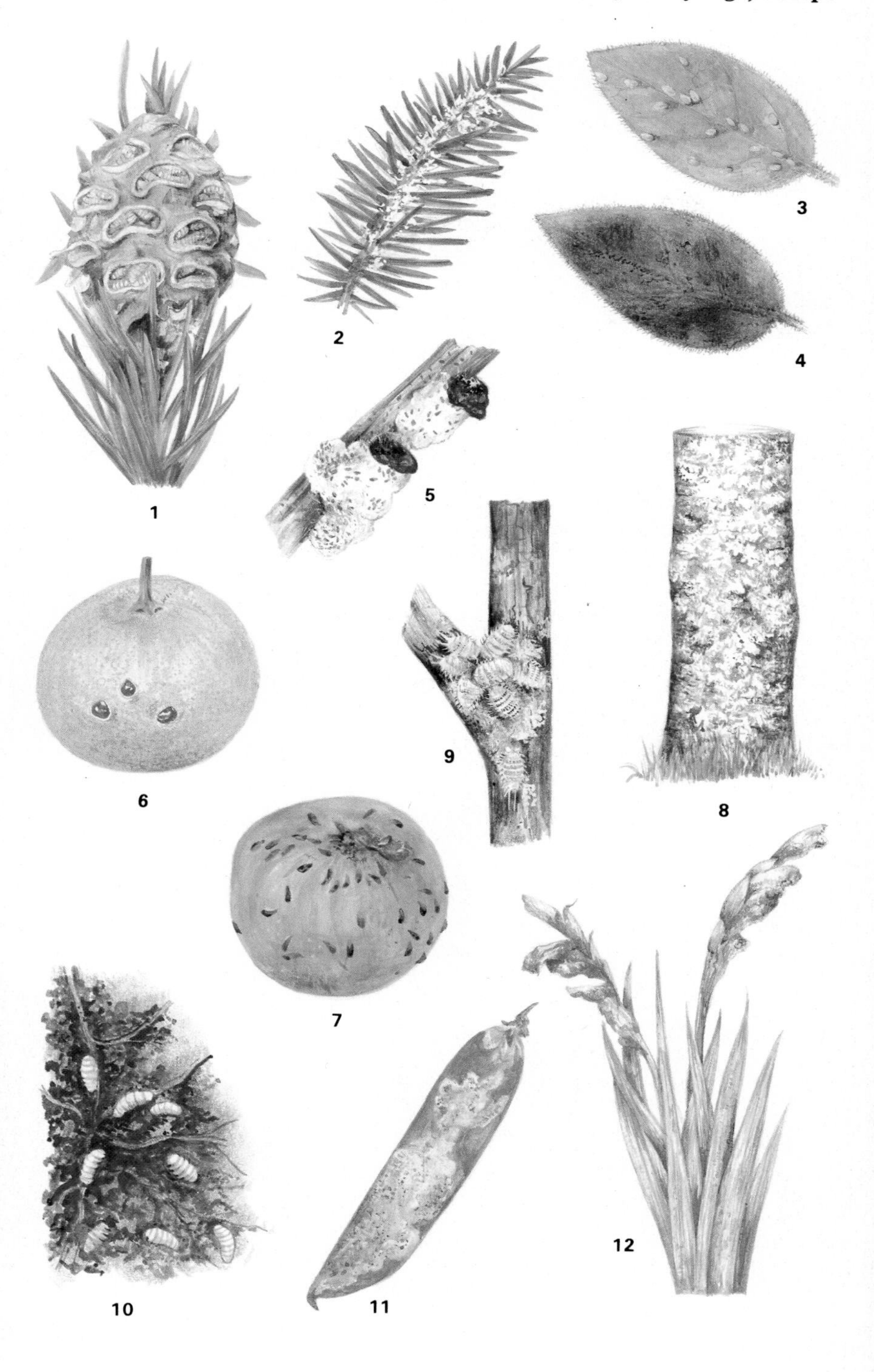
1
2
3
4
5
6
7
8
9
10
11
12

PLATE 5 Caterpillars

Winter Moths 133

1. Hornbeam leaves showing typical injury caused by caterpillars of the winter moth, *Operophtera brumata*, and related species feeding on buds and young growths in spring.
2. Caterpillar of the mottled umber moth, *Erannis defoliaria*, feeding on hornbeam leaf.

Codling Moth *Cydia pomonella* 134

3. Apple fruit damaged by codling moth caterpillar tunnelling into core.

Leopard Moth *Zeuzera pyrina* 136

4. Caterpillar tunnelling in woody branch of apple tree.

Cutworms 136

5. Caterpillars of the turnip moth, *Agrotis segetum*, in soil.

Swift Moths 137

6. Caterpillar of the garden swift moth, *Hepialus lupulinus*, in soil.

Cabbage Caterpillars 138

7. Caterpillar of the large white butterfly, *Pieris brassicae*, feeding on cabbage leaf.
8. Caterpillar of the small white butterfly, *Pieris rapae*.

Pea Moth *Cydia nigricana* 139

9. Caterpillars feeding on peas inside a pea pod.

Silver Y Moth *Autographa gamma* 139

10. Caterpillar feeding on leaf of glasshouse chrysanthemum.

Angle Shades Moth *Phlogophora meticulosa* 140

11. Caterpillar feeding on leaf of glasshouse plant.

Carnation Tortrix Moth *Cacoecimorpha pronubana* 142

12. Caterpillar on damaged leaf surrounded by silk webbing which it spins to draw leaves together into a protective covering.

Vapourer Moth *Orgyia antiqua* 141

13. Caterpillar feeding on leaves of dahlia.

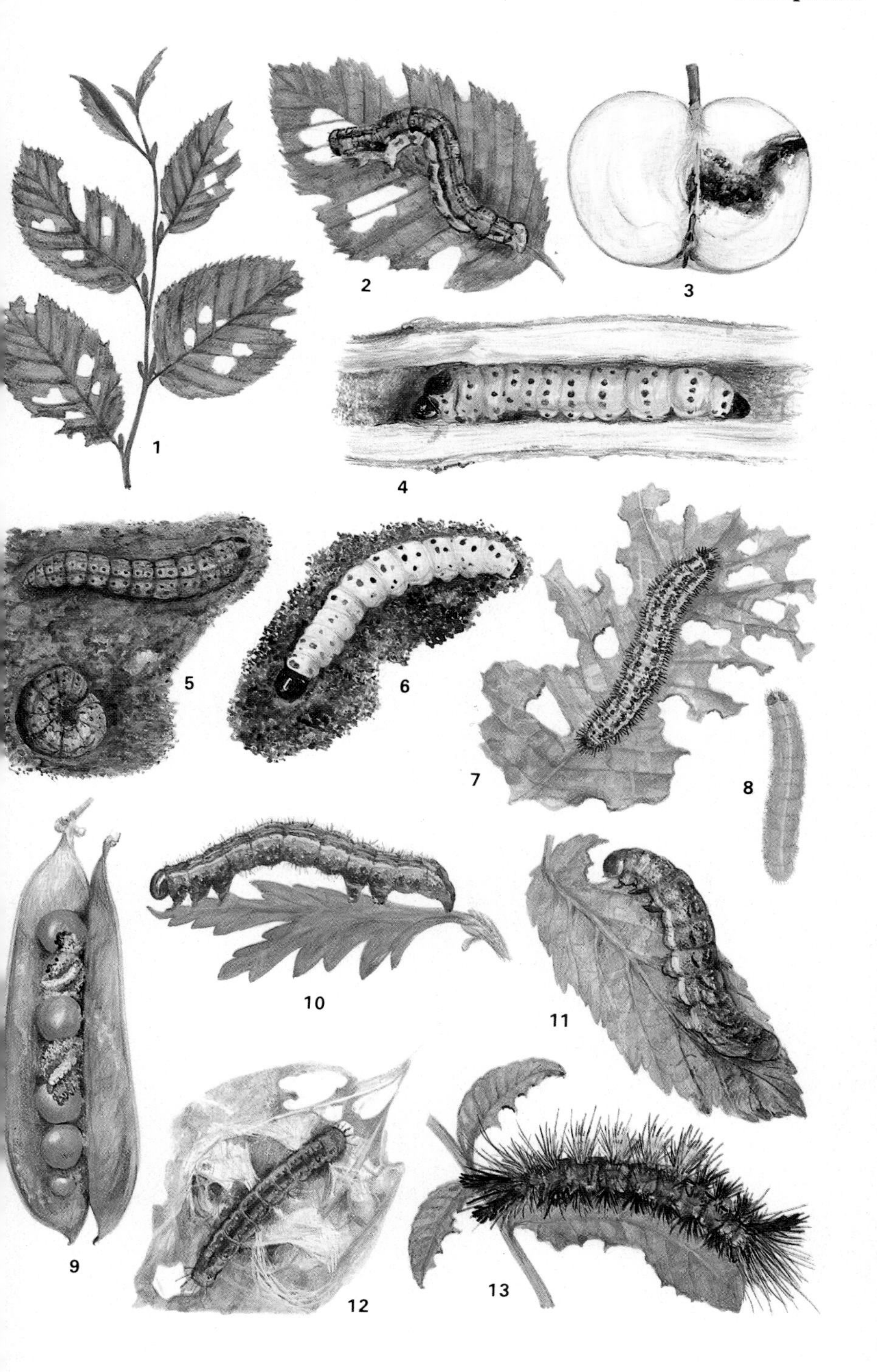
1
2
3
4
5
6
7
8
9
10
11
12
13

PLATE 6 **Flies**

Pear Midge *Contarinia pyrivora* 145
1. Pear fruitlet cut open to show midge larvae feeding in internal cavity.

Leatherjackets 147
2. Larvae of the crane-fly, *Tipula oleracea*, in soil.

Celery Fly *Euleia heraclei* 149
3. Blotch mines produced by celery fly maggots feeding in leaves.

Cabbage Root Fly *Delia radicum* 150
4. Young cabbage transplant wilting and collapsing after the root system has been severely damaged by cabbage root fly maggots.

Carrot Fly *Psila rosae* 149
5. Carrot showing typical injury caused by carrot fly maggots tunnelling in tissues.

Onion Fly *Delia antiqua* 151
6. Maggot and pupa (puparium), as seen through a × 10 magnifier.
7. Young onion plants collapsing and dying after the roots and stem bases have been damaged by onion fly maggots.

Bean Seed Fly *Delia platura* 151
8. Bean seedling showing typical injury to the cotyledons and growing point caused by bean seed fly maggots feeding on them in the soil during the early stages of development.

Yew Gall Midge *Taxomyia taxi* 152
9. Tips of yew shoots enlarged to form two galls (left) resembling miniature artichokes; normal shoot on right.

Large Narcissus Fly *Merodon equestris* 152
10. Narcissus bulb cut open to show narcissus fly maggot in large internal cavity.

Chrysanthemum Leaf Miner *Phytomyza syngenesiae* 153
11. Sinuous white mines caused by maggots feeding in chrysanthemum leaf.

Holly Leaf Miner *Phytomyza ilicis* 154
12. Blotch mine caused by maggots feeding in holly leaf.

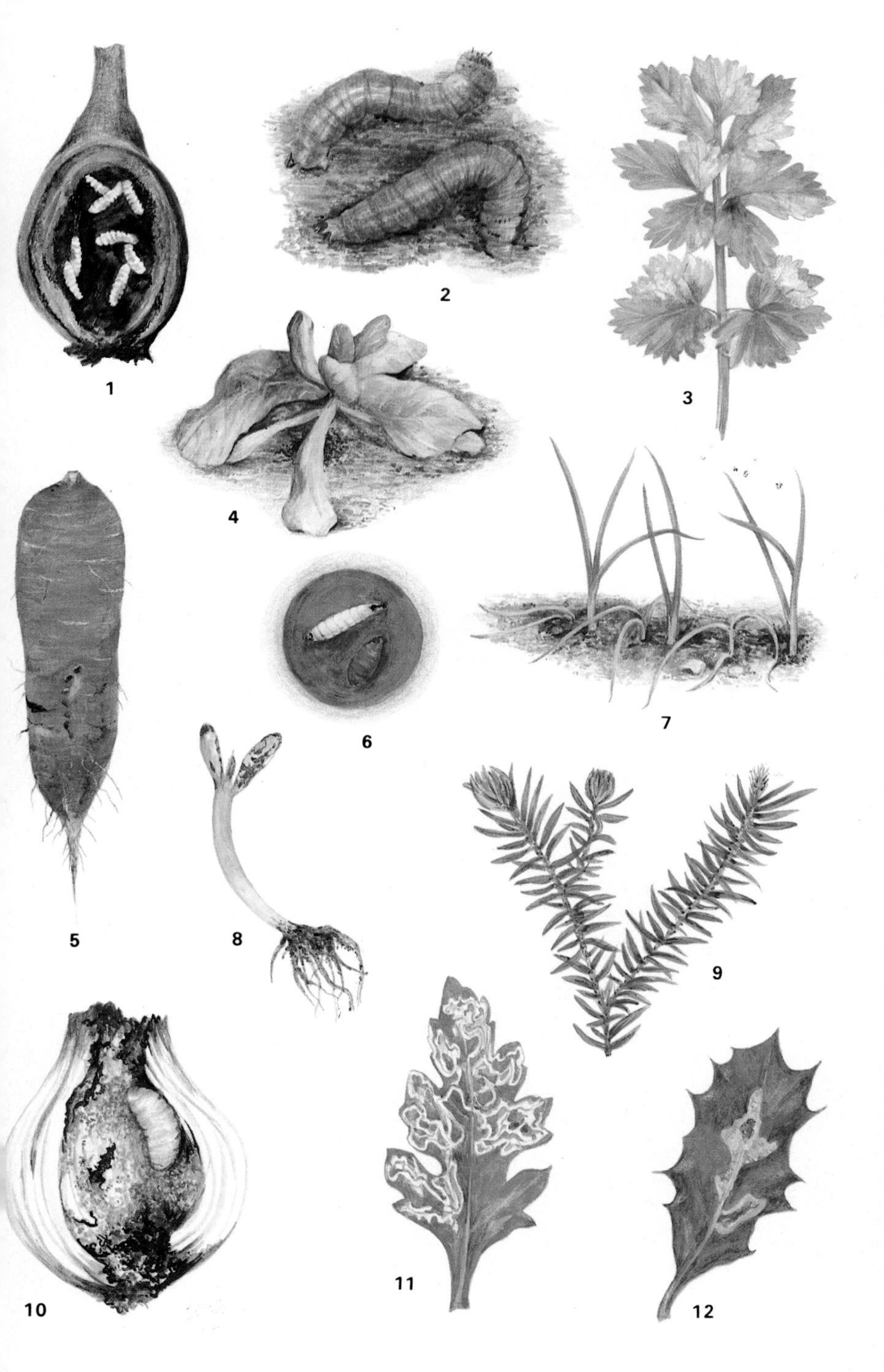
1
2
3
4
5
6
7
8
9
10
11
12

PLATE 7 Sawflies, Gall Wasps, Leaf-cutter Bee, Wasps

Apple Sawfly *Hoplocampa testudinea* 154

1. Apple fruitlets showing holes and scars caused by sawfly larvae tunnelling in tissues.
2. Older fruit showing characteristic superficial scarring resulting from sawfly attack during the earlier stages of development.

Pear and Cherry Slugworm *Caliroa cerasi* 155

3. Larvae eating away surface tissues from a leaf of *Chaenomeles*.

Common Gooseberry Sawfly *Nematus ribesii* 156

4. Larva feeding on gooseberry leaf.

Rose Slug Sawfly *Endelomyia aethiops* 156

5. Larvae feeding on upper surface of rose leaf, eating away surface tissues to produce transparent 'windows'.

Leaf-rolling Rose Sawfly *Blennocampa pusilla* 157

6. Rose shoot showing the effect of a severe attack by female sawflies. Each rolled leaflet has been pierced by the female's ovipositor during egg-laying.

Willow Bean-gall Sawfly *Pontania proxima* 157

7. Willow leaves with typical hard, raised galls containing sawfly larvae.

Marble Gall Wasp *Andricus kollari* 159

8. Marble galls on oak. Galls develop when buds are attacked by gall wasps and each gall contains a single gall wasp larva in a small internal chamber.

Silk-button Spangle Gall Wasp *Neuroterus numismalis* 159

9. Silk-button galls on underside of oak leaf.

Leaf-cutter Bee *Megachile centuncularis* 162

10. Rose leaf with semi-circular pieces removed by bees to construct cells in their nests.

Wasps 161

11. Adult wasps feeding on ripe pear, probably extending a wound made by birds or by mechanical injury.

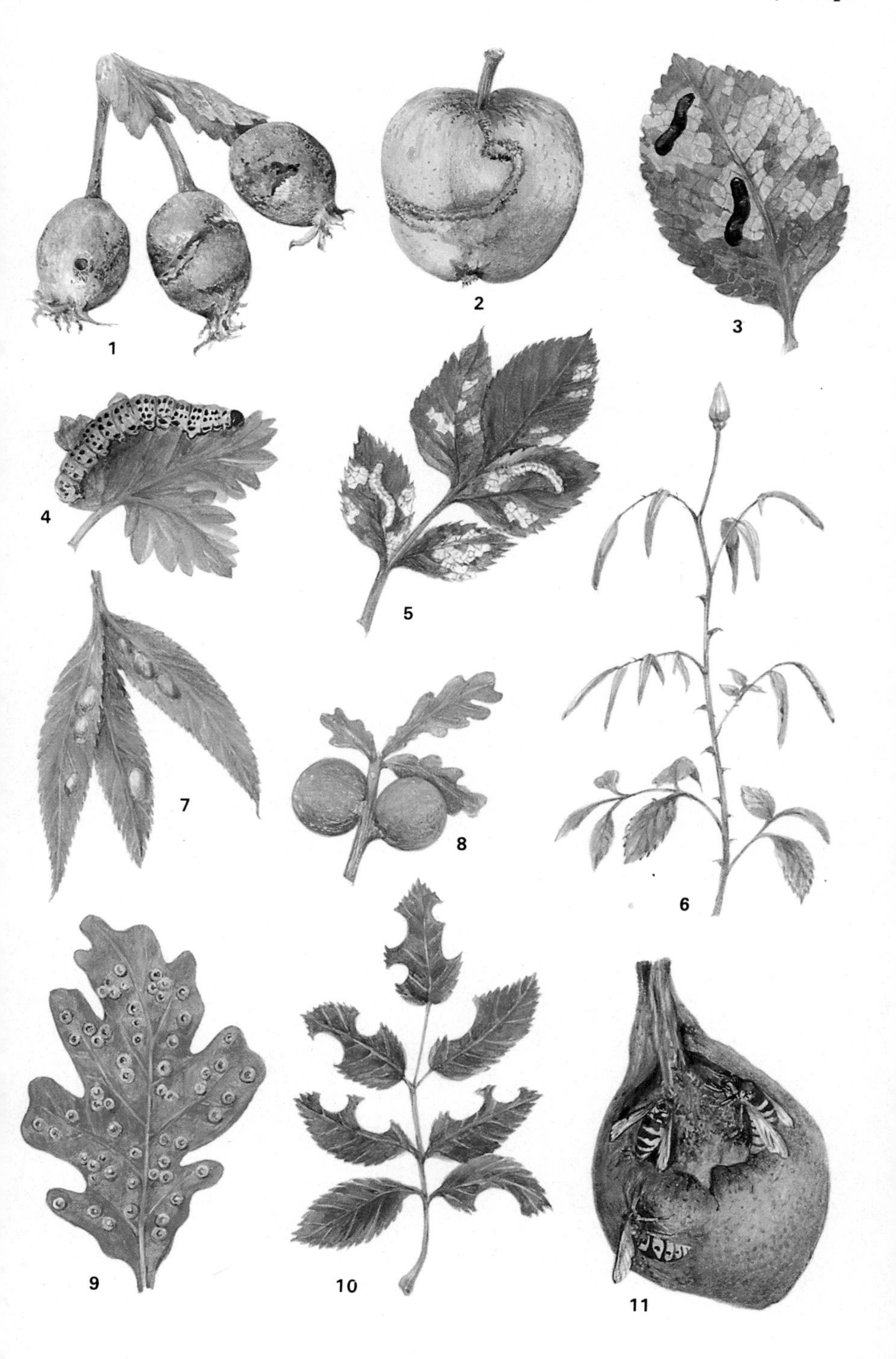
1
2
3
4
5
6
7
8
9
10
11

PLATE 8 **Beetles**

Chafers 163

1. Larva feeding in potato tuber.

Wireworms 163

2. Larvae of common click beetle, *Agriotes lineatus*, in soil.

Raspberry Beetle *Byturus tomentosus* 165

3. Larva feeding on ripe raspberry fruit.

Flea Beetles 165

4. Adult flea beetles feeding on young turnip plant, showing typical damage to young leaves.

Colorado Beetle *Leptinotarsa decemlineata* 166

5. Adult beetle on potato leaf.

Water-lily Beetle *Galerucella nymphaeae* 167

6. Water-lily leaf showing typical damage caused by adults and larvae feeding on the upper surface.

Lily Beetle *Lilioceris lilii* 167

7. Adults feeding on lily leaf.

Apple Blossom Weevil *Anthonomus pomorum* 168

8. Apple blossom that has failed to open following attack by weevil larvae. The larvae develop within the 'capped' flowers.

Turnip Gall Weevil *Ceutorhynchus pleurostigma* 169

9. Cabbage stem with weevil galls. Each gall contains a single larva in an internal chamber.

Pea and Bean Weevil *Sitona lineatus* 169

10. Broad bean plant with edges of leaves eaten away by adult weevils, producing a characteristic scalloped effect.

Vine Weevil *Otiorhynchus sulcatus* 170

11. Larvae in potting compost.

Elm Bark Beetle *Scolytus scolytus* 171

12. Elm branch with bark removed to expose typical galleries in which the bark beetle larvae develop.

1
2
3
4
5
6
7
8
9
10
11
12

PLATE 9 Mites, Birds

Glasshouse Red Spider Mite *Tetranychus urticae* 173

1. Typical symptoms of early stages of attack on leaves of *Impatiens*.
2. Adult mites and eggs on underside of leaf, as seen through a ×10 magnifier.

Fruit Tree Red Spider Mite *Panonychus ulmi* 175

3. Overwintering eggs on branch of apple tree.

Conifer Spinning Mite *Oligonychus ununguis* 175

4. Typical discolouration of leaves of *Picea* resulting from mite infestation.

Strawberry Mite *Tarsonemus pallidus* 177

5. Pot cyclamen buds showing characteristic discolouration caused by mites feeding in the buds. Flowers developing from damaged buds are discoloured and distorted.

Bulb Scale Mite *Steneotarsonemus laticeps* 177

6. Leaves of narcissus showing typical scarring caused by mites feeding on young leaves.

Black Currant Gall Mite *Cecidophyopsis ribis* 178

7. Enlarged buds of black currant ('big bud') caused by mite infestation. This symptom is generally most obvious in early spring.

Pear Leaf Blister Mite *Eriophyes pyri* 178

8. Pear leaf showing typical blistering and discolouration caused by mites feeding in young tissues.

Nail Gall Mite *Eriophyes tiliae* 179

9. Nail galls projecting from upper surface of lime leaf.

Bird Damage 179

10. Pear buds attacked by bullfinches in late winter.
11. Cabbage plant attacked by wood pigeons.
12. Ripening apple pecked by blackbird.

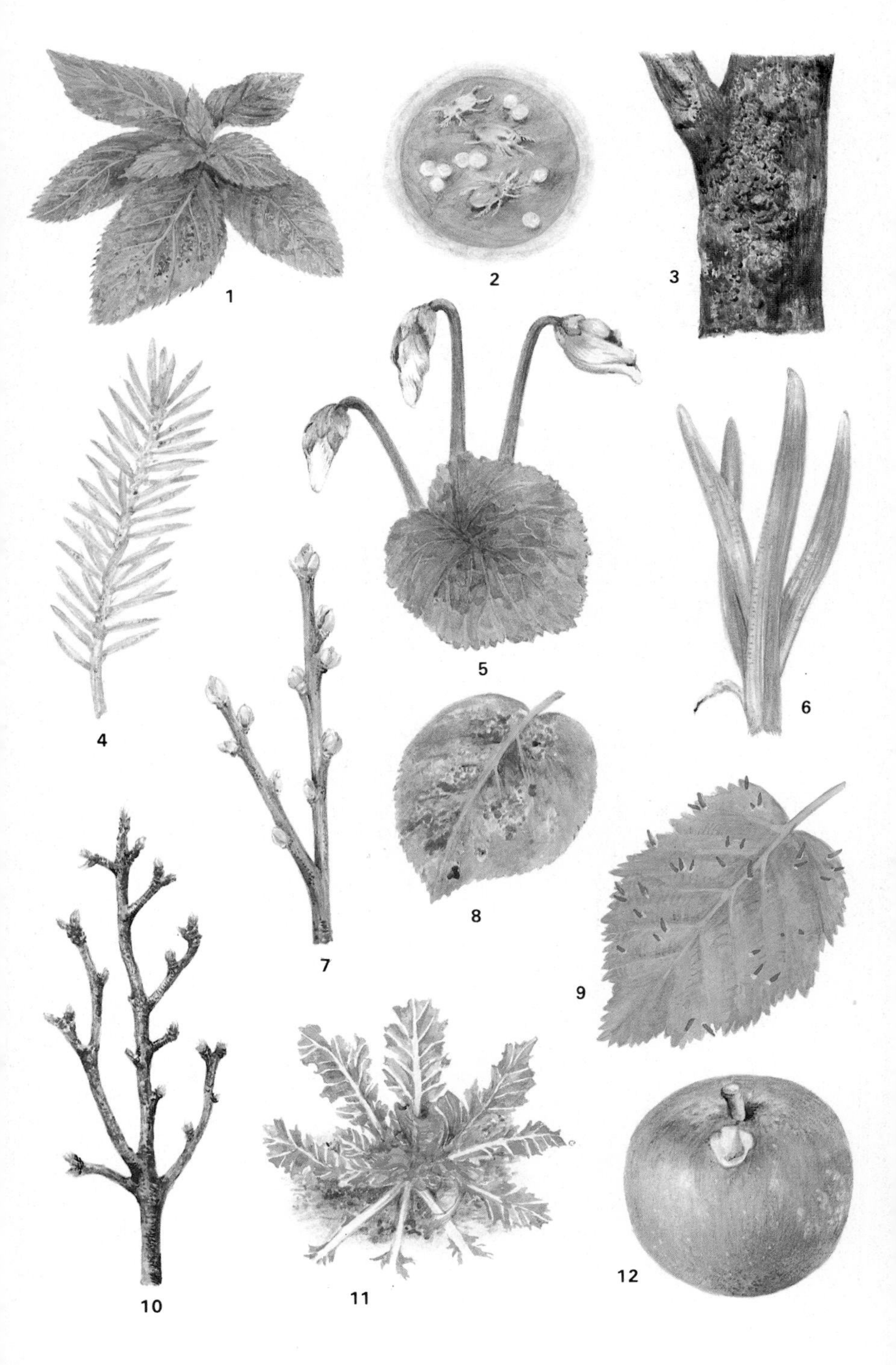
1
2
3
4
5
6
7
8
9
10
11
12

PLATE 10 Rusts, Smuts

Blackberry Common Rust *Phragmidium violaceum* 193

1. Aeciospore-producing lesion on stem.
2. Aeciospore and urediniospore (yellow) and teliospore (black) -producing pustules on underside of leaf.

Blackberry Stem Rust *Kuehneola uredinis* 193

3. Aeciospore-producing pustules on upperside of leaf.

Carnation Rust *Uromyces dianthi* 194

4. Plant bearing masses of urediniospore-producing pustules.

Chrysanthemum Rust *Puccinia chrysanthemi* 194

5. Urediniospore-producing pustules on underside of leaf.

Chrysanthemum White Rust *Puccinia horiana* 195

6. Plant bearing typical white pustules brought about by the germination *in situ* of teliospores to produce basidiospores.

Hollyhock Rust *Puccinia malvacearum* 196

7. Teliospore-producing pustules on underside of leaf.

Leek Rust *Puccinia allii* 197

8. Slit-like urediniospore-producing lesions on leaf.

Mint Rust *Puccinia menthae* 197

9. Plant distorted by systemic infection and bearing two or three types of spore-producing pustule.

Pelargonium Rust *Puccinia pelargonii-zonalis* 198

10. Urediniospore-producing pustules on underside of leaf.

Plum Rust *Tranzschelia discolor* 198

11. Upperside of plum leaf with characteristic yellow spots indicating positions of pustules beneath.
12. Powdery urediniospore-producing pustules on underside of plum leaf.
13. Cluster cups on underside of anemone leaf; the alternate host.

Rose Rust *Phragmidium tuberculatum* 199

14. Masses of aeciospores on briar shoot.
15. Yellow urediniospore and black teliospore-producing pustules on underside of rose leaf.

Mahonia Rust *Cumminsiella mirabilissima* 197

16. Upperside of leaf with dark spots and red colouration; often, but not invariably, associated with the disease.
17. Underside of leaf with powdery urediniospore and teliospore-producing pustules.

Sweet Corn Smut *Ustilago maydis* 201

18. Cob distorted by systemic infection and bursting to reveal masses of black teliospores.

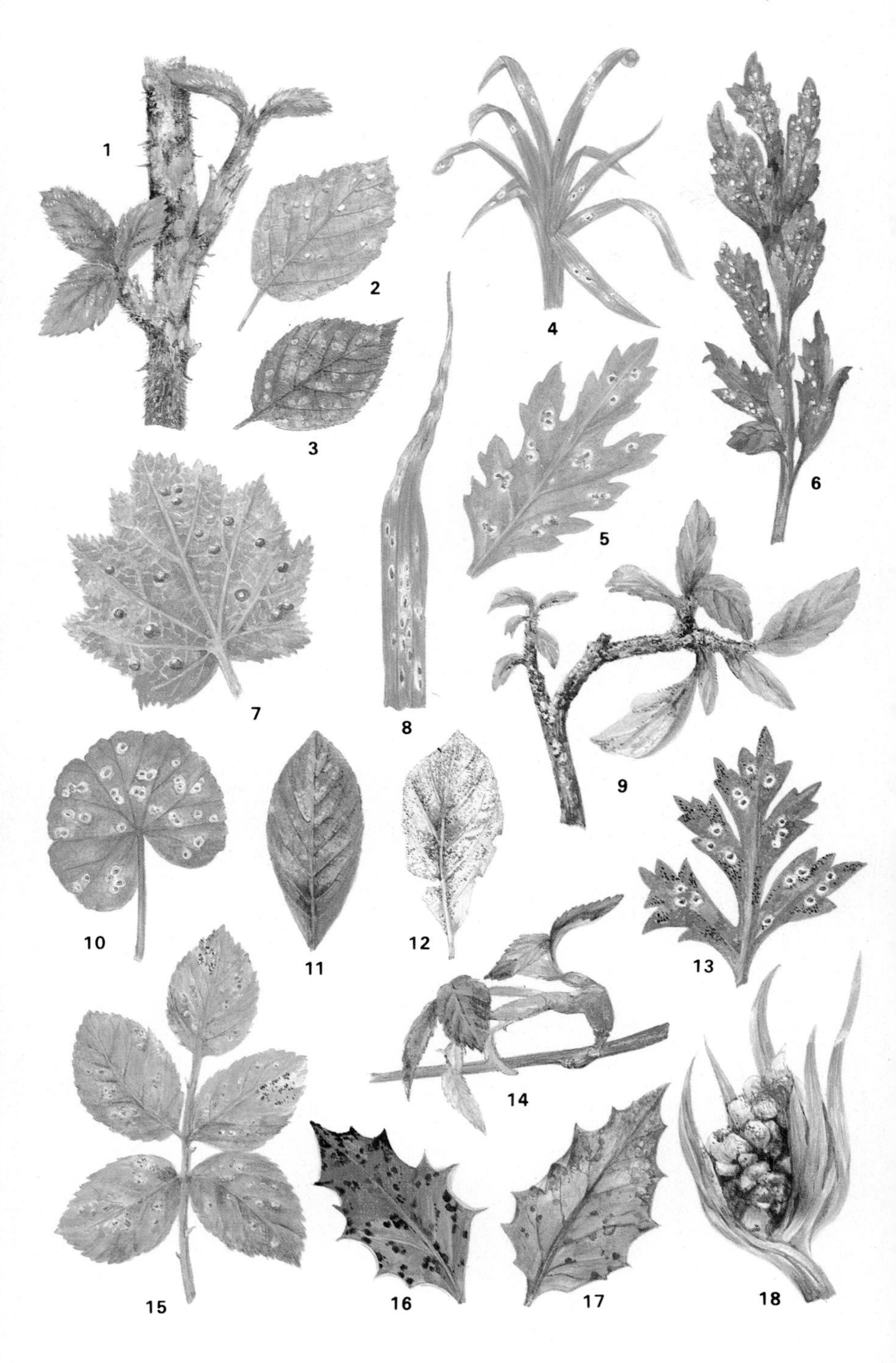
1
2
3
4
5
6
7
8
9
10
11
12
13
14
15
16
17
18

PLATE 11 Downy Mildews, Powdery Mildews, Sooty Mould, White Blister, Needle Cast, Wilts

Lettuce Downy Mildew *Bremia lactucae* 203

1. Plant with angular, dead patches of tissue on leaves.
2. Detail of underside of affected patch with the whitish mould that develops in damp conditions.

Crucifer Downy Mildew *Peronospora parasitica* 202

3. Patch of off-white mould growth on underside of leaf lesion.

Apple Powdery Mildew *Podosphaera leucotricha* 205

4. Shoot with characteristic terminal tuft of remaining leaves.

Rose Powdery Mildew *Sphaerotheca pannosa* 207

5. Affected shoot.

Sooty Mould 209

6. Beech leaves affected by sooty mould growing on insect-produced honeydew; contrasted with healthy foliage.

White Blister *Albugo candida* 210

7. Underside of affected cauliflower leaf.

Needle Cast 210

8. Browning and bleaching of pine needles caused by a needle-cast fungus.

Wilts 211

9. Tomato plant affected by *Verticillium* wilt with older leaves drooping first.
10. Longitudinal section of tomato stem *c.* 30 cm above ground level with darkened conducting tissues.
11. Young English elm with symptoms of Dutch elm disease.
12. Elm shoot affected with Dutch elm disease with bark removed to show dark streaks.

1
2
3
4
5
6
7
8
9
10
11
12

PLATE 12 Cankers, Diebacks, Stem and Twig Blights, Galls, Witches' Brooms, Leaf Curls

Apple Canker *Nectria galligena* f.sp. *mali* 215

1. Four- to five-year-old lesion on young stem.

Plum and Cherry Bacterial Canker *Pseudomonas mors-prunorum* 218

2. Canker symptom on cherry branch with copious exudation of gum.
3. 'Shot-hole' symptoms on cherry leaves in early summer.

Coral Spot *Nectria cinnabarina* 216

4. Conidia-producing pustules on old pea stick.
5. Clusters of perithecia on dying gooseberry twig.

Fireblight *Erwinia amylovora* 217

6. Scorched appearance of foliage on hawthorn hedge.

Clubroot *Plasmodiophora brassicae* 223

7. Swollen lateral roots on swede.
8. 'Finger and toe' symptoms on young cauliflower root.
9. 'Club' symptom on cabbage.

Potato Wart *Synchytrium endobioticum* 226

10. Knobbly gall on tuber.

Crown Gall *Agrobacterium radiobacter* var. *tumefaciens* 224

11. Elm trunk with a type of gall common on many trees and believed to be caused by the crown gall organism.
12. Gall at base of stem on young apple tree.

Witches' Broom *Taphrina turgida* 227

13. Bird's nest type brooms on silver birch; probably the commonest host plant for witches' brooms.

Peach Leaf Curl *Taphrina deformans* 225

14. Appearance of affected foliage in early summer.
15. Single affected shoot in summer with white coating imparted by the layer of ascospores formed on the tissues.

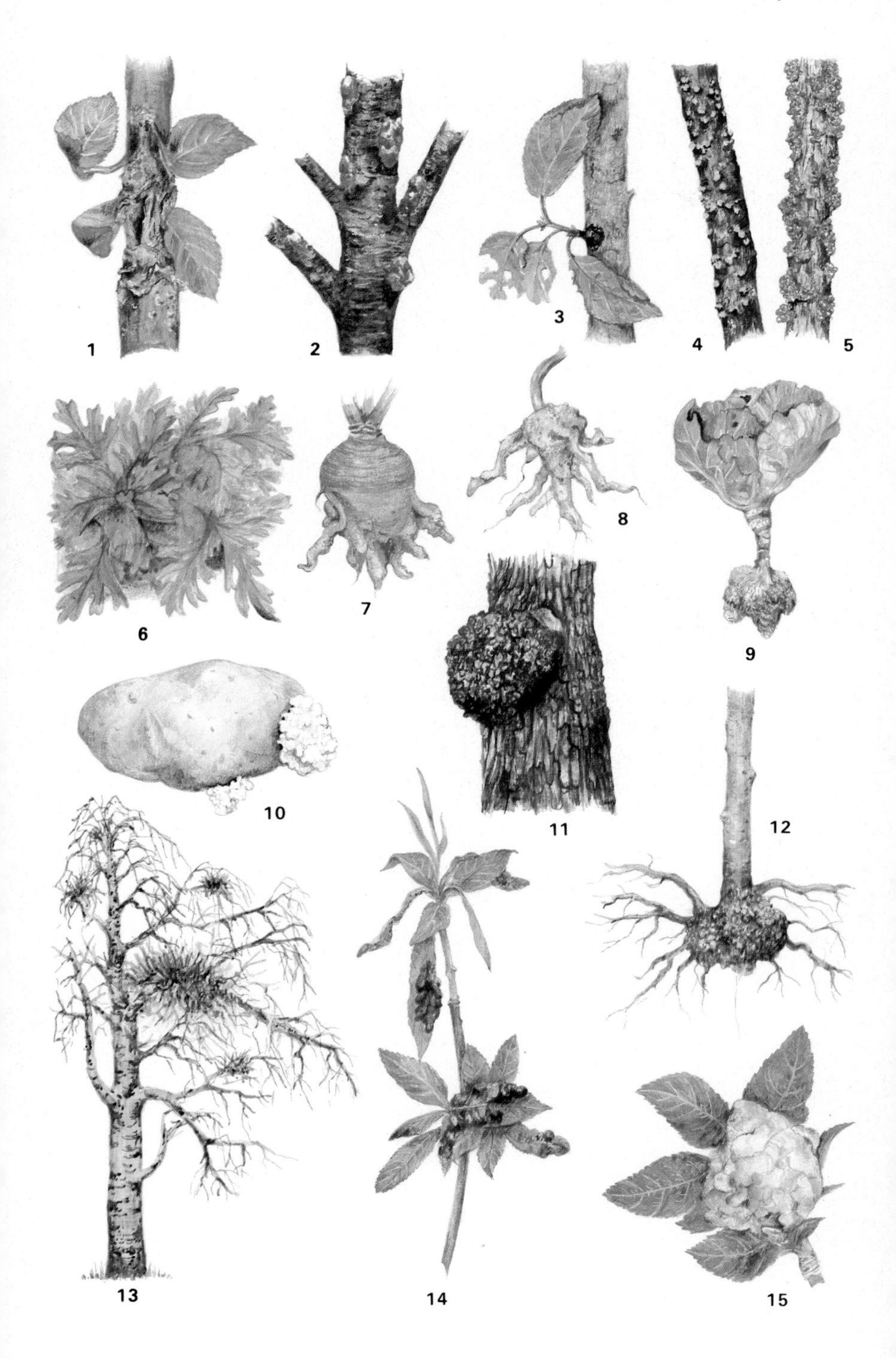

1
2
3
4
5
6
7
8
9
10
11
12
13
14
15

PLATE 13 Scabs, Corm, Bulb and Tuber Rots, Flower and Bud Rots

Apple Scab *Venturia inaequalis* 228

1. Cracked and corky patches on fruit; the most obvious symptom.

Potato Common Scab *Streptomyces scabies* 229

2. Spots of corky tissue over tuber surface.

Potato Powdery Scab *Spongospora subterranea* var. *subterranea* 230

3. Severe symptoms with considerable distortion of tuber; when less severe, the effects are similar to those of common scab.

Bulb and Corm Rots 231

4–10. Examples of some of the commonest symptom types.

Blue Mould Rot *Penicillium* sp.

4. Vertical section through narcissus bulb with mould growth on and between the fleshy scales.

Gladiolus Core Rot *Sclerotinia draytoni*

5. Vertical view of affected corm with decay and mould growth in centre.
6. Vertical section of corm with decayed centre.

Gladiolus Dry Rot *Stromatinia gladioli*

7. Corm with scales removed, to reveal rings of shallow, sunken lesions.
8. Dead leaf base with many black sclerotia.

Narcissus Basal Rot *Fusarium oxysporum* f.sp. *narcissi*

9. Vertical section through affected bulb with brown rot spreading upwards from basal ring.

Tulip Grey Bulb Rot *Rhizoctonia tuliparum*

10. Bulb with scales partly removed to reveal large sclerotia.

Grey Mould *Botrytis cinerea* 232

11. Moribund rose head with grey mould growth.
12. Petal spotting symptoms on impatiens.

Chrysanthemum Ray Blight *Didymella chrysanthemi* 232

13. Rotting and collapse of terminal bud on affected shoot.
14. Bloom beginning to collapse with incipient decay.

Rhododendron Petal Blight *Ovulinia azaleae* 233

15. Limp and slimy blooms hanging on affected shoot.

Rhododendron Bud Blast *Pycnostysanus azaleae* 232

16. Pin-head like coremia (conidia-producing bodies) on dried bud.

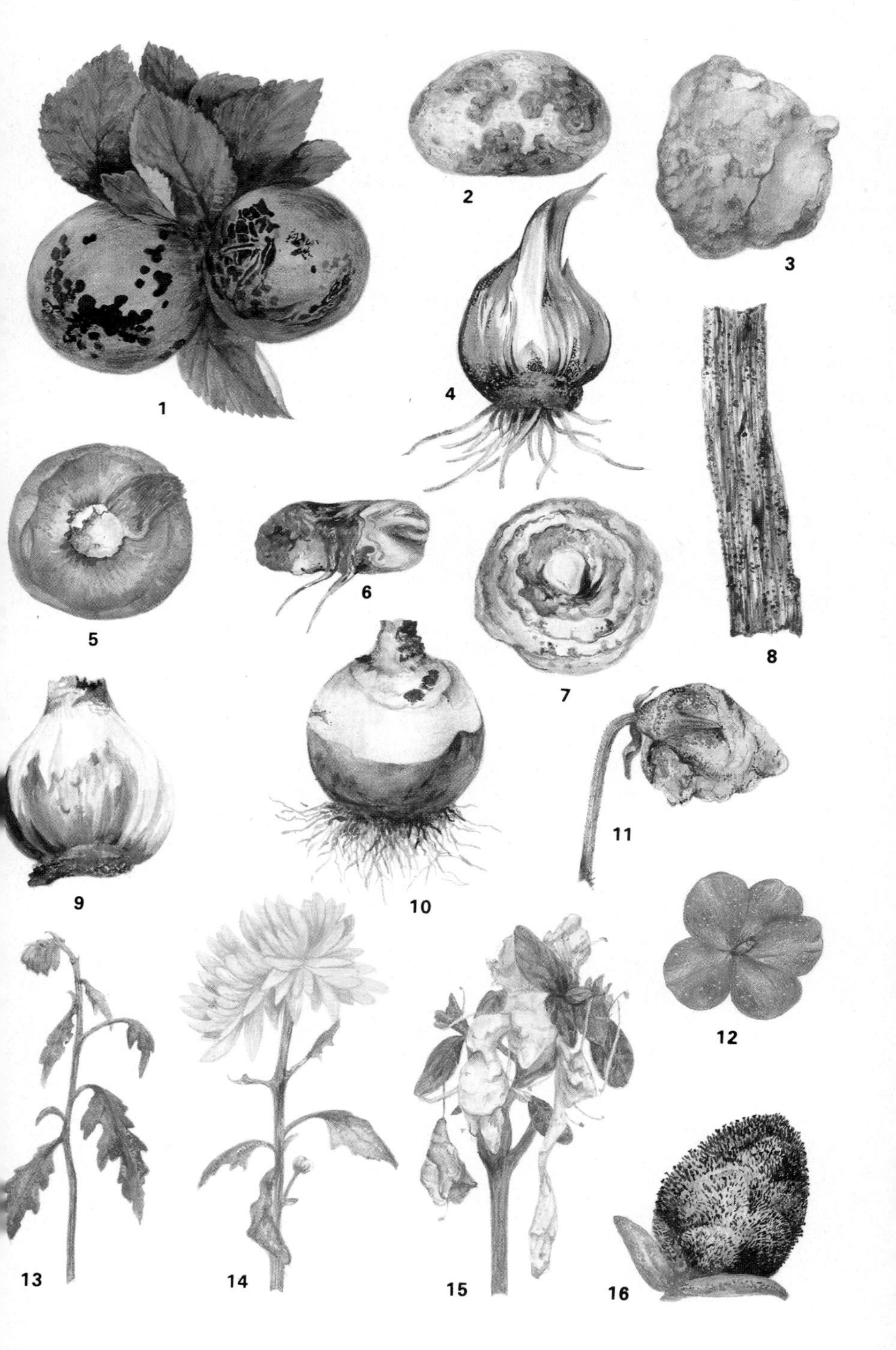
1
2
3
4
5
6
7
8
9
10
11
12
13
14
15
16

PLATE 14 Fruit and Vegetable Rots

Bacterial Soft Rot *Erwinia carotovora* 234
1. Soft, slimy decay spreading down from neck into carrot root.
2. Slimy outer leaves of Brussels sprout buttons.

Violet Root Rot *Helicobasidium purpureum* 241
3. Carrot root enmeshed by deep purple mycelium.

Brown Rot *Sclerotinia fructigena* 235
4. Decay spreading from diseased to healthy apple fruit.
5. Small canker bearing conidial pustules on affected apple shoot.

Blue Mould Rot *Penicillium* sp. 231/8
6. Affected apple fruit in store.

Bitter Rot *Pezicula malicorticis* 234
7. Depressed lesion developed on apple in store.

Onion Neck Rot *Botrytis allii* 238
8. Greyish mould growth around the softened neck in store.

Onion White Rot *Sclerotium cepivorum* 245
9. Decayed roots, softening at bulb base, and small black sclerotia over bulb surface of salad onion.

Potato Dry Rot *Fusarium* sp. 239
10. Shrinkage and concentric wrinkling of tuber with fluffy mould growth.

Potato Gangrene *Phoma* sp. 240
11. 'Thumb-print' lesions on tuber.

Potato Pink Rot *Phytophthora erythroseptica* 240
12. Section through affected tuber as seen about half an hour after cutting; the pink later darkens to black.

Grey Mould *Botrytis cinerea* 236
13. Raspberries.
14. Grapes.
15. Broad bean, with decay beginning characteristically at one end of the pod.

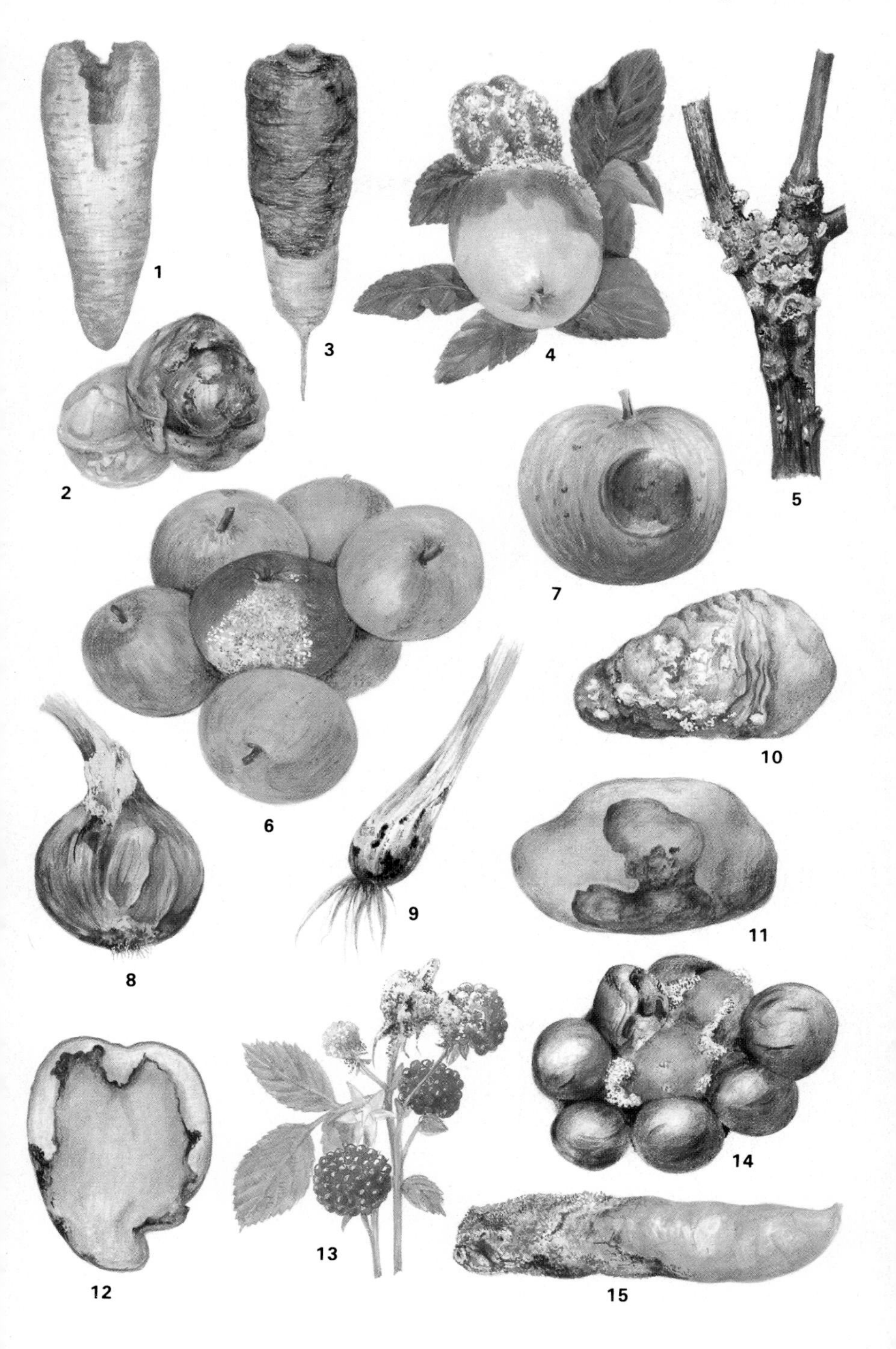
1
2
3
4
5
6
7
8
9
10
11
12
13
14
15

PLATE 15

Root and Foot Rots (herbaceous plants), Tree and Shrub Rots, Stem and Leaf Rots (herbaceous plants)

Damping-off *Pythium* sp. 243

1. Affected seedbox with circular patch of dead and dying seedlings.

Wirestem *Rhizoctonia solani* 243

2. Young cabbage plant with pinched and wiry stem.

Sclerotinia Disease *Sclerotinia sclerotiorum* 247

3. Fluffy white mould at base of celery crown.

Strawberry Red Core *Phytophthora fragariae* 248

4. Plant with stunted central leaves and roots that have been split open to reveal the dark red core.

Potato Black Leg *Erwinia carotovora* var. *atroseptica* 246

5. Blackened and slimy base to affected stem.
6. Tuber rotting in store.

Honey Fungus *Armillaria mellea* 249

7. Toadstools at base of dead apple stump.

Birch Polypore *Piptoporus betulinus* 248

8. Bracket-like fructification, typical of many wood-rotting fungi.

Lettuce Grey Mould *Botrytis cinerea* 252

9. Severence of rotted stem as the plant is disturbed.

Paeony Grey Mould Blight *Botrytis* spp. 254

10. Discolouration and mould growth at shoot base.

Potato Blight *Phytophthora infestans* 254

11. Dark areas of decay on foliage with mould developing on undersides in damp conditions.
12. Surface lesions on tuber.
13. Discolouration of internal tuber tissues.

Tomato Leaf Mould *Fulvia fulva* 256

14. Mould growth on undersides of leaves.

Tulip Fire *Botrytis tulipae* 257

15. Distorted leaf bearing mould growth in damp conditions.
16. Small sclerotia on remains of flower stalk base.

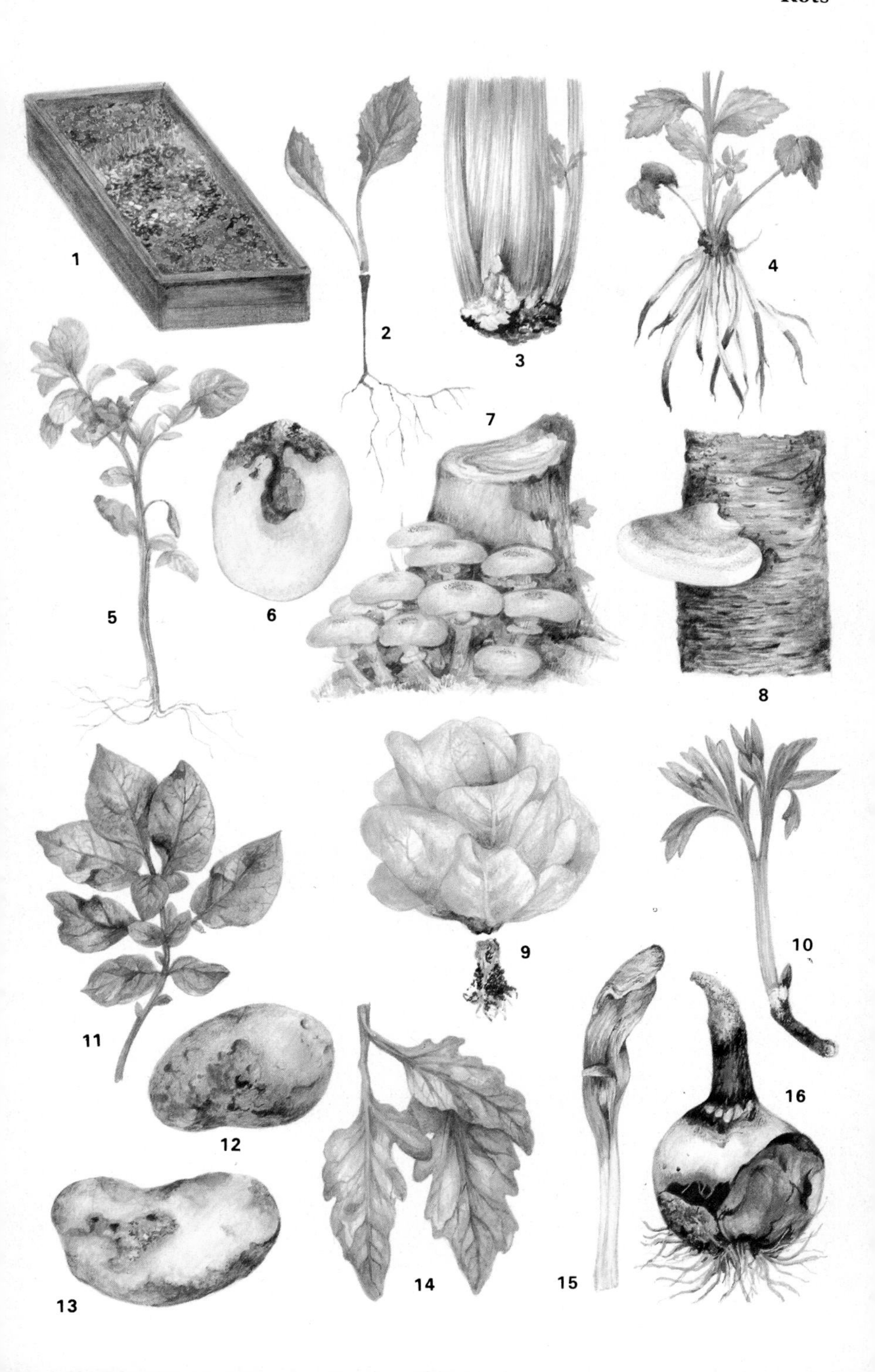
1
2
3
4
5
6
7
8
9
10
11
12
13
14
15
16

PLATE 16 **Spots**

Acer Tar Spot *Rhytisma acerinum* 260

1. Bitumen-like blobs on sycamore leaf.

Antirrhinum Leaf Spot *Phyllosticta antirrhini* 260

2. Early symptoms before individual spots merge.

Bean Anthracnose *Colletotrichum lindemuthianum* 260

3. Affected pod.

Bean Halo Blight *Pseudomonas phaseolicola* 261

4. Leaf bearing spots with characteristic yellow halos.
5. Greasy spots on pod.

Blackberry Purple Blotch *Septocyta ramealis* 262

6. Cane lesions; often confused with those of cane spot disease.

Brassica Ring Spot *Mycosphaerella brassicicola* 263

7. Cabbage leaf.
8. Brussels sprout buttons.

Celery Leaf Spot *Septoria apiicola* 263

9. Early symptoms; the spots may later fuse to affect large areas of leaf.

Currant Leaf Spot *Pseudopeziza ribis* 265

10. Blackcurrant leaf; symptoms often more severe on redcurrants.

Dianthus Ring Spot *Mycosphaerella dianthi* 265

11. Symptoms on carnation; similar effects are caused by a different strain of the fungus on sweet williams.

Helleborus Leaf Spot *Coniothyrium hellebori* 265

12. Symptoms on *H. corsicus*, not usually affected as severely as *H. niger*.

Horse Chestnut Leaf Blotch *Guignardia aesculi* 266

13. Lesions, commonly confused with normal autumnal necrosis.

1
2
3
4
5
6
7
8
9
10
11
12
13

PLATE 17 Spots

Iris Leaf Spot *Mycosphaerella macrospora* 266

1. & 2. Leaf symptoms of differing intensity.

Narcissus Leaf Scorch *Stagonospora curtisii* 267

3. Early leaf-tip symptoms.

Pea Leaf and Pod Spot 268

4. Pod lesions formed by *Ascochyta pisi.*
5. Leaf lesions formed by *Ascochyta pisi.*
6. Leaf lesions formed by *Mycosphaerella pinodes.*

Potato Silver Scurf *Helminthosporium solani* 268

7. Moderate tuber symptoms.
8. Severe tuber symptoms.

Potato Skin Spot *Polyscytalum pustulans* 268

9. Moderate tuber symptoms; sprout tips are often killed.

Raspberry Cane and Leaf Spot *Elsinoë veneta* 269

10. Moderate cane symptoms; leaves are often much more severely spotted.

Rhododendron Leaf Spots 269

11. & 12. Two of several common types of leaf lesion.

Rose Black Spot *Diplocarpon rosae* 270

13. Leaf lesions at the stage shortly before the leaves are likely to drop.

Sooty Blotch *Gloeodes pomigena* 271

14. Apple.

Strawberry Leaf Blotch *Gnomonia fragariae* 271

15. Typical leaf lesions which are commonly associated with a fruit rot.

Strawberry Leaf Spot *Mycosphaerella fragariae* 272

16. Leaf symptoms which arise in the absence of a fruit rot.

Tomato Ghost Spot *Botrytis cinerea* 272

17. Fruit spots which are common late in the season in cool glasshouses and may lead to grey mould rot.

Walnut Leaf Blotch *Gnomonia leptostyla* 273

18. Leaf lesions.
19. Green nut damage.

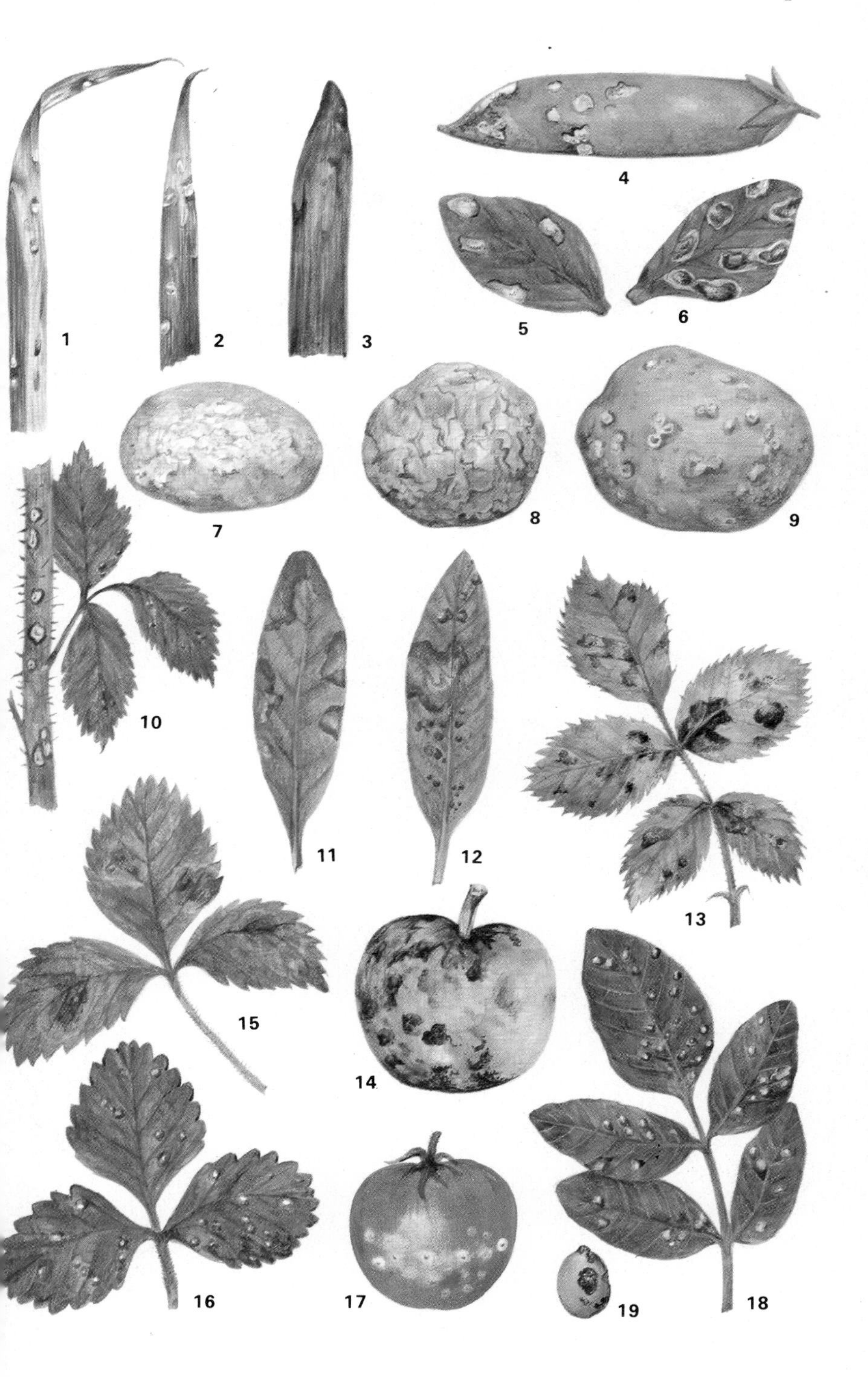
1
2
3
4
5
6
7
8
9
10
11
12
13
14
15
16
17
18
19

PLATE 18 Miscellaneous Non-pathogenic Conditions

Slime Moulds 273

1. Plasmodium of *Fuligo septica* on tree stump.
2. Sporocarps of *Physarum* on dead grass stem.

Lichens 273

3. Young growth of leafy lichens on spruce shoot.
4. Old and prolific mixed growth of several leafy lichens on moribund branch.

Lichen and Alga 273–4

5. Old tree trunk with covering of crustose lichen and green alga.

Harmful Flowering Plants 274–6

6. Mistletoe (*Viscum album*) on black poplar in winter.
7. Flowering spike of broomrape (*Orobanche*).
8. Dodder (*Cuscuta*); flowering shoots parasitising gorse.
9. Ivy (*Hedera helix*) smothering a hedgerow ash tree.
10. Honeysuckle (*Lonicera periclymenum*); strangled stem of beech sapling.

Root Nodules 276

11. Stem base and roots of broad bean showing nodulation.

Mycorrhiza 276

12. Toadstools of *Boletus*, one of the fungi which appears beneath affected trees.
13. Left: beech rootlet growing in poor soil without mycorrhiza; right: with enveloping mycorrhizal mycelium.

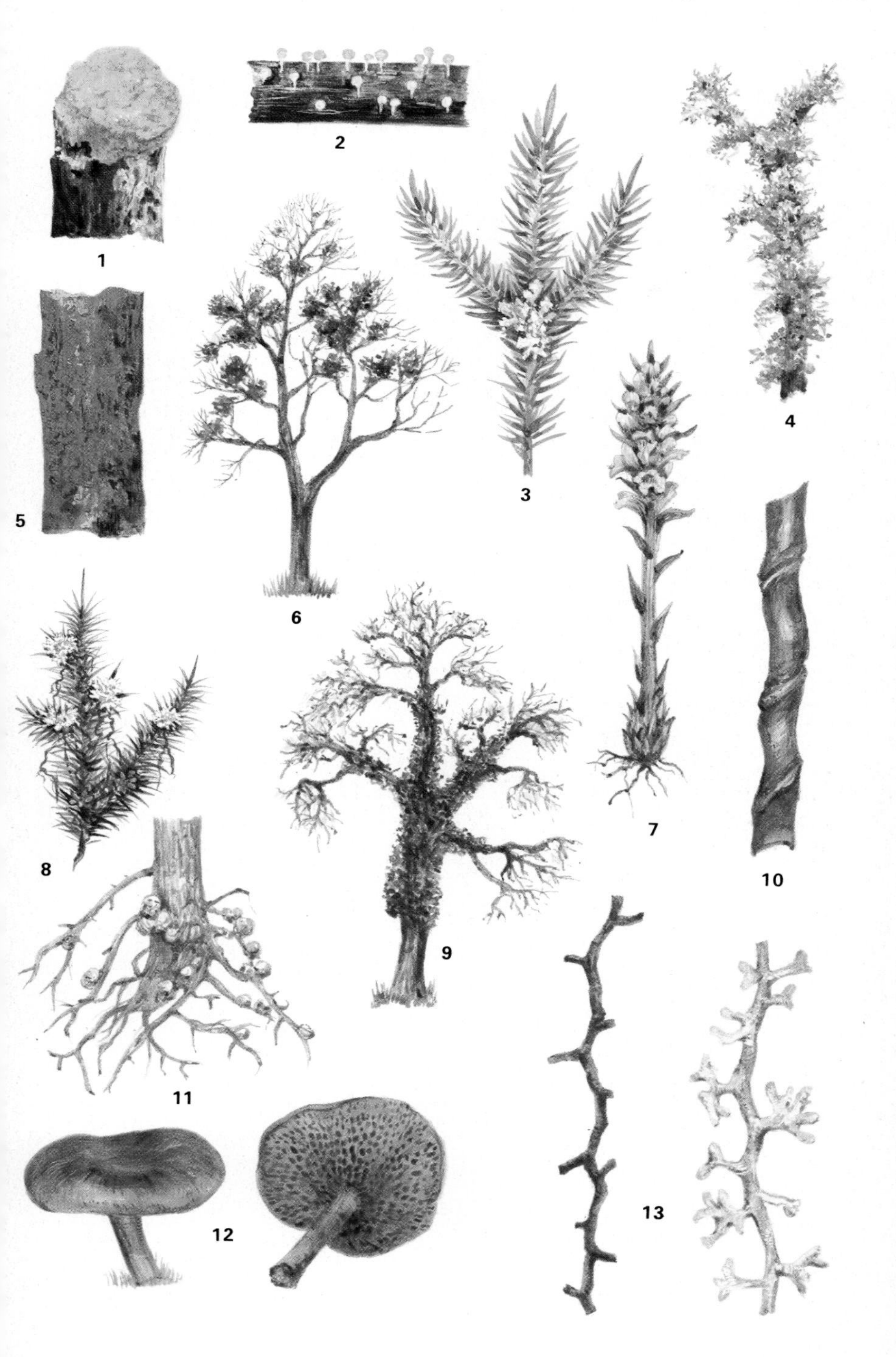
1
2
3
4
5
6
7
8
9
10
11
12
13

PLATE 19 Viruses and Virus-like Organisms

Refer to pp. 277–82 for general types of symptom.

Mosaics and Mottles

1. Abutilon mosaic.
2. Cucumber mosaic.
3. Raspberry mosaic.

Line Patterns and Ringspots

4. Apple mosaic.
5. Rose mosaic.
6. Chaenomeles (apple mosaic virus).

Vein Yellowing

7. Forsythia (arabis mosaic virus).

Vein Banding and Yellowing

8. Cauliflower mosaic.
9. Narcissus yellow stripe.

Necrotic Spots

10. Cabbage black ring spot (turnip mosaic virus).
11. Apple star-crack.

Enations

12. Pea enation.

Leaf Roll

13. Potato leaf roll.

1
2
3
4
5
6
7
8
9
10
11
12
13

PLATE 20 Viruses and Virus-like Organisms

Refer to pp. 277–82 for general types of symptom.

Flower-breaking

1. Wallflower (turnip mosaic virus).
2. Tulip.

Stunting

3. Rubus stunt (raspberry).
4. Apple rubbery wood.

Leaf Crinkling

5. Lettuce big vein.

Leaf Narrowing

6. Tomato mosaic (fern-leaf) (tobacco mosaic virus).

Fruit Discolouration

7. Plum pox; symptoms on cultivar 'Victoria'.

Fruit Malformation

8. Pear stony pit.

Tuber Discolouration

9. Potato spraing; tuber in section (tobacco rattle virus).

Yellowing

10. Strawberry yellow edge; normal and affected leaf.

Grassiness.

11. Narcissus.

Green Flowers

12. Chrysanthemum.
13. Strawberry.

1
2
3
4
5
6
7
8
9
10
11
12
13

PLATE 21 Mineral Nutrient Deficiencies

Nitrogen 284

1. Cabbage.
2. Potato.
3. Runner bean.
4. Apple.

Phosphorus 285

5. Celery.
6. Apple.
7. Carrot.
8. Broad bean.

Potassium 285

9. Potato.
10. Apple.
11. Raspberry.
12. Cauliflower.

Iron 288

13. Azalea.
14. Blackcurrant.
15. Cherry.
16. Strawberry.

1
2
3
4
5
6
7
8
9
10
11
12
3
14
15
16

PLATE 22 Mineral Nutrient Deficiencies

Magnesium 287

1. Potato.
2. Swede.
3. Lettuce.
4. Sweet corn.

Manganese 289

5. Potato.
6. Beetroot.
7. Blackcurrant.
8. Pea, split in half; marsh spot

Boron 289

9. Swede.
10. Cauliflower.
11. Parsnip.

Molybdenum 290

12. Cauliflower.

Calcium 286

13. Tomato; blossom-end rot.
14. Apple; internal bitter-pit.
15. Lettuce.
16. Brussels sprout, split in half to show internal browning.

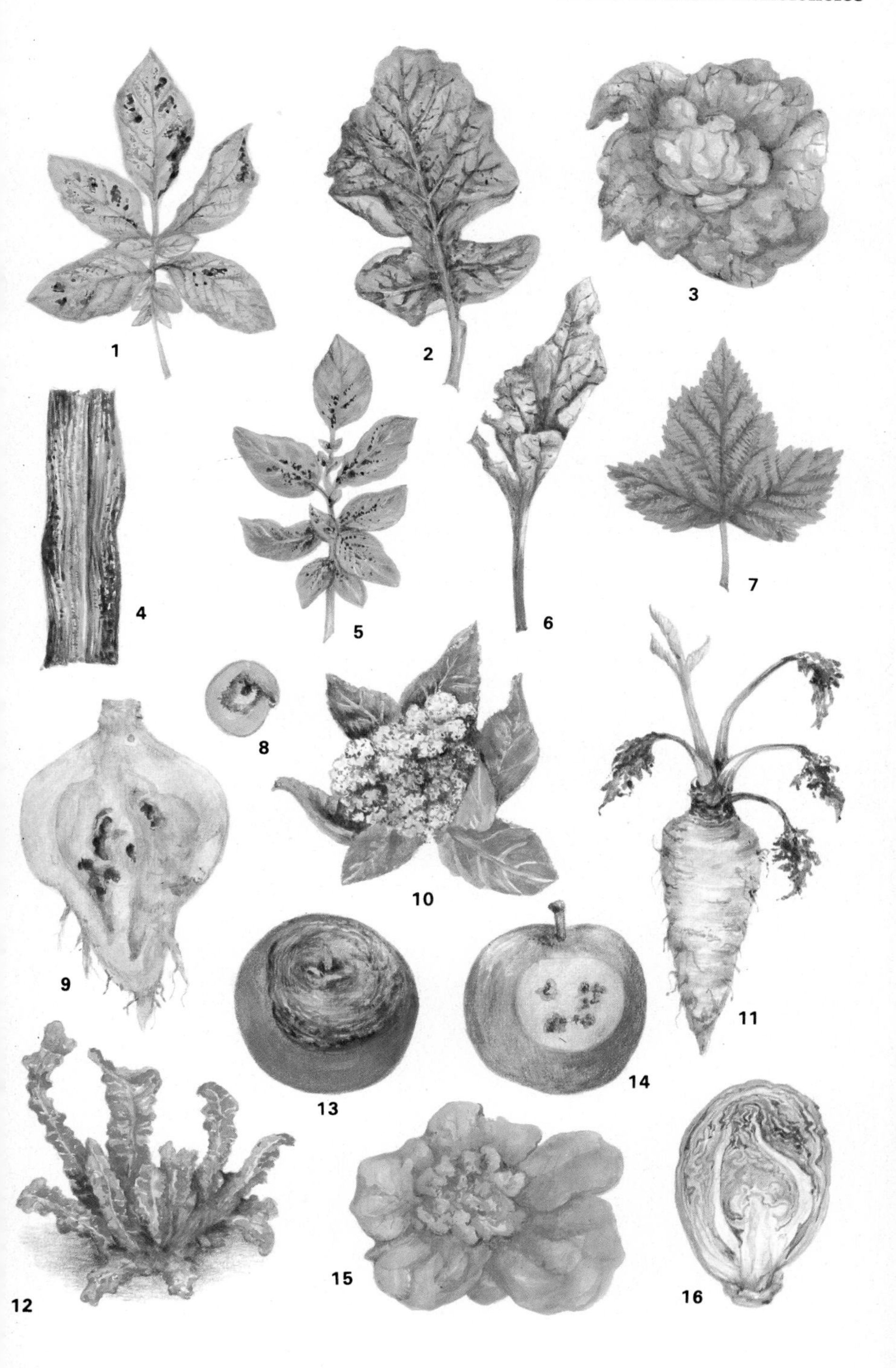
1
2
3
4
5
6
7
8
9
10
11
12
13
14
15
16

PLATE 23 Non-nutritional Disorders

Disturbed Growth 297

1. Bolting by lettuce plant after prolonged drought stress.
2. Oedema on tomato stem.
3. Splitting of tomato fruit.
4. Splitting of carrot root.

Drought 291

5. Pot plant wilting through water shortage.
6. Dry set of tomato fruit resulting from dry air at pollination time.
7. Drought-induced lesions on fuchsia leaf.

Frost 292

8. Spring frost scorching of young beech leaves.
9. Chilling injury in internal potato tuber tissues.

Genetic Abnormalities 298

10. Severe hybridisation nodule development on swede.
11. Silvering of tomato foliage.

Mechanical Injury 298

12. Vandalised beech tree.
13. Root cramping arising from incorrect planting of a shrub.
14. Constriction of stem brought about by over-tight support.

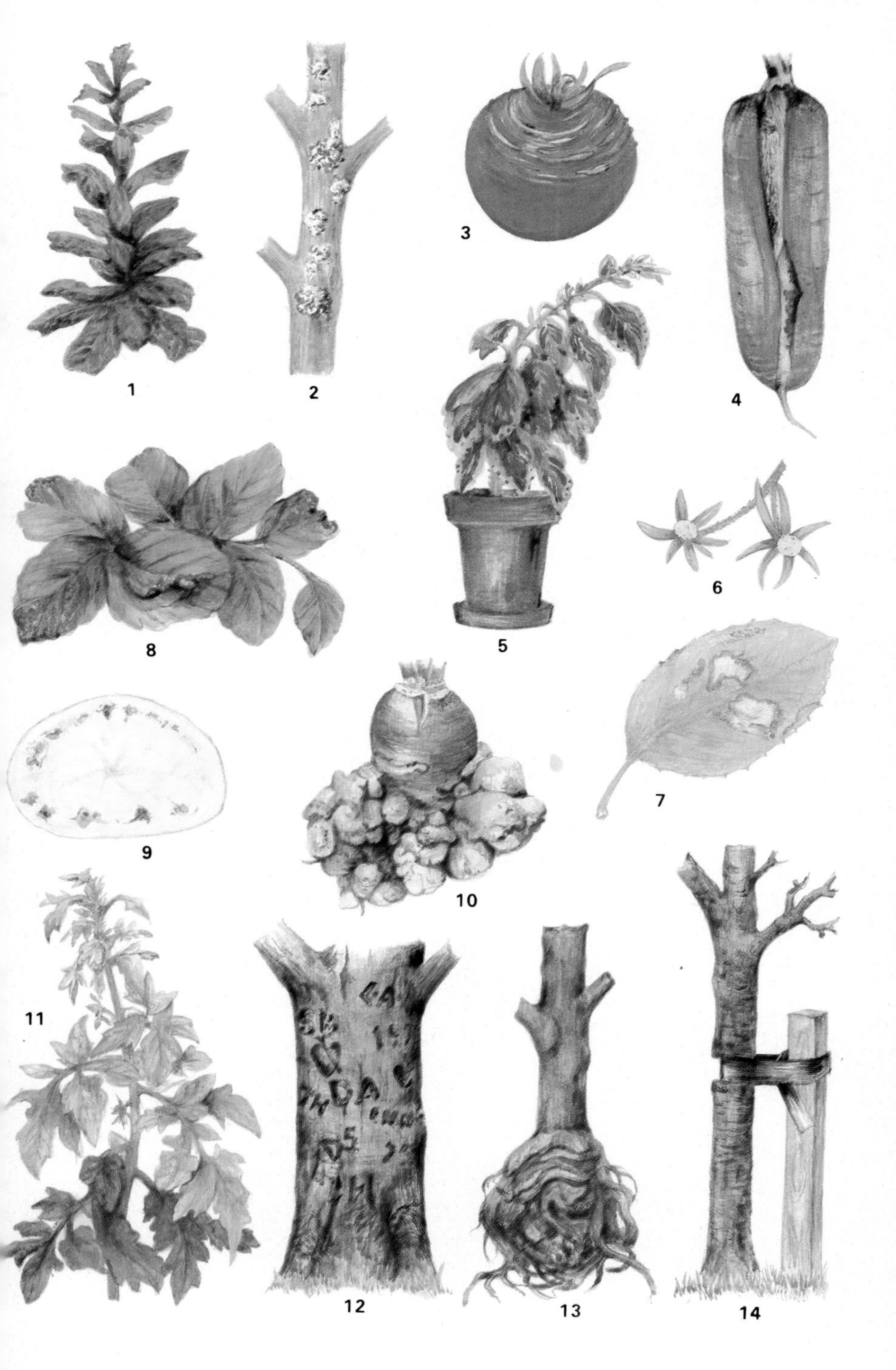
1
2
3
4
5
6
7
8
9
10
11
12
13
14

PLATE 24 Non-nutritional Disorders

High Temperature 294

1. Heat scorch on tomato fruit.

Light 294

2. Greening of potato tuber flesh.

Lightning 295

3. Shattered lesion down one side of tree trunk.

Pollution 301

4. Hormone herbicide damage on tomato.

Miscellaneous Pollutant Effects 299–301

5. Plum.
6. Rose.
7. Marrow.
8. Grapevine.

Cold Water and Light 294–5

9. Ring patterns on saintpaulia following watering with cold water and exposure to bright light and warmth.

Wind 296

10. Wind pruning of coastal larch.
11. Wind-break of mature cedar following winter gale.
12. Wind-scorching and salt spray damage on coastal holly.

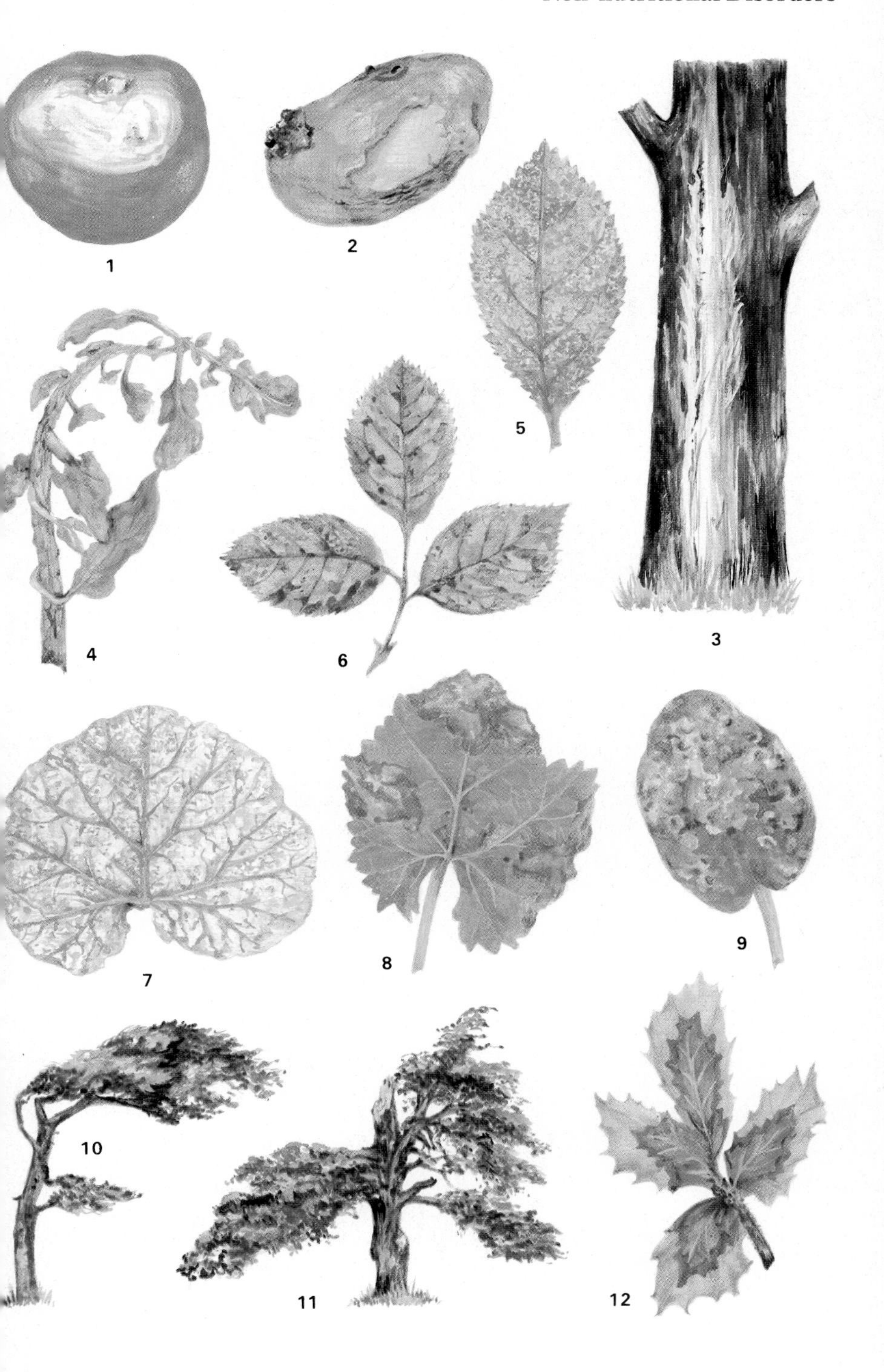
1
2
3
4
5
6
7
8
9
10
11
12

ANTS

All ants are social insects (Hymenoptera: Formicidae) and they live in nests of varied types and sizes which generally contain large numbers of wingless workers. Winged males and females are produced at certain times, usually during warm weather in summer, and these flying ants swarm in mating flights. Fertilised females (queens) then shed their wings and either enter existing nests or establish new nests. Individual queen ants live for several years and maintain colonies by continuing to lay eggs throughout this long reproductive period. The detailed biology of ants is very complex and interesting. Some species are carnivorous and some harvest pieces of plants on which fungi are cultured to create fungus gardens inside their nests. Some colonies keep slave ants, as well as maintaining various inquilines which inhabit their nests, and many species tend aphids, scale insects and mealybugs, feeding on the honeydew that they produce and affording them some protection from parasites and predators. The most troublesome species in gardens are the common black ant, *Lasius niger* and the mound ant *Lasius flavus*. In glasshouses and houses various introduced species occur, especially Pharaoh's ant, *Monomorium pharaonis* and the Argentine ant, *Iridomyrmex humilis*.

Symptoms. Symptoms vary according to the situation and the species of ant concerned. Occasionally ants eat small pieces of tissue out of leaves but this type of injury is seldom important, except on choice pot plants in glasshouses. More damage is caused, both in glasshouses and outdoors, by ants collected seeds from seed boxes, pots and open ground and carrying them away to their nests where they are used as food for larvae. Seeds with a high oil content are often selected and those of buddleias, meconopsis, rhododendrons and violas are often taken. Plants may also be damaged by ants tunnelling in soil under their roots and in dry borders and rock gardens on light soils root function may be seriously affected so that plants wilt and die. The mound ant causes similar trouble in lawns and rough grass by throwing up heaps of soil over nests. These mounds are often as large as mole hills and can interfere with mowing. Much indirect damage is also caused by ants tending aphids, mealybugs and scales since this can encourage the spread of these pests and the maintenance of healthy colonies.

Biology. Nests are usually constructed in soil, under paving stones, in walls, woodwork and other structures, and even in flower pots. Each nest contains at least one egg-laying female (the queen) and the nest is serviced by many wingless worker ants which construct galleries, tend eggs, rear larvae, forage for food and protect nests from invaders. Nests persist for many years and each year they produce mating flights of winged males and females which extend infestations.

Treatment. Direct treatment of nests is the best method of control as it eradicates these pests at source. If nests are accessible, treat them by watering a spray-strength solution of HCH or trichlorphon into the entrances, using sufficient solution to permeate the whole nest. If nests are inaccessible they may be poisoned indirectly by putting down baits or dusts in areas where workers are active. Proprietary ant baits usually consist of sugar or other attractants mixed with a persistent insecticide. These are applied to the soil or are placed in shallow lids or other containers to which ants have easy access. Workers then carry particles of poisoned bait back to the nest. Baits should be renewed regularly so long as ants continue to visit them and it may take weeks of baiting before there is any marked reduction of ant populations. Many different baits are available but those that contain trichlorphon or propoxur generally give best results.

WASPS

(Plate 7)

Wasps are relatively large insects (Hymenoptera: Vespidae), up to 20 mm long, and with conspicuous yellow and black markings (Pl. 7). Six species of wasp and the similar, but larger hornet, *Vespa crabro*, occur in Britain and northern Europe.

Symptoms. Adult wasps are usually most troublesome in summer and early autumn when they feed on ripening fruits, especially apples, pears, plums and grapes, often extending damage caused by other pests, such as birds, and by diseases and disorders (Pl. 7). Large cavities are eaten in fruits and people are sometimes stung by wasps when picking fruit. These pests may also damage plants such as dahlias by scraping the stems.

Biology. The two commonest species, the common wasp (*Paravespula vulgaris*) and the German wasp (*Paravespula germanica*), usually construct nests in cavities in soil, walls and buildings but some of the other species make nests amongst twigs and branches of shrubs and trees. Nests are constructed from a paper-like material which the wasps make by chewing small pieces of wood and mixing them with saliva. Fertilised female wasps (queens) overwinter under loose bark on trees, in garden sheds, in outbuildings and in similar dry, protected situations and establish new nests in the spring. Initially the nests are small, with only a few open hexagonal cells in which the queen rears the first brood of larvae, feeding them on a high-protein diet of caterpillars and other insects. When the first worker wasps of the new season emerge in early June they take over nest-building and feeding functions from the queen and by mid-summer the nests are greatly enlarged, often containing thousands of workers. At this stage males and females are reared and the young fertilised queens seek suitable sites in which they can overwinter. Nests continue to thrive until the first hard frosts kill them out in late October and early November.

Treatment. Wasp populations fluctuate considerably from year to year and in years when conditions favour them they may be so numerous that it may be almost impossible to protect all susceptible plants from attack. Nest destruction may have some effect but workers may often fly into gardens from nests situated some distance away. Nests found within gardens may be destroyed by applying carbaryl or derris dust to the entrances at night when most of the workers are inside. It is best to wait until at least an hour after sunset before applying this treatment. Wasps leaving and entering treated nests during the next few days will be contaminated by the dust and the nests may eventually die out. Wasps visiting fruit trees can be trapped in great numbers by baiting jam jars or other containers with a little jam and then partly filling them with water and detergent. Prevention of bird damage to fruit (p. 182) will also reduce wasp damage by limiting the initial injuries that the wasps find so attractive. Wasp stings should be treated with a mild antiseptic and with cold compresses and anti-histamine creams. Individuals who are hypersensitive to stings should seek medical advice.

LEAF-CUTTER BEES

(Plate 7)

These solitary bees are closely related to honey bees but do not live in communal nests. *Megachile centuncularis* is the commonest species in gardens but other species also occur.

Symptoms. Neat semi-circular to oblong pieces are cut out of leaves of roses (Pl. 7), laburnums, lilacs, privet, rhododendrons and other ornamental plants during the summer by small, hairy bees which are about 10 mm long. Damage to plants is seldom severe but the sudden appearance of the unusual symptoms may cause concern.

Biology. Female bees cut pieces out of leaves with their mandibles and use them to construct series of thimble-like cells in cavities in decaying wood, old brickwork, light soils, or even in flower pots. The female bee provisions each cell with a mixture of pollen and honey before laying a single egg and then sealing the top with a neat, circular piece of leaf. About six cells are built end to end in each series. Larvae feed within the cells during the summer and then overwinter in them. They pupate in the following spring and adults emerge in June, eating their way out of the cells in an orderly fashion so that adults developing from the first eggs laid are the last to leave.

Treatment. Prevention of damage is difficult and is seldom necessary since plants are not normally seriously affected. If necessary, plants can be protected by spraying or dusting with HCH and nests can be located and destroyed by following the bees when they are working.

BEETLES

(Plate 8)

Beetles (Coleoptera), comprise the largest order of insects with more than 250,000 species known and at least 5,000 of these recorded from Britain and northern Europe. The fore-wings of adult beetles are characteristically modified to form a pair of hard wing-covers (elytra) which hinge over the abdomen and over the membranous hind-wings. The head is generally relatively small but well developed, with prominent eyes, a pair of antennae, and strong mouthparts capable of biting and chewing hard or soft food. Size of pest species varies from very small (1 mm long) to large (3 cm long). Most species are black, grey or brown but some are brightly coloured. Reproduction is normally sexual but a few species are parthenogenetic. Females lay eggs on or near food, depositing them singly or in clusters. Larvae vary considerably in structure from active, predaceous types with three pairs of well developed thoracic legs and hard, pigmented bodies to relatively inactive, colourless, legless, maggot-like larvae with soft bodies. Most larvae have a well developed head with biting mouthparts. Both adults and larvae feed and their feeding habits are varied.

Predators (ground beetles, ladybirds) feed on insects and other small invertebrates and may therefore be beneficial in gardens. Some groups are aquatic (dytiscid and whirligig beetles); others feed mainly on dead wood (furniture, longhorn and death-watch beetles) and many species feed on living plant tissues and are pests of cultivated and wild plants. The most important pests of garden plants are dealt with in detail in the following section.

CHAFERS

Pl. 8

The larvae of at least five different species of chafer beetle (Scarabaeidae), also known as white grubs, live in soil, usually in old grassland and overgrown gardens, and both adults and larvae attack cultivated plants. The main species found in gardens are the cockchafer, *Melolontha melolontha* and the garden chafer, *Phyllopertha horticola.*

Symptoms. Soft-bodied, white, C-shaped larvae, up to 40 mm long, with well developed brown head and three pairs of thoracic legs (Pl. 8) feed on roots, corms, tubers and stems of fruits, vegetables and ornamental plants and also attack lawns. Raspberries, strawberries, potatoes, lettuces, young trees and various herbaceous ornamentals are especially susceptible. Affected plants wilt and die when the main root is severed. Similar symptoms are produced by vine weevil larvae (p. 170) but they can be distinguished by the absence of any thoracic legs. Adult chafers also cause some damage by feeding on leaves, buds, flowers and fruits of apples, roses and some other plants. When lawns are attacked by larvae, brown, withered areas appear during dry weather and chafer larvae can usually be found by lifting affected turf. Similar symptoms are produced by leatherjackets (p. 147) and other factors.

Biology. The biology of the five main chafers found in gardens is basically the same. Females lay eggs in soil near plants during summer and larvae hatch a few weeks later. They then feed underground on roots, corms and tubers or in rotting wood until they are ready to pupate, which is generally within a year of hatching for the smaller species but may take up to five years for the larger cockchafer. Before pupating, larvae construct pupal cells in the soil at depths down to about 60 cm. These cells may be exposed during winter digging and, if opened carefully, will be found to contain a chafer larva, a pupa, or even a fully grown adult ready to emerge in the following spring.

Treatment. Chafer larvae are mainly pests in newly-cultivated land and are soon eliminated by thorough cultivation and good weed control. Valuable plants may be protected by working a relatively persistent insecticide, such as HCH, bromophos or diazinon, into the soil around the roots, preferably before planting. Infested lawns benefit from heavy rolling in late spring to kill pupae and emerging adults and, if necessary, HCH dusts or sprays may be used.

WIREWORMS

Pl. 8

Wireworms are the larvae of various species of click beetle (Elateridae), which are well known for their ability to flick themselves into the air when lying on their backs. This acrobatic click jump puts them back onto their legs after a fall. The larvae mainly develop in grassland but are occasionally troublesome in gardens, the main species being the garden click beetle, *Athous haemorrhoidalis*, and the common click beetle, *Agriotes lineatus*.

Symptoms. Elongate, cylindrical, white to golden yellow, tough-skinned larvae, up to 25 mm long, with three pairs of thoracic legs (Pl. 8) live in soil and feed on roots, corms, tubers and stems of many plants. Larvae tunnel into mature potato tubers, leaving small holes, 2–3 mm across, which may be enlarged later by slugs and millepedes. Wireworms also attack strawberries, cabbages and other brassicas, beans, beetroot, carrots, lettuces, onions, tomatoes and many ornamental plants, especially anemones, carnations, chrysanthemums, dahlias, gladioli and primulas. Most damage is done in spring but wireworms are present throughout the year and may attack plants at other times.

Biology. Female click beetles lay eggs in soil during June/July and larvae hatch about a month later. They feed for up to five years, with the main periods of active feeding in March–May and September/October. Fully fed larvae construct oval pupal cells about 20 cm below the soil surface before pupating. Adults emerge from pupae in late summer and early autumn but remain within the cells until the following summer when they come to the surface, mate, and continue the cycle.

Treatment. Thorough cultivation and good weed control should soon eliminate wireworms from newly cultivated ground and, if susceptible plants need temporary protection, the insecticides recommended for chafer control should be adequate (see above). Compost heaps and heaps of turf stacked to produce loam are sometimes infested by wireworms and should be checked before use. If many wireworms are seen to be present, the compost or loam should be exposed to weather and birds to reduce the numbers of wireworms before use. Main-crop potatoes should always be lifted early when wireworms are likely to be present since damage will be greatest when they are left too long in the soil after maturing.

STRAWBERRY BEETLES

Most ground beetles (Carabidae) are predators on insects and other small invertebrates but a few species, notably the strawberry seed beetle, *Harpalus rufipes*, and the strawberry ground beetles, *Pterostichus madidus* and *Pterostichus melanarius*, are omnivorous or specialist seed-feeders and may damage ripening strawberry fruits.

Symptoms. Black beetles, up to 20 mm long feed on ripening strawberries, removing seeds and eating out pieces of flesh. Similar damage is caused by birds and slugs but when strawberry beetles are the cause they can usually be found by looking under the straw beneath damaged fruit trusses.

Biology. Adults and larvae overwinter in burrows in soil, in accumulations of plant debris, and in overgrown areas of gardens. They become active in spring and females lay eggs in the soil from May onwards.

Treatment. Clean up strawberry beds in autumn by removing old straw and other plant debris and also clear adjacent areas of rough grass or other overgrowth that could harbour beetles. In early spring, reduce beetle populations by sinking jam jars level with the soil surface to act as pit-fall traps. Examine these regularly and kill any strawberry beetles found in them. Methiocarb pellets, used to control slugs, may have some effect on strawberry beetles but should not be used during the harvesting period since ripe fruit could easily be contaminated.

RASPBERRY BEETLE *Byturus tomentosus* Pl. 8

Symptoms. Yellow-brown larvae, up to 8 mm long, with brown heads and brown dorsal markings, feed in and on ripening fruits of raspberries (Pl. 8), loganberries and blackberries, causing direct damage by feeding on the fruits and reducing the palatability of picked fruit by their presence, which is often first noticed when the fruit is being prepared for eating. Adult raspberry beetles may also cause some damage by feeding on buds and flowers earlier in the season.

Biology. The small, inconspicuous adult beetles, which are up to 4 mm long, overwinter in small earthern cells in the soil near their host plants and emerge from hibernation in April/May. They then fly to hawthorn, apple blossom and other flowers to feed and move onto raspberry, loganberry and blackberry blossom as it opens later in the season. In June/July females lay eggs on the stamens and other floral parts of these host plants. Larvae hatch about two weeks later and feed for about a month by tunnelling into the developing fruits. Fully fed larvae pupate in earthern cells in the soil and adults emerge in the autumn but remain within the pupal cells until the following spring.

Treatment. This is a common species and most cultivated raspberries, loganberries and blackberries are likely to be attacked by adults flying into gardens from adjacent hedgerows and uncultivated areas where wild blackberries and raspberries thrive. Under these circumstances, only chemical control can effectively check this pest and correct timing is critical since the larvae must be killed before they tunnel into the fruit. Fenitrothion is probably the best insecticide currently available for use in gardens, with malathion or derris as possible alternatives. One or other of these insecticides should be applied as a spray or dust as soon as flowering has finished. Reduce risks to pollinating insects by applying insecticides in the late evening and do not harvest fruit until at least a week after application of insecticides.

FLEA BEETLES Pl. 8

Many species of flea beetle (Chrysomelidae) attack cultivated plants. The main species in gardens are the small striped flea beetle, *Phyllotreta undulata*, the large striped flea beetle, *Phyllotreta nemorum*, the turnip flea beetles, *Phyllotreta atra* and *Phyllotreta cruciferae*, and *Phyllotreta nigripes*. These *Phyllotreta* species are mainly pests of brassicas and other cruciferous plants but other garden plants may be attacked by similar species belonging to other genera. Some species transmit radish mosaic and turnip crinkle viruses (p. 277).

Symptoms. Adult flea beetles attack germinating brassica and other seedlings as they first emerge from the soil in spring. Small holes and pits, 2–3 mm across, are eaten out of the young leaves (Pl. 8) and sustained attacks check growth and may kill plants. Most damage is done in April/May, especially during dry weather, and at this time the small adult beetles, up to 3 mm long, may be seen jumping like fleas on and near affected plants. Larvae also damage some plants by feeding on roots or mining leaves. Radishes, swedes, turnips, cabbages, kale, beet and also various ornamentals, especially alyssums, anemones, drabas, godetias, irises, nasturtiums (*Tropaeolum*), stocks and wallflowers are especially susceptible.

Biology. Adult flea beetles hibernate in accumulations of plant debris under hedges, in grass tussocks, under loose bark on trees, and in similar situations. They emerge from hibernation in early spring and move onto young plants to feed. Adults may fly for a kilometre or more from their hibernation sites and are especially attracted to brassicas and related plants. Females lay eggs in soil near plants during May/June and larvae feed in leaf mines (large striped flea beetle) or on plant roots (other species). Larvae pupate in the soil and the next generation of adults emerges in August–October. These adults feed for a few weeks and then seek hibernation sites to overwinter.

Treatment. Clear accumulations of plant debris to limit numbers of adults overwintering and protect susceptible young plants in spring by applying a combined insecticide/fungicide seed-dressing to seed before sowing. If necessary, protect plants after germination by applying an insecticidal dust, such as pirimiphos-methyl, derris or HCH, to the young leaves and to the soil around plants. The effects of flea beetle attack may also be reduced by thorough preparation of the soil before sowing, to encourage rapid establishment and healthy growth, and by watering young plants in dry weather.

COLORADO BEETLE *Leptinotarsa decemlineata* **Pl. 8**

This species is native to N. America where it feeds on wild plants that are related to cultivated potatoes. It was accidentally introduced into France about 1921 and has gradually become established throughout most of western Europe. Adults are often found in Britain, mainly on imported horticultural produce, but constant vigilance and strict control measures applied by the Ministry of Agriculture have prevented the establishment of breeding populations here. Any suspected outbreak found in Britain must, by law, be reported immediately to the Ministry of Agriculture.

Symptoms. Conspicuous black and yellow striped adult beetles, up to 12 mm long (Pl. 8) and equally conspicuous bright red larvae feed on leaves of potatoes, tomatoes and related plants, often reducing them to a skeleton of bare stems. Infested plants are characteristically fouled by black excrement produced by the beetles and their larvae. Severe infestations cause substantial or complete loss of crops.

Biology. Adult beetles hibernate in the soil at depths down to about 25 cm. They emerge from hibernation on warm days in spring and early summer and make short flights of a few kilometres in search of potato plants. When they find these or other suitable host plants, they settle to feed on the leaves and each female lays about 500 orange-yellow eggs in small batches on the undersides of the leaves. Eggs hatch about a week later and larvae feed for about a month before going to the soil to pupate. A second generation of adults may lay eggs and produce further larvae in late summer but by the autumn most beetles will have gone to the soil to hibernate.

Treatment. Any infestation discovered in Britain must be reported immediately to the Ministry of Agriculture, which will then take responsibility for investigation and treatment of the affected area. In continental Europe contact insecticides applied to potato plants in June/July may give adequate control.

ASPARAGUS BEETLE *Crioceris asparagi*

Symptoms. Conspicuous adult beetles, up to 6 mm long, with distinctively marked yellow and black wing cases and grey-black, hump-backed larvae feed on leaves and stems of asparagus from May onwards. Persistent attacks defoliate plants, damage stems and may check growth.

Biology. Adults hibernate under stones, in plant debris, in soil, and in similar protected situations. They emerge in May to feed on young asparagus shoots and females lay small batches of brown eggs on the leaves in June. Eggs hatch about a week later and larvae feed for about two weeks before going to the soil to pupate in cocoons. One or two further generations develop during July–October and towards the end of this period adults seek hibernation sites.

Treatment. Limit overwintering populations by clearing up accumulations of plant debris and spray or dust asparagus with a non-persistent insecticide, such as derris or malathion, if beetles or larvae appear in spring. Repeat this treatment later if infestations persist.

WATER-LILY BEETLE *Galerucella nymphaeae* **Pl. 8**

Symptoms. Small, brown, adult beetles, up to 6 mm long, and soft-bodied, brown-black larvae, eat irregular, narrow furrows and small holes in the upper surface of water-lily leaves in spring and summer (Pl. 8). Affected leaves rot and disintegrate.

Biology. Adult beetles hibernate in coarse vegetation and plant debris at the sides of pools. They emerge in May/June and move onto water-lily leaves to feed. Females then lay batches of eggs and the larvae, which hatch about a week later, feed for 2–3 weeks before pupating on the leaves. Two or three further generations develop during the growing season and adults leave the water-lilies in autumn to seek hibernation sites.

Treatment. Insecticides should not be used against this pest if fish are present in pools or if there is any possibility of insecticides contaminating water-courses. In these circumstances the best method is to knock adults and larvae off leaves with a powerful jet of water from a garden hose. Fish will then be able to feed on them in the water and the treatment can be repeated as often as is necessary. If there is no danger to fish, non-persistent insecticides, such as derris, malathion or nicotine, may be used, either as dusts or sprays.

LILY BEETLE *Lilioceris lilii* **Pl. 8**

Symptoms. Conspicuous, scarlet-red adult beetles, up to 6 mm long (Pl. 8) and reddish-yellow, hump-backed larvae, covered with black slime, feed on leaves, stems and seed pods of lilies and also attack fritillarias, nomocharis and polygonatum (Solomon's seal) from May onwards. Both adults and larvae feed voraciously and cause considerable damage when conditions favour them.

Biology. Adult beetles overwinter in plant debris and coarse vegetation and move onto lilies and other host plants in May/June. Females lay

200–300 eggs each on leaves and stems, and larvae, which hatch about a week later, feed for about a month before going to the soil to pupate in earthen cells.
Treatment. Apply a contact insecticide, such as malathion, resmethrin or HCH, as soon as beetles or larvae are seen in the spring and repeat the treatment later if infestations persist.

WILLOW and POPLAR LEAF BEETLES

Various beetles attack the leaves of willows and poplars, causing similar damage. The three commonest are the brassy willow beetle, *Phyllodecta vitellinae*, the blue willow beetle, *Phyllodecta vulgatissima*, and the willow flea beetle, *Chalcoides aurata*.
Symptoms. Small, metallic blue, red or green beetles, up to 5 mm long, and groups of black-spotted larvae feed on leaves of willows and poplars in spring and summer, stripping away the tissues and exposing the leaf veins. Persistent infestations make affected plants look unsightly.
Biology. Adults hibernate under dead bark, in plant debris and in similar situations and move onto willow and poplar leaves in May/June. Females lay small batches of eggs on leaves and larvae, which hatch after about two weeks, feed on the undersides of the leaves in small groups, gradually extending the area of attack. After feeding for 2–3 weeks the larvae pupate in the soil and a second generation of adults appears in August/September.
Treatment. Spray adults and larvae with a contact insectide such as malathion, nicotine or resmethrin, as soon as they are seen on plants.

WEEVILS **Pl. 8**

Weevils belong to a remarkably successful family of beetles (Curculionidae) with more than 50,000 world species. At least 500 of these are recorded from Britain and about 1,000 from northern Europe. They vary in size from small seed weevils, less than 2 mm long, to the large pine weevils, 20–25 mm long. All weevils have a characteristic snout (rostrum) projecting forward from the head, with terminal mouthparts and many have elbowed antennae. The long-nosed weevils have an exceptionally long rostrum, which may exceed the length of the rest of the body, but in most weevils it is much shorter. Adults and larvae of all species feed either on living or on dead plant tissues and many species are important pests of cultivated plants. Larvae are relatively featureless, with a well-developed head, no thoracic legs, and a soft, white body (Pl. 8). The main pest species are dealt with below but there are many other species that may occur in gardens as minor pests.

APPLE BLOSSOM WEEVIL *Anthonomus pomorum* **Pl. 8**

Symptoms. Apple blossom fails to develop normally in spring. Flowers remain closed, with dead petals attached (Pl. 8), and careful examination of affected flowers may reveal weevil larvae, pupae or adults inside. Similar symptoms are caused by frost (p. 292).
Biology. The small, black to brown adult weevils, up to 4 mm long, hibernate under loose bark and in dead leaves and other accumulations of debris near apple trees. In early spring they crawl up trees and feed on young leaves. Females then lay up to 20 eggs each in flower buds and the

larvae, which hatch after 1–2 weeks, feed on the stamens and other parts of the young flowers and prevent the normal opening of the petals. Usually a single larva develops in each affected flower and, after feeding for a few weeks, the larvae pupate in the flowers, under the dead petals. Adults emerge in June/July and feed on the leaves for about a month before seeking hibernation sites.

Treatment. This pest does not normally cause appreciable damage since it tends to act as a natural thinning agent, reducing the amount of fruit setting. If it is known to be locally important, protect blossom by spraying trees with fenitrothion or HCH just before the flower buds open, to kill female weevils before they lay eggs.

LEAF WEEVILS *Phyllobius* spp.

Small, (5–10 mm long), dark brown to black weevils, densely covered by metallic gold or greenish-bronze scales, feed on leaves of apples and other fruits and on leaves of birch, limes, flowering cherries, crab-apples, poplars and rhododendrons, eating small holes in the leaves and occasionally damaging blossom. The main species are the brown leaf weevil, *Phyllobius oblongus*, the silver-green leaf weevil, *Phyllobius argentatus*, and the common leaf weevil, *Phyllobius pyri*, but some other species also occur in gardens. These weevils are usually seen on plants in May–June. They seldom cause severe damage and can easily be controlled, if necessary, by spraying with a contact insecticide, such as malathion or resmethrin.

TURNIP GALL WEEVIL *Ceutorhynchus pleurostigma* Pl. 8

Symptoms. Characteristic bumpy round galls develop on roots of turnips, cabbages (Pl. 8) and other brassicas. They resemble symptoms of clubroot disease (p. 223) but the galls are hollow and contain weevil larvae. Extensive galling stunts growth and may make turnips unusable.

Biology. The small adult weevils, up to 3 mm long, are active from March onwards. Females lay eggs in holes that they make in the roots of their host plants and as the larvae develop the plant tissues form galls around them. Larvae feed in the galls until the following spring and then leave them to pupate in the soil.

Treatment. Remove and destroy affected roots of old brassica crops in early winter and cultivate the soil thoroughly. Protect spring and early summer sowings of cabbages and turnips by dressing the seed with a combined insecticide/fungicide seed-dressing before sowing. Discard any brassica transplants that show signs of attack.

PEA and BEAN WEEVIL *Sitona lineatus* Pl. 8

This is one of several different species of *Sitona* that feed on cultivated plants. Similar damage is caused by these weevils on roses, lupins, cytisus, sorbus, laburnum and carnations, among others. Some species transmit certain viruses that infect broad beans (p. 277).

Symptoms. Small, semi-circular pieces are eaten out of the edges of pea and broad bean leaves in spring and summer, producing a characteristic scalloped effect (Pl. 8). Small, short-snouted weevils, up to 5 mm long, may be seen on affected plants but often drop off when disturbed.

Biology. Adult weevils overwinter in plant debris and coarse vegetation and move onto peas, beans and related plants in early spring. Females lay eggs in the soil during warm weather and the larvae, which hatch about two weeks later, feed on the root nodules for about a month before pupating in the soil. Adults emerge in June/July and feed on various plants until the autumn, when they seek hibernation sites. There is only one generation a year.

Treatment. Encourage good germination and rapid growth by preparing the ground thoroughly before sowing and by treating the seed with a combined insecticide/fungicide seed-dressing. If necessary, protect young plants by dusting the leaves with pirimiphos-methyl, fenitrothion or HCH. Older plants are not greatly affected by this pest and need not be treated unless damage is excessive.

VINE WEEVIL *Otiorhynchus sulcatus* **Pl. 8**

This is the most important species of *Otiorhynchus* attacking garden plants in glasshouses, houses and out of doors but two other species, the clay-coloured weevil, *Otiorhynchus singularis*, and the strawberry root weevil, *Otiorhynchus rugifrons*, attack some plants out of doors. The clay-coloured weevil is particularly associated with damage to apples, currants, gooseberries, raspberries, yew, roses, rhododendrons, polyanthus and clematis and the strawberry root weevil is mainly a pest of strawberries. The biology and treatment of both of these weevils is essentially the same as for the vine weevil.

Symptoms. Legless, white larvae, up to 8 mm long, feed on roots, corms and tubers of many plants. They look like miniature chafer larvae but lack thoracic legs (Pl. 8). They are especially troublesome on pot plants and container-grown plants in houses and glasshouses but also affect plants growing outdoors in borders, rock gardens and similar situations. Pot cyclamen, primulas and begonias are most susceptible to attack but this pest also affects crassulas, ferns, gloxinias, saxifrages, sanseverias, camellias, orchids and many others. Destruction of roots by larvae checks growth and may cause sudden wilting and collapse of shoots and leaves. Adult vine weevils are seldom seen since they are mainly nocturnal and hide during the day. Their presence is generally indicated by irregular notches and holes eaten out of leaves and by the death of young shoots following ring-barking. Camellias and rhododendrons are most susceptible to this damage, especially in woodland plantings.

Biology. The biology of the vine weevil is unusual. Most other beetles reproduce sexually but virtually all vine weevils are female and they must therefore reproduce parthenogenetically. Male vine weevils have been found occasionally but are very rare. Each female lays up to 1,000 eggs in soil or potting media over a period of 3–4 months during spring and early summer and, although many of these eggs are infertile, this means that a single female has the potential to start a serious infestation. The eggs are usually laid close to suitable host plants and the larvae, which hatch after about two weeks, feed for three months or more before pupating in small earthen cells in the soil or other growing medium. Adults mostly emerge in the autumn under glass but not until the following spring out of doors. There is basically one generation a year but, because of the staggered emergence of adults, there is some overlap in late winter and early spring when eggs, larvae, pupae and adults may all be present at the same time,

especially in glasshouses and houses. Adult weevils are unable to fly but crawl into glasshouses through doors and ventilators or are introduced on plants. They hide at soil level during the day, in leaf litter, loose brickwork and woodwork and similar situations, and crawl up onto plants after dark.
Treatment. In glasshouses damage can be prevented by regular inspection, good hygiene, and the use of chemicals. Remove all accumulations of plant debris that could provide cover for adults and, if necessary, fumigate or spray with HCH to kill adults before they lay eggs. Protect susceptible plants, such as cyclamen, primulas, and begonias, by incorporating HCH dust or chlorpyrifos granules in the potting medium when potting up. This will protect young plants while they are establishing and additional protection may be given later by working HCH dust into the surface layer of the potting medium or by watering in a spray strength solution of HCH. During re-potting destroy any larvae, pupae or adults seen and use the above treatments to eliminate survivors.

Protection of plants growing out of doors is not so easy since the damage is usually done before the presence of the pest is realised. Saxifrages and sedums growing in light soils are especially susceptible and may be protected by working HCH dust into the soil around them in spring and early summer. Leaf feeding by adult weevils seldom causes severe damage although it may make rhododendron and other foliage look unsightly. If necessary, adult weevils could be killed by spraying affected plants with HCH in May/June.

ELM BARK BEETLES *Scolytus scolytus* and *Scolytus multistriatus* **Pl. 8**

Symptoms. These beetles are serious pests of elms since they are mainly responsible for spreading Dutch elm disease, which causes sudden yellowing of leaves on affected branches and subsequent death of most infected trees (p. 212). If the dead branches and trunks of affected trees are examined, bark beetles and their larvae will be found in characteristic tunnels under the loose bark. These tunnels consist of a main gallery, about 25 mm long, in which the female beetle lives, and a characteristic series of radiating side galleries, in which the larvae develop (Pl. 8). The beetles are 3–6 mm long, with brown wing cases and shining black thorax.
Biology. Adults, pupae and larvae overwinter in dead trees and branches and adults emerge from May onwards. Development is greatly influenced by the weather and may vary considerably from year to year, from place to place, or even from one side of a log to the other. Adults fly to the tops of healthy trees to feed on the smaller twigs. Spores of the Dutch elm disease fungus are carried on their bodies and mouthparts and are introduced into the tissues of healthy trees as the beetles feed on them. Transmission of the disease is mainly due to this feeding activity of adult beetles and infections therefore tend to spread most rapidly in warm springs and summers when the beetles are most active.
Treatment. There is no really effective way of controlling elm bark beetles. Destruction of infected trees removes potential breeding sites and limits local populations but the beetles can probably fly for several kilometres so that these measures will only have an effect if used over large areas. Even when this is done, beetles may survive in sufficient numbers to

initiate further infestations. In North America large-scale spraying from the ground and from the air has failed to eradicate *Scolytus scolytus* and it seems unlikely that chemical control of the beetles will ever be really effective. Biological control has been suggested as a possible alternative solution to the problem, both in North America and in Europe, but will require a substantial research input if it is to have any hope of succeeding.

Timber from infected trees is not seriously affected either by the disease or the beetles. It may therefore be used but all branch wood, trimmings and bark should be removed during the winter and should be burned by the end of March to kill the beetles before they emerge.

MITES

(Plate 9)

Mites differ from insects in having four, not three, pairs of jointed legs in the nymphal and adult stages and in lacking any clear division of the body into head, thorax and abdomen. They are generally small (1–2 mm long) or very small (less than 0.5 mm long) and are extremely abundant in most terrestrial habitats. Many species are general scavengers, feeding in soil, in decaying organic matter and in similar situations; others prey on small invertebrates, including other mites and many species of insect, and some feed on healthy plant tissues and may therefore be pests of cultivated and wild plants. Reproduction is generally sexual and the main stages of development are: egg, larva, various nymphal stages and adult. Males are absent or rare in some species and reproduction is then parthenogenetic.

Despite their relatively small size, mites are often serious pests of cultivated plants since they are able to breed rapidly when conditions are favourable and they are often less susceptible to chemical control than many insects. The main pest species in gardens are:

RED SPIDER MITES Pl. 9

These are small mites (Acarina: Tetranychidae), up to about 1 mm long. They move relatively quickly and resemble small spiders, to which they are distantly related. Colonies develop on leaves and other aerial parts of plants and usually contain all stages, from eggs to adults (Pl. 9). Young and adult mites feed by extracting sap and cell contents from plant tissues, producing characteristic fine light mottling and other discolourations (Pl. 9). Many cultivated plants are attacked by various species of red spider mite and serious damage is done when populations increase to astronomical numbers in heated glasshouses and during warm summer weather outdoors. Glasshouse and house plants may be almost covered by seething masses of mites and the webbing that they spin and this may even happen on large trees, such as limes, which may have vast numbers of mites swarming over leaves, branches and trunks during hot dry weather in summer.

The red spider mites dealt with here are those that feed on plants but there are other groups of red, spider-like mites that feed on decaying organic matter or prey on small invertebrates. These are sometimes seen in or on soil, on walls and paths, or on tree trunks and branches and may be mistaken for the plant-feeding red spider mites (especially since the latter are often not particularly red-coloured). If in doubt, seek expert advice.

GLASSHOUSE RED SPIDER MITE *Tetranychus urticae* and **CARMINE SPIDER MITE** *Tetranychus cinnabarinus* **Pl. 9**

These are two of the most troublesome pest species found in glasshouses and houses. *Tetranychus urticae* is generally commoner and more widespread than *Tetranychus cinnabarinus.*

Symptoms. Infestations first show as a very fine light speckling or as localised pale yellow spots on the upper surfaces of leaves (Pl. 9). Careful examination of the undersides of affected leaves, preferably with a hand lens or magnifying glass, should reveal colonies of mites, with numerous minute spherical eggs and, if the mites have been present for some time, scurfy accumulations of egg shells and of mite moult skins will also be present, especially at the sides of the leaf veins. As mite numbers increase, the damage to leaves, buds and flowers is extended. Leaves usually become progressively discoloured, often showing characteristic bronzing, and in severe attacks the leaves may wither and die. Mites then swarm over plants on fine silk webbing and when populations are exceptionally high, ropes of webbing, swarming with mites, hang off the tips of leaves. Adult female mites are about 0.5 mm long and the males are slightly smaller. They have four pairs of relatively short legs and the body colour during most of the growing season is usually yellow or green with darker green markings. Hibernating females of *T. urticae* turn bright red as they stop feeding in autumn and active females of *T. cinnabarinus* are reddish brown during most of the year.

The worst red spider mite infestations develop between June and September, both outdoors and under glass,but damage may occur at other times in heated glasshouses. Many different plants are attacked, including strawberries, peaches and nectarines, vines, cucumbers, tomatoes, beans, aubergines, capsicums, cacti, carnations, chrysanthemums, fuchsias, impatiens ('busy Lizzie'), orchids, pelargoniums, poinsettias, primulas, roses and violets.

Bryobia mites are sometimes confused with red spider mites but are quite distinct (see p. 176).

Biology. Female red spider mites live for a month or more and lay up to 100 eggs each, mostly on the undersides of leaves. Eggs hatch after 3–30 days, depending on temperature, and the six-legged larvae feed for a few days before moulting and transforming into the first nymphal stage (protonymph). The protonymph also feeds for a time before transforming into the second nymphal stage (deutonymph) which later develops into the adult. Development from egg to adult takes only about 8 days at an average temperature of 26.5°C (80°F) but more than two months at 10°C (50°F). Breeding continues throughout spring, summer and early autumn but as the days shorten in September females of *T. urticae* stop laying eggs, change colour and leave plants to seek hibernation sites in cracks in woodwork, in straw and leaf litter, under loose bark on stakes, in canes, in soil and potting media and in similar situations outdoors and in glasshouses and houses. They then remain dormant until the weather warms up in March and April when they gradually leave their hibernation sites and seek plants on which to lay eggs and establish the first infestations of the new season.

Some infestations may also remain active throughout the winter and this is especially the case with *T. cinnabarinus*.

Treatment. The simplest way of checking glasshouse red spider mite infestations is to spray susceptible plants with a fine mist of plain water twice a day. The high humidity depresses mite activity and, provided the plants are not affected, this treatment can be used effectively on glasshouse and house plants, and possibly to some extent outdoors on tomatoes and beans. Red spider mite attacks are often most severe on plants that are growing under unfavourable conditions or on plants that are ageing and lacking vigour and pot plants growing at high temperatures in dry, over-crowded glasshouses are especially susceptible. Provision of good growing conditions and frequent propagation of new plants, followed by rigorous discarding of old infested plants, will help to prevent serious attacks. Any severely infested plants present in glasshouses and houses in early autumn are best removed and destroyed, preferably by burning immediately. This will kill off many female mites that would otherwise carry over to the next season in hibernation and numbers of mites can be further reduced by tidying up accumulations of plant debris, straw, old canes, plant ties and other materials that may provide hibernating sites. If glasshouses can be cleared of plants, they should be thoroughly washed down and sterilised.

Chemical control of glasshouse red spider mites is generally unsatisfactory and is best avoided, if possible. Few of the chemicals available to gardeners are specifically active against these pests and, even when they are, mite populations can soon become resistant to most of the main groups of chemicals. If chemical control is attempted, the main choice is between derris, dicofol, malathion, dimethoate or pirimiphos-methyl, applied as sprays. Derris is usually the safest chemical to use on delicate plants but is of such short persistence that it has to be applied more frequently than other materials.

A biological method of controlling glasshouse red spider mites has been developed in recent years and overcomes some of the difficulties of chemical control. It involves introducing a predaceous species of mite that feeds on all stages of the glasshouse red spider mites. This red spider mite predator is *Phytoseiulus persimilis*, a species that is native to Chile but is now maintained in cultures in Europe and N. America. Adult mites are slightly larger than red spider mites, with longer legs and an orange-red body. They move rapidly over plants, searching for their prey, and each individual can kill about 5 adults or about 20 immature stages a day. Females lay eggs amongst red spider mite colonies and when temperatures are high eggs soon hatch and predator populations increase, often reaching sufficiently high numbers to eliminate all red spider mites. When this happens, the predator eventually starves and dies out, so must be reintroduced if new red spider mite infestations develop. *Phytoseiulus* is mainly used on commercial crops of cucumbers and tomatoes and is sold by commercial suppliers in batches of 100 or more adult mites. Best control is given when the predator is introduced into glasshouses early in the season. It should be established on infested plants throughout the glasshouse since it does not spread very quickly if left to its own devices. The subsequent use of chemicals to control other pests must be restricted as they would kill out the predators and when mite populations have already reached damaging levels it is best to spray with a non-persistent chemical, such as malathion or derris, a week before introducing the predator. Further details of this method of biological control can be obtained from the Ministry of Agriculture and from the Royal Horticultural Society.

FRUIT TREE RED SPIDER MITE *Panonychus ulmi* Pl. 9

This is the most important red spider mite attacking apple and plum trees but the similar glasshouse red spider mites (see above) also attack some fruits, especially peaches, nectarines and strawberries.

Symptoms. Mite colonies build up on leaves from April onwards, causing progressive light speckling, bronzing and desiccation. Severe attacks cause extensive damage to foliage in June/July and may reduce fruit yields both in the year of attack and in the following year. The general appearance of mite colonies on the undersides of leaves is very similar to that described for glasshouse red spider mites (see above). Fruit tree red spider mite mainly attacks apples, pears, plums, damsons, cotoneasters, hawthorns and rowans but may also affect some other related plants.

Biology. Small, spherical red-brown eggs, about 0.15 mm diameter, overwinter on twigs and branches of host plants (Pl. 9), often in such great numbers that the reddish colour of the eggs on the branches can be seen from 20–30 metres away. Eggs hatch during April–June and mites feed and breed on the undersides of the leaves throughout the growing season, producing 4–5 successive generations, which results in rapid increases of populations. When temperatures start to fall in September the females lay overwintering eggs and then die out.

Treatment. Examine susceptible host plants carefully in December/January to determine the extent of autumn egg laying. If eggs are abundant, occurring in clusters of a dozen or more rather than as isolated single eggs, apply a soaking spray of DNOC/petroleum to fully dormant plants in January/February, paying strict attention to the instructions for safe use. Otherwise wait until after blossoming and examine leaves for the presence of mite colonies. If they are detected, spray in May or early June with malathion or dimethoate to check these colonies before they reach peak numbers. Benomyl and some other fungicides are partially effective against fruit tree red spider mite and their regular use against diseases may be sufficient to keep this pest under control.

Populations of fruit tree red spider mites have become resistant to organophosphorus acaricides, such as malathion, and to other groups of chemicals, and expert advice should be sought if resistance is suspected. Fruit tree red spider mites can also become troublesome if tar oil winter washes are used regularly to control aphids and other insects since tar oil reduces the numbers of predaceous insects feeding on overwintering red spider mite eggs.

CONIFER SPINNING MITE *Oligonychus ununguis* Pl. 9

Symptoms. Colonies of this mite build up on conifers, especially dwarf conifers, in May, June and July. Affected foliage turns yellow (Pl. 9) and in severe attacks the damaged leaves may be shed prematurely. Spruces, cedars, cypresses, junipers, thujas and pines are susceptible to attack.

Biology. Eggs laid on trees in autumn overwinter and hatch in early spring. Mite colonies then become established on young shoots and breeding continues until the autumn.

Treatment. Small ornamental conifers can be treated by spraying thoroughly on two or three occasions in early spring with malathion to check the initial colonies.

BRYOBIA MITES *Bryobia* spp.

Various species of mites belonging to the genus *Bryobia* attack some fruit and ornamental plants, producing symptoms that resemble those produced by red spider mites.

Symptoms. Mites feed on leaves in spring and summer causing progressive discolouration which may result in general bronzing and desiccation, followed by premature leaf fall. Adult bryobia mites can be distinguished from red spider mites by their relatively long fore-legs and by the absence of any long bristles on their bodies. They also prefer to feed on the upper surfaces of leaves and do not produce silk webbing. Apple, gooseberry, pear, polyanthus, ivy and various alpine plants, especially campanulas, dianthus, gentians and saxifrages, are susceptible to attack. In autumn large numbers of bryobia mites move off cultivated plants and weeds and may be seen swarming over paths and invading garden sheds, glasshouses and buildings.

Biology. Most species of *Bryobia* reproduce parthenogenetically and males are unknown. Some species overwinter as eggs on host plants but others survive as adults on plants or in buildings, walls and similar protected situations. Eggs hatch and adults become active from March onwards and up to five successive generations develop during the growing season. Some species breed slowly but others reproduce rapidly, giving rise to high populations in summer and early autumn.

Treatment. Chemicals applied to control fruit tree red spider mites and aphids on apples and other fruits will check bryobia mites. If local infestations on other plants justify control, use malathion sprays, repeating applications after a week, if necessary.

TARSONEMID MITES **Pl. 9**

Tarsonemid mites (Tarsonemidae) are very small (up to 0.25 mm long), relatively slow moving mites with elongate, rounded, shiny cream to light brown bodies. They generally feed in buds, under leaf sheaths, in the tips of young shoots and in similar situations on plants, and are therefore more difficult to detect than are the red spider mites, which feed openly on leaves. The main stages of development are: egg, larva, quiescent pre-adult stage (sometimes inaccurately known as a pupa), and adult. Males occur regularly in most species but reproduction may be parthenogenetic for much of the time. Females lay about 50 eggs each, either singly or in small clusters, on or near young buds, leaves and flowers. Eggs hatch after a few days and larvae feed for a week or more before entering the quiescent pre-adult stage. The rate of development from egg to adult is greatly influenced by temperature and at 75°F (24°C) the complete cycle may take less than a week. Mites continue to breed throughout the year but the rate of development slows down considerably during the winter. Females extend infestations by crawling over plants and are sometimes assisted by males which carry female 'pupae' on their backs to new feeding and breeding sites. Such movements are generally restricted so that infestations tend to be relatively local. Effects on plants vary but symptoms mostly result from mites feeding on young tissues. New growth is checked and distorted; buds and flowers may be killed, and damaged stems and leaf bases often show characteristic light brown, russet-like scarring (Pl. 9). Leaves of infested plants are often puckered, curled, slightly thickened and rather brittle and damaged flowers are generally discoloured and distorted (Pl. 9). Damage is often out of all proportion to the numbers of mites present since localised death of plant tissues in attacked buds results in extensive symptoms on the leaves and flowers that later develop from them. Both indoor and outdoor plants are attacked by tarsonemids but damage is often greatest in heated glasshouses and in houses, where higher temperatures encourage rapid and continuous breeding.

The main species attacking garden plants are the strawberry mite, *Tarsonemus pallidus* (also known as the cyclamen mite); the broad mite, *Polyphagotarsonemus latus*, and the bulb scale mite, *Steneotarsonemus laticeps*.

Treatment. None of the chemicals currently available for garden use is likely to give effective control of tarsonemid mites. Pot plants may be protected to some extent by dusting with powdered sulphur if temperatures are above 65°F (18°C) but this leaves an unsightly deposit on foliage and flowers. Spraying with malathion or one of the other organophosphorus acaracides is sometimes recommended but there is evidence that use of these chemicals can actually increase mite populations, probably by eliminating natural predators and also by altering the nutritional value of the plants so that they have a beneficial effect on the mites. Apart from chemical control, good hygiene can prevent serious outbreaks, especially in glasshouses. Do not introduce suspect plants into glasshouses, houses or gardens and isolate or destroy affected plants as soon as they are noticed. Avoid undue disturbance of infested plants by handling or re-potting since infestations may be spread by mites dropping onto other plants and onto staging. Heat treatments may sometimes be used to eliminate mites from certain plants but must be carefully applied. Strawberry runners, saintpaulias and cyclamen are treated by immersing whole plants in water maintained at 46°C (115°F) for 7 minutes and forced narcissus bulbs can be treated by sudden cooling, which can be achieved quite simply by putting them outside on one or two frosty nights about a week after forcing has started.

GALL MITES

Pl. 9

Many different species of eriophyid mites (Eriophyidae), commonly known as gall mites, induce galls and other malformations on wild and cultivated plants. Adult mites are very small, usually less than 0.25 mm long, with narrow white or yellow bodies and only two pairs of legs. Adults and immature stages feed on plant tissues, usually inside buds or in galls, and colonies of gall mites often contain many thousands of individuals. Although the galls caused by these mites are often conspicuous, most species cause little or no permanent damage to their host plants. The only real exception to this is the black currant gall mite, which transmits the agent causing reversion disease.

The main species in gardens are:

BLACKCURRANT GALL MITE

Cecidophyopsis ribis **Pl. 9**

This is an important and widespread pest of blackcurrants.

Symptoms. Gall mites infest buds which then become swollen and rounded and fail to develop normally (Pl. 9). This condition is commonly known as 'big bud' and is most apparent on infested blackcurrant bushes in winter and early spring. Direct damage to buds is generally less important than secondary effects resulting from the transmission by the mites of the agent that causes reversion disease.

Biology. Mites breed inside buds in summer and autumn and many mites overwinter in them. Populations increase from January onwards and when the buds start to open in March/April mites disperse from them and invade healthy young dormant buds that will develop in the following season. Mites can only crawl over short distances on plants but may be carried passively over longer distances by wind and rain or on flying insects, such as aphids. Most dispersal occurs during warm, humid weather in May/June and by July the mites are established and breeding in the dormant buds, where colonies persist until the following spring.

Treatment. If possible, remove enlarged buds from bushes during the winter and early spring to limit the numbers of mites carrying over from one season to the next. Destroy these affected buds immediately, preferably by burning, so that the enclosed mites are killed before they can disperse. The fungicides benomyl or carbendazium applied during early April with a repeat application about 3 weeks later, will give some control of this pest. Once reversion disease has become established the affected plants will have to be replaced by healthy plants on a new site. To limit the spread of mites and the disease from diseased to healthy plants it is best to lift and burn all infested plants during the winter, well before the new plants are brought into the garden.

NUT GALL MITE *Phytoptus avellanae*

This species resembles the black currant gall mite and produces similar enlarged buds on hazels. It is a distinct species and cannot transfer from hazels to black currants. Damage to hazels is slight and does not justify the use of any control measures, other than picking off and destroying affected buds.

PEAR LEAF BLISTER MITE *Eriophyes pyri* **Pl. 9**

Symptoms. Irregular pink or yellow blisters appear on young pear leaves in spring and, as the leaves age during summer and autumn, these blisters turn dark brown and black (Pl. 9). Severely infested leaves may be killed and growth of young shoots may be checked. Some other host plants, especially apples, cotoneasters, mountain ash, whitebeams and wild service trees are occasionally attacked by this or by closely related species. These symptoms may be confused with those of pear leaf curl disease.

Biology. Adult mites overwinter under bud scales and feed on young leaves, causing blistering. Mite colonies then develop within the tissues and breeding continues throughout the summer. Mites move out of infested leaves just before leaf-fall in autumn and seek overwintering sites in dormant buds.

Treatment. If possible, remove and destroy affected leaves as soon as they are seen. Otherwise, treat persistent and severe infestations by spraying with benomyl or carbendazium, towards the end of March, just as the buds begin to open.

NAIL GALL MITE *Eriophyes tiliae* **Pl. 9**

Small, conical red galls appear on the upper surfaces of the leaves of lime trees in May/June (Pl. 9). A single leaf may bear hundreds of galls and their bright red colour contrasts sharply with the fresh green colour of the young leaves. This unusual and dramatic appearance often causes concern to gardeners but healthy trees are not seriously affected and control measures are not necessary.

SYCAMORE GALL MITE *Eriophyes macrorhynchus*

The effects of this species are similar to those of the nail gall mite but it only affects sycamores and hedgerow maple. Numerous small red galls, each about the size of a pin head, develop on the upper surfaces of young leaves from April onwards, producing characteristic rashes of red pimples. These galls tend to be common on young trees, especially those growing in hedges, but do little harm to them.

BIRDS

(Plate 9)

Most birds are welcome visitors to gardens but a few species are destructive pests of fruits, vegetables and ornamental plants and are especially troublesome because of their mobility and their ability to adapt quickly to changing circumstances. Their rate of reproduction, compared with that of insects and mites, is relatively low. Each female lays only a dozen or so eggs a year but this low egg count is compensated for by parental care of the young, by the relatively long life-span of individuals, and by alert awareness of danger and consequent ability to avoid hazards. The main pest species are noted below and general advice on the prevention of damage is given on p. 182.

BULLFINCH *Pyrrhula pyrrhula* **Pl. 9**

Three distinct races of this species occur in Europe: the British bullfinch, which is confined to the British Isles; the Northern bullfinch of Scandinavia and the Baltic, and the Continental bullfinch, which occurs in France, the Netherlands and other countries of Western Europe.

Symptoms. During winter and early spring the flower and leaf buds of various fruit and ornamental trees and shrubs (Pl. 9) are attacked by marauding parties of bullfinches working surreptitiously in groups of about 6–12 individuals. They nip off buds systematically, working from the tops to the bottoms of shoots and branches, and taking up to 30 buds a minute. The succulent centres are eaten and the harder outer bud scales are dropped and accumulations of dropped scales and other debris may be noticed under attacked plants, especially on frosty mornings or after falls of snow. Persistent attacks seriously affect subsequent flowering, fruiting and growth. Plums, fruiting and flowering cherries, gooseberries, apples, pears, forsythias, wistarias, viburnums and lilacs are particularly susceptible and in spring the damaged branches have bare lengths devoid of buds.

Biology. Bullfinches are shy birds and they generally frequent the fringes of woodland, coppices, thickets, overgrown scrubland and similar habitats that provide them with adequate cover. Females lay up to three successive clutches of 4–5 eggs during May/September in insubstantial nests made of fine twigs, roots and hairs, usually in hedgerows and thickets. Parties of birds forage together during late summer, autumn and winter, feeding mainly on seeds of various weeds, grasses and trees. By mid-winter most of these food sources are exhausted and birds then feed on buds of wild and cultivated plants until the spring when the parties split up as birds pair and nest. Most bullfinches remain within about a 16 km (10 mile) radius of the nest in which they were reared and, despite occasional reports to the contrary, there are no substantial long-range movements of birds.

Treatment. Repellents are sometimes recommended but are seldom really effective and the only certain way to prevent damage is to erect permanent fruit cages or temporary netting, which should be in place by the end of November (see p. 182). Trapping and shooting are unlikely to have any marked effect on populations and are illegal in most areas.

WOOD PIGEON *Columba palumbus* **Pl. 9**

Wood pigeons are mainly pests of agricultural crops but can also cause substantial damage in gardens. Collared doves occur in gardens in some areas and may cause similar damage.

Symptoms. Leaves of brassica plants are torn and eaten and are often reduced to a skeleton (Pl. 9). Young transplants may be uprooted and killed and seeds of peas, beans and other crops are taken. Buds, leaves and fruits may be stripped from black currants and other fruit bushes and branches are sometimes broken. Wood pigeons cause most damage in spring and early summer when a few individuals making regular raids into gardens, usually in the early morning, can have quite disastrous effects. Adult wood pigeons are mainly blue-grey with a distinct white patch at the base of the neck and white bars visible on the wings in flight. The presence of wood pigeons near gardens is often indicated by their characteristic call, which is a soft 'coo-cooo-coo, coo-coo'.

Biology. Wood pigeon nests consist of loose platforms of twigs, usually constructed in the lower branches of conifers, hawthorns and other woodland trees, often in thickets and hedges. Nests may be occupied for most of the year and females rear a succession of clutches, which average about two eggs to a clutch. Eggs are incubated for about three weeks and young birds leave the nests after about another month. The peak nesting period is during August/September and it is at this time that most young birds appear. Many of these die through starvation during the winter and, although predators take some toll, wood pigeon populations are mainly regulated by severe winter weather and food shortages. When weather is particularly severe in western Europe, wood pigeons may migrate south and west in search of food, but they do not undertake regular large-scale migrations.

Treatment. Netting or fruit cages provide the only certain protection for susceptible plants although scaring devices may have some deterrent effect (see p. 182). Trapping and shooting are unlikely to have any permanent effect on populations.

HOUSE-SPARROW *Passer domesticus*

House-sparrows are closely associated with houses and other buildings and therefore tend to be particularly destructive in gardens, especially in urban and suburban areas.

Symptoms. Flowers, leaves and buds of many garden plants are attacked and torn to pieces in winter, spring and early summer. House-sparrows mainly feed on seeds and much of the damage that they do in gardens seems quite wanton as it is not directly connected with normal feeding. It is probably a displacement activity that the birds indulge in when they are not fully occupied with essential activities. Plums, currants and gooseberries are disbudded in late winter and early spring, although similar damage is also caused by bullfinches (p. 179), and many spring and early summer flowers, especially crocuses, primulas and polyanthus, may be torn to pieces and even uprooted. Carnations, chrysanthemums, lettuces, beetroot, peas, onion sets and other plants are similarly attacked and, in addition, house-sparrows eat seeds and take dust baths in newly sown lawns.

Biology. Nests are built from straw and dried grasses and are sited in holes in walls, under eaves, in drain pipes, in ivy and other climbers, and in similar situations on or near buildings. The main breeding season lasts from May to August and 2–3 successive batches of about 4–6 eggs are hatched and reared. Adults and immature birds stay near buildings for most of the year but during late summer and early autumn large flocks fly off to feed on maturing cereal crops on farm land.

Treatment. Protect susceptible plants with netting or cages whenever possible. Black cotton or other scaring devices and chemical repellents may prove partially effective (see p. 182). Trapping or shooting will have little effect since cleared areas are soon reinvaded by roving flocks of young birds looking for new territories. Putting out food for birds in gardens attracts house-sparrows and probably gives them more free time to attack plants.

Other bird species that occasionally cause damage are listed below. See p. 182 for treatment.

BLUE TIT *Parus caeruleus* **Pl. 9**

Blue tits damage ripening fruits, especially apples and pears, by pecking small pieces out of them. These wounds are quickly infected by fungal and bacterial rots (p. 242) and may also be extended by wasps (p. 161). Blue tits also peck camellia, magnolia and other flower buds and flowers in early spring. Damage done by blue tits is counterbalanced to some extent by the fact that they also feed on insects, especially aphids and caterpillars, and may therefore help to reduce pest populations.

BLACKBIRD *Turdus merula*
SONG-THRUSH *Turdus philomelos*
FIELDFARE *Turdus pilaris*
REDWING *Turdus iliacus*

These four related species all eat fruits and berries. Blackbirds and song thrushes are resident in the British Isles but fieldfares and redwings are winter migrants which move into Britain from northern Europe in large flocks, especially during severe winter weather. During spring, summer and autumn blackbirds and thrushes attack strawberries, apples, pears and other ripening fruits and during late autumn and winter all four species attack ornamental berries, especially hollies, berberis, pyracanthas and cotoneasters. Netting is the only certain protection although scaring devices may have some effect.

STARLING *Sturnus vulgaris*

Parties of starlings often work over lawns, pecking at the turf and sometimes leaving holes and loose tufts of grass. They are usually feeding on leatherjackets (p. 147) or chafer grubs (p. 163) and their activities are therefore mainly beneficial. In some areas they may cause damage to fruits, especially cherries.

JAY *Garrulus glandarius*

Jays raid gardens from adjacent woodland and scrub. They peck conspicuous V-shaped pieces out of developing pods of peas and beans and eat the seeds. If jays are known to occur locally, protect peas and beans with temporary or permanent netting.

General Treatment. In Britain all birds are protected by law and it is illegal to kill them by shooting, trapping or other means or to take their eggs and destroy their nests. Only authorised persons are excluded from this general provision so far as pest species are concerned. Gardeners must therefore rely on preventive measures. Many different techniques have been developed to prevent or reduce bird damage on agricultural and horticultural crops and on garden plants but man's ingenuity in devising them has often been matched by the ability of birds to avoid or circumvent them.

The main methods worth considering for garden use are:

A. *Nets and cages.* In areas where birds regularly attack plants, the best solution is to use temporary or permanent netting to exclude them. The erection of fruit cages to contain soft and top fruits is especially worthwhile since this can prevent both winter attacks on buds by bullfinches and sparrows and summer attacks on ripening fruits by tits, blackbirds and other species of bird. It also gives protection against squirrels (p. 184). A wide range of wire, cord and plastic nettings is available, as well as ready-made fruit cages, and it should be fairly easy to select materials to suit individual requirements. The smallest meshes, 20 mm ($\frac{3}{4}''$) rigid or 12 mm ($\frac{1}{2}''$) pliable, should be used to exclude blue tits but larger meshes can be used against other birds. Nets should be closed by early November, to prevent winter damage to buds, and should be inspected regularly to ensure that they are secure. They should be removed temporarily in spring to allow free access of pollinating insects, but should be replaced as soon as fruits have set.

B. *Scaring devices.* Bird-scaring devices range from traditional scare-crows to modern recorded transmissions of distress calls. Distress calls, explosive devices and other techniques that rely on noises to scare the birds are used in horticulture and agriculture but are generally unsuitable for use in gardens, especially in small suburban gardens where neighbours may object. Techniques that are better suited to garden use include:

i. Black cotton, string or similar materials strung above plants from canes, stakes or sticks.

ii. Glittering strips of foil or similar material hung from lines or canes.

iii. Small windmills, sometimes with rattles, mounted on stakes.

iv. Scare-crows simulating human forms.

Birds soon become accustomed to a particular device and these techniques therefore give best results if they are changed frequently.

C. *Chemical repellents.* Various chemicals with unpleasant tastes are used either as dusts or sprays applied to plants to repel birds from them. Alum and anthraquinone are probably the most widely used active ingredients in proprietary repellents but other materials are also available. These chemical repellents may be partially effective but are limited in use and erratic in performance. They cannot be used to protect ripening fruits, since the fruits will be tainted, and they are not very effective in preventing winter damage to buds by bullfinches and other birds since severe weather quickly removes deposits of repellents from buds and, in any case, starving birds may not be sufficiently deterred from feeding.

Other methods of bird control, such as the use of stupefying baits, trapping, shooting or nest destruction are not recommended for garden use although they may sometimes be used in agriculture, horticulture and forestry. To be effective, they must be used consistently and efficiently over wide areas and care must be taken to avoid illegal killing of non-pest species.

MAMMALS

Some of the smaller mammals, such as mice, voles, moles and rabbits, are often common pests of garden plants, even in urban and suburban areas, and larger mammals, such as deer, are occasional or regular pests in rural areas.

All mammals give birth to live young and these are protected by the parents during the early weeks and months of growth. Populations never reach the astronomical numbers commonly achieved by many insects and mites but the adaptable behaviour of most mammals, combined with their powerful senses of sight, smell and hearing, may make it difficult to prevent damage to plants.

RABBIT *Oryctolagus cuniculus*

Symptoms. Young and adult rabbits nibble and graze many different wild and cultivated plants. They eat young shoots and leaves, strip bark from young trees, especially in severe winters, and feed on flowers, fruits and seeds. In gardens lettuces, hostas, heathers and lilies and many herbaceous perennials are particularly susceptible to attack and may be seriously damaged in spring and early summer.

Biology. Rabbits are burrowing animals. They live in tunnels excavated in hedge banks, under thickets of hawthorn and bramble, and in similar situations and they emerge at night to feed on plants. Each rabbit eats about 0.5 kg (1 lb) of greenstuff a day and large colonies of rabbits therefore have a marked effect on vegetation growing near their warrens. Each female produces 2–4 litters a year, mostly between January and June, and each litter contains 3–6 young rabbits. These mature and start to breed within a year and populations can increase rapidly when conditions are favourable. This high reproductive potential may be checked by predators, such as foxes and weasels, and by diseases, such as myxomatosis. This virus disease was introduced into Europe in the early 1950's and was initially very virulent. Fleas and mosquitoes transmitted it from unhealthy to healthy rabbits and rabbit populations were rapidly reduced by as much as 90 per cent. In Britain rabbits almost disappeared and in 1955 it was estimated that the value of cereal crops increased by £15 million following reduction of rabbit populations by myxomatosis. Since then the disease has become less virulent and rabbits have become immune to it so that numbers have increased again, but in some areas there may be an annual cycle with the disease reaching a peak in late summer and early autumn.

Treatment. When rabbits are abundant on land adjoining gardens, the only way to prevent persistent damage to plants is to erect and maintain a rabbit-proof fence. This should be made from 1¼–1½ m (4–5 ft) widths of 18 or 19 gauge wire netting with a 2.5–3.0 cm (1–1¼″) mesh. About 30 cm (12″) of this width is buried in the soil to stop rabbits burrowing under it and the remaining 1–1¼ m (3–4 ft) must be well supported by posts and straining wires. Fences should be inspected regularly to ensure that there are no holes through which rabbits can pass.

If rabbits are not particularly abundant, valuable trees, shrubs and other plants may be adequately protected by netting, spiral tree-protectors or other devices. Chemical repellents may give some protection, especially when applied to the bark of trees to prevent bark-stripping, but are not always effective. Some plants are unattractive to rabbits and a list of these may be obtained from the Royal Horticultural Society. Trapping, shooting and gassing are not suitable for general garden use.

HARES

Hares are related to rabbits but are less numerous and therefore seldom cause appreciable damage. Brown hares, *Lepus capensis*, occasionally occur in gardens, especially when these adjoin farmland, and may damage young fruit trees and ornamental trees and shrubs by stripping bark from the stems. Spiral tree-protectors or wire netting should be used to prevent such damage and susceptible young trees may need protection for many years.

GREY SQUIRREL *Sciurus carolinensis*

Symptoms. Grey squirrels usually enter gardens from adjacent deciduous woodland and may cause considerable damage by digging up and eating bulbs, especially crocuses, lilies and tulips, by taking berries and fruits, especially strawberries, hazel nuts and walnuts, and by eating bark off stems and branches of trees, especially ash, beech, sycamore and spruce. They also eat young shoots, buds and flowers of various trees and shrubs in spring and the cones of conifers, such as pine and larch, at other times of year. They have also been known to gnaw hose pipes and plastic or metal plant labels.

Biology. The grey squirrel is a N. American species that was introduced into zoos and menageries in Europe about a century ago. It escaped from captivity and became widely established, eventually replacing the indigenous red squirrel in much of Britain and parts of Europe. Grey squirrels mainly frequent woods containing broad-leaved trees, such as oaks, and during the winter they live together in large nest-like structures (dreys) made from leafy branches and constructed high in the branches of trees. The does live alone in large breeding dreys or in holes in trees and produce litters of 3–4 young, either in late February or in July.

Treatment. Squirrels can be well controlled on woodland estates by shooting, trapping and the destruction of dreys but these measures cannot usually be used in gardens. Bulbs can be protected with wire netting until they are through the ground and squirrels may also be discouraged from digging them up if lengths of prickly gorse stem are buried amongst the bulbs at planting time. Fruit cages and netting used to protect fruits from birds (see p. 182) will also deter squirrels and temporary netting can be used to protect particularly valuable ornamental shrubs. Stem barking is best prevented by using spiral tree-protectors or small mesh wire netting.

WOOD MOUSE *Apodemus sylvaticus*

Also known as the long-tailed field mouse.

Symptoms. This species will eat almost anything but in gardens the main damage is to bulbs and corms, especially those of lilies, narcissus and tulips, and to seeds, particularly seeds of peas and beans which are dug up and eaten after they have been sown. In autumn and winter this mouse enters garden sheds and glasshouses and can cause considerable damage to apples and other stored fruits and to packeted seeds. It is much more common in outbuildings than the house-mouse, with which it is sometimes confused. Populations of long-tailed field mice fluctuate and may be exceptionally high in some years.

Biology. Adults are brown with greyish-white underparts and a relatively long tail. They live in burrows in hedge banks and similar situations and breed from March until October. They do not hibernate but remain active throughout the winter and it is at this time that many individuals move into outbuildings. They are preyed on by owls, weasels, cats and other predacious birds and mammals.

Treatment. Traditional mouse-traps should be set in garden sheds, seed stores, glasshouses and other buildings in autumn and winter to catch mice before they cause any damage. Carrot, apple, melon seeds or pieces of potato should be used as bait. Traps can also be set outdoors but should then be covered with cloches or some other form of protection that will prevent birds and pet animals from getting to them. Seeds of peas and beans should be dressed with a combined insecticide/fungicide seed dressing before sowing, as that makes them less palatable to mice, and seed beds and bulbs may also be protected with 1 cm (⅜″) mesh wire netting. Anticoagulant (warfarin) and other proprietary mouse poisons may be used with baits but precautions must be taken to lay them so that domestic and other animals are not affected.

SHORT-TAILED VOLE *Microtus agrestis*

Symptoms. This pest causes serious damage when it eats the bark off young trees and shrubs at about soil level but it also eats seeds, bulbs and roots of outdoor plants. It does not normally enter buildings.

Biology. Short-tailed voles, also known as field voles, are the commonest small rodents in Britain. They have short stout bodies with small ears and short tails and look like miniature guinea-pigs. They prefer to live in unkempt grassy areas where they make extensive networks of runs near the surface of the soil. These runs may include chambers provisioned with short lengths of grass stem, shoots eaten off bulbs, or other succulent pieces of plants. Short-tailed voles do not hibernate but are inactive for short periods during very cold weather. Plague populations tend to develop in some years and up to 500 voles may then be found per 0.2 ha (½ acre).

Treatment. Clear overgrown areas of grass, especially around trees, and protect the bases of valuable trees and shrubs with spiral tree-protectors or with wire netting. Trapping and baiting are unlikely to be effective when populations are high since cleared areas would soon be recolonised.

WATER VOLE *Arvicola amphibius*

This is a much larger species than the short-tailed vole with adults growing to a length of about 20 cm (8″). It is sometimes mistakenly referred to as the water rat. Water voles tunnel in banks of streams and pools and may be a nuisance in gardens that include or adjoin water. Apart from physically undermining banks, they also feed on plants near their burrows. Populations are usually small and it may be possible to eradicate them by trapping which should be done by an expert. Failing this, wire netting may be used to protect banks of pools.

MOLE *Talpa europaea*

Symptoms. Small mounds of loose earth (molehills) appear on lawns, rough ground and cultivated areas where moles are active. Light, well-drained soils are most affected but moles can thrive in a variety of situations ranging from lowland suburban gardens to upland moors. Mole activity in gardens is usually greatest in late winter and early spring but new tunnels and molehills can be made at any time of year. Moles do not feed directly on plants but damage them indirectly by undermining the roots, which can seriously affect the growth of young plants, especially vegetables and strawberries. Production of molehills also makes lawns unsightly and difficult to mow.

Biology. Moles spend virtually all of their lives underground in a ramifying system of tunnels and chambers that they excavate with their unusual shovel-like fore limbs. Adults are about 15 cm (6″) long, with dense dark brown fur. The main breeding season runs from February to June, and each female rears a litter of about four young in a subterranean nest, sometimes known as the fortress. A single family may inhabit a tunnel system extending over 0.2 ha (½ acre) and individuals patrol the tunnels regularly to feed on earthworms and other small invertebrates that find their way into them. Young moles leave the parental tunnel system after a few months and either establish new systems or enter old systems that are unoccupied.

Treatment. The main methods used to check mole damage are trapping, poisoning and the use of repellent devices or substances.

Two types of mole trap are approved for general use and can be bought from some garden shops and hardware stores. These are the Duffus half-barrel trap and the caliper trap. Permanent mole runs must first be located by careful observation, probing and excavation and traps are then set so that moles are killed instantaneously as they pass along the runs. The Duffus trap is generally easiest to use and gives best results when inserted in relatively straight lengths of run within 15–20 cm (6–8″) of the soil surface. Such runs often follow the lines of fences, walls, buildings and paths and can be located by probing with a thin cane or a metal rod. Once located, the run is carefully exposed, using a trowel or similar tool, the trap is set and inserted and earth and turf are placed over it so that light is excluded but operation of the trap is not obstructed. Caliper traps are inserted in a similar way and are generally easier to use in deeper runs. Traps should be examined at least once a day and if they fail to catch any moles within four days they should be moved to new sites. The best period for trapping is usually in late winter and early spring when mole activity can be easily observed by looking for new molehills and surface runs but traps can be set at any time of year, and continuous trapping may often be necessary if cleared runs are invaded by new moles moving into gardens from adjoining land.

Poisoning is not suitable for use by gardeners since the poisons used are highly toxic and can only be obtained on licence. It may be the best method for clearing large gardens but should then be done by an expert.

Many different repellents are claimed to prevent invasion of gardens by moles or to drive them away once they have become established. Most rely on smell (mothballs, creosote, smoke cartridges, garlic, etc., inserted into tunnels) and some rely on vibrations (empty bottles or tins sunk in the soil so that wind produces vibrations as it blows across them). Moles are certainly sensitive to unusual odours and to vibrations in the soil and it is therefore possible that some of these repellents may have a brief deterrent effect. It is also true that moles can quickly block off their tunnels temporarily so that the effects of repellents could be restricted to small sections of the whole system. It therefore seems that they are unlikely to have a permanent effect on mole activity in a garden.

DEER

Roe deer, *Capreolus capreolus*, and fallow deer, *Cervus dama* are the two species that are most likely to be troublesome in gardens although other species, such as the sika and muntjac may occur in some areas.

Symptoms. Plants in gardens are mainly damaged in March, April and May when deer browse on new shoots and leaves of many shrubs and trees. They also strip bark from conifers and other trees during the winter and bucks may fray the stems and branches of trees and shrubs in spring when they are marking out their territories. Deer feed at dusk and dawn and are seldom seen in gardens but their tracks may be found in soft ground and their presence should be suspected where shoots and stems have been cut through cleanly on one side but left with a frayed edge on the other side. This characteristic symptom results from the fact that deer lack teeth in the upper jaw.

Biology. Roe deer are usually solitary but may sometimes form small herds. The rutting period is generally from mid-July to mid-August and each doe gives birth to a pair of fawns in the following April–July. These remain with the mother until the following season and become sexually mature at about 15 months. Adult roe deer are only about 0.6 m (2 ft) high at the shoulder and are able to work their way through small gaps in hedges and fences. They can also jump over a height of about 1.5 m (5 ft).

Fallow deer are slightly larger. They form separate herds of bucks and of does with fawns and a herd breaking into a garden overnight can cause a great deal of damage to shrubs and trees. In summer their chestnut coloured coats are generally marked with cream white spots, which are lost in winter, and they have a distinctive black and white tail.

Treatment. In districts where deer are common and damage to plants in gardens is persistent, the only adequate solution is to have deer-proof fences and hedges. Fences must be at least 1.8 m (6 ft) high and should be made from large mesh wire netting, such as two widths of sheep fencing well overlapped. Plastic netting is not suitable for this type of fence. In addition to fencing and hedging the perimeter, deer-proof gates on drives and paths may also be necessary.

If complete exclusion of deer is not possible, susceptible plants should be protected by wire netting around the stems and trunks to limit bark stripping and fraying. Chemical repellents and scaring devices are seldom really effective but temporary protection may be given by tinsel, tin cans, twine, coloured rags or feathers strung across pathways that deer are likely to use. Leading shoots of valuable plants may also be protected by winding lengths of wool around them in spring to enable them to grow out of reach of deer.

Local Deer Control Societies operate in some areas, under the auspices of the British Deer Society, and may be willing to give advice to gardeners.

DOGS *Canis familiaris*

Domestic dogs damage plants by urinating on them, which kills leaves and produces brown discoloured patches on the foliage of dwarf conifers and low-lying shrubs and on lawns. Usually the damage is confined to the owner's garden but on open-plan housing estates passing dogs can become a nuisance. Vulnerable plants should be sited away from pavements and paths where dogs are a problem or should be protected by netting or low fencing. Chemical repellents may prove effective in some situations.

CATS *Felis catus*

Cats are attracted to newly cultivated areas of soil which they use as toilet areas and they often scratch up seed beds and newly sown lawns. They prefer dry soil and can therefore be discouraged by keeping affected areas well watered. Pepper dust and other repellents may also have some deterrent effects.

Diseases

Diseases are malfunctions of plants caused by fungi, bacteria, viruses or virus-like organisms. Any such organism causing a disease is known as a pathogen and the science of their study is plant pathology. In this book, diseases have been mainly grouped together on the basis of similarity of symptoms as different types of causal organism can have essentially similar effects and require similar treatments. It is appropriate to consider briefly therefore some general aspects of fungal and bacterial biology (viruses are dealt with separately on pp. 277–82). There are probably at least 100,000 species of fungi and they are usually considered to be closely related to, if not actually members of, the plant kingdom. They differ from almost all other plants however in lacking the chlorophyll that enables plants to photosynthesise organic nutrients from the raw materials of carbon dioxide gas and water. Fungi must therefore obtain their nourishment by other means and they do this by growing on dead or living organic matter which they digest extracellularly; that is, by secreting enzymes into the material and subsequently absorbing the digested products.

Varying degrees of specialisation have evolved among fungi and it is generally thought that, within any particular group, the ability to live only on dead matter (saprophytism) is less specialised than the ability to live on either dead or living matter (facultative parasitism). Exclusive dependence on living matter (obligate parasitism) is believed to be the most highly specialised. Most of the fungi described in this book are facultative parasites which can thus live on dead or dying organic matter and use this as a springboard to attack healthy plants or healthy tissues. Relatively few of the fungi important in causing garden diseases are obligate parasites and the rusts and powdery mildews are probably the best known of them.

The basic structural units of almost all fungi are microscopic tubular threads termed hyphae. En masse, such hyphae constitute a mycelium and this, in varying degrees of aggregation, is responsible for the form of all the familiar types of fungal structure, ranging in complexity from toadstools downwards. Fungal mycelium grows and ramifies through the soil, through decaying compost and vegetation and through the diseased tissues of plants. It is usually only visible to the naked eye when it forms reproductive bodies and other relatively large structures. Unlike flowering plants, fungi do not produce seeds but spread and multiply by much simpler structures termed spores. Whereas all seeds are the result of sexual reproduction however, spores may be produced by sexual or asexual means. Most fungi do both and the killing of spores or the prevention of their germination is the means of action of many fungicidal chemicals. Spores produced by different types of fungi or in different ways have different names but the term conidium (plural, conidia) is applied to virtually all asexually produced spores and is used repeatedly throughout this section of the book. The types of spore produced by different fungi are used as the basis for much of the classification of the group. Fungi that produce only asexual conidia and for which no sexual reproductive process is known constitute the group Deuteromycetes, sometimes called the fungi imperfecti. Fungi that produce spores termed ascospores in microscopic, enclosed bag-like structures, by sexual reproduction, constitute the Ascomycetes. This is the largest group of fungi and familiar macroscopic examples are the cup-fungi such as *Peziza*. Fungi that produce sexual spores on unenclosed surfaces are the Basidiomycetes and these spores are termed basidiospores. All the familiar mushrooms and toadstools as well as rusts and smuts belong to this group which is generally thought the most advanced fungal type. Sometimes, most notably in the rusts, other spore types are produced also but it is the presence of basidiospores that remains the important classificatory feature. All remaining fungi are placed in an assorted group termed the Phycomycetes in which are classified such widely diverse organisms as the causal agents of clubroot, potato blight, downy mildews and potato wart. They have no particular spore type in common although many of the important pathogenic forms produce free-swimming swarm spores which move in films of water in the soil or on plant surfaces.

In temperate climates, all fungi face the problem of survival during the winter when the low temperatures do not favour their growth and when their host plants may have died down or entered a dormant state. Some survive in sheltered sites as mycelium but most produce specially toughened structures to resist the adverse conditions. Often these structures are spores but many fungi also develop toughened masses of mycelium (usually known as sclerotia) which serve the same purpose. The success of much disease control depends on preventing the formation, survival or germination of these over-wintering bodies, so breaking the life cycle.

As with all other living organisms, fungi are named for scientific purposes using the Latin binomial system which also serves to indicate affinities between related forms. Again, as with other groups, these names are changed from time to time, usually as detailed study reveals close relationships between types previously thought different. With some fungi however a special problem arises. The Deuteromycetes were referred to above as having no known sexual reproductive process, the emphasis being on the word known. Detailed research often reveals however that a fungus classified and named as a Deuteromycete is in fact only the asexual state of another fungus, named or classified quite separately in another group, usually the Ascomycetes. Thus the same organism has two names. According to internationally agreed rules, the name of the sexually reproducing (or 'perfect') state takes priority and the old Deuteromycete name thus becomes virtually redundant. In this book however, the Deuteromycete names have been retained in those instances where the name is already very familiar to gardeners and/or where it is the asexual state of the fungus that is largely responsible for the disease symptoms. Thus the familiar name *Botrytis cinerea* will be found for the grey mould fungus and not the more strictly correct *Botryotinia fuckeliana*, which is its ascospore producing state. In a few instances where both names may be familiar, both are given.

The effects of parasitic fungi on the plants they infect range from the mild, through chronic to acute and are produced in a wide variety of ways. They may be localised, resulting in restricted damage such as leaf spots. Alternatively, they may be systemic, spreading throughout the entire tissues of an affected plant which may then display a general distortion, rotting or other debilitating effect. Obligate parasites develop specialised hyphae that are able to drain nutrients from host cells without killing the plant; for if this were to happen, they would die also. Facultative parasites on the other hand are much more destructive and grow into and between host cells, producing extensive damage by enzymic or sometimes toxic or growth regulatory (hormonal) action.

There are fewer species of bacteria, (probably about 1600), than there are of fungi and in general they are less significant as pathogens although there are a number of important exceptions. Of these, the effects of the soft-rotting bacteria are those with which gardeners are most likely to be familiar.

Structurally bacteria are much simpler than fungi, each bacterium normally comprising a single microscopic cell which may be rod-shaped, spherical or more or less thread-like. Some bacterial cells are capable of movement and some can produce spores although many do not. They reproduce by simple binary fission – by dividing themselves in two, and can multiply with incredible rapidity, especially under warm conditions. Bacteria occur almost everywhere in the environment but relatively few species ever cause any harm to man, animals or plants.

The classification of bacteria is of little importance to the gardener but it is worth stressing that, once established, bacterial diseases often prove difficult to control for relatively few fungicides or other chemicals are effective against them. Both the symptoms and the gross effects of bacterial infections are similar to those produced by fungi.

RUSTS

(Plate 10)

Basidiomycete fungi (Order Uredinales) which produce rust-like areas of fungal growth on leaves, stems or other plant organs. Rusts affect a wide range of vegetables, fruit, trees and ornamentals and several types are very common in gardens. They have a world-wide distribution with about 4500 species; more than 200 in Britain and W. Europe, the majority in the genus *Puccinia*. Many species have complex, highly sophisticated life cycles and appreciation of some of the basic variations will make it easier to understand and to deal with the harmful effects of the diseases on garden plants. Up to five different spore types may be produced by a rust fungus during its development. These are pycniospores, aeciospores, urediniospores (or summer spores) which spread rust diseases rapidly during the summer, teliospores (or winter spores) which are often the means of overwintering, and basidiospores. Many rusts regularly alternate between different host plants. Pycniospores and aeciospores are then produced on one host species and the remaining spore types on another. The two host plants are often quite unrelated botanically and some rust diseases may therefore be controlled by eradicating one of the alternate hosts to benefit the other.

The effect of rust infection on plants is a general debilitating one. As highly specialised parasites, most develop hyphae within the host tissues and by means of special feeding structures are able to drain nutrient from the plant without killing it.

A number of fungicides are fairly effective in controlling rust diseases. Copper compounds have been widely used in the past but dithiocarbamates, such as mancozeb, as well as sulphur in various forms, are valuable for the treatment of certain rust diseases. The systemic fungicide oxycarboxin is highly effective against many rusts although it is not sold in garden packs and must be obtained from wholesalers in larger quantities. It is certainly worth trying, applied at fortnightly intervals, on ornamentals if other treatments fail. Varieties and cultivars of many plants are resistant to some strains or races of rusts but few plants are resistant to all strains of any particular rust.

It is a usual convention to describe and name rust fungi with reference to the host on which the teliospores are developed. This has not always been followed here however and the various rusts are described under the host plant which is considered most significant from a gardener's point of view. In common parlance, certain rusts are sometimes named according to the most obvious symptoms on the most important host plants. Thus cluster cup rusts are those that produce only aeciospores on the major host plant and urediniospores and teliospores (if at all) on other plants that are horticulturally insignificant whereas blister rusts produce masses of powdery aecia on swellings on woody hosts.

ANTIRRHINUM RUST *Puccinia antirrhini*

First discovered in California, and first definitely reported in England in 1933 and on the Continent soon afterwards. It is commonest in hot, dry seasons and is now the most serious antirrhinum disease.

Symptoms. Chocolate-brown pustules, usually with a surrounding yellow halo, develop on the undersides of leaves with corresponding pale yellowish spots on the upper surfaces. In severe attacks the stems, capsules and sepals are also diseased. The leaves may die and the flowers are either distorted or fail to develop.

Biology. The pustules normally produce urediniospores; occasionally teliospores, but aeciospores are unknown. Teliospores may also be produced in separate pustules from the urediniospores but their role is uncertain and it seems that the rust can overwinter as mycelium on plants in glasshouses or other protected situations. It may also be carried in infected seed.

Treatment. Many antirrhinum cultivars, long thought to be resistant to rust in Britain, have, in recent years, developed the disease. More than one race of the fungus exists in North America and it seems that this must now be the case here. Spraying every two or three weeks from early July to late September with mancozeb or oxycarboxin provides some protection. Diseased plants should be destroyed and antirrhinums not left in the ground over the winter unless absolutely necessary nor grown on land that has carried a diseased crop during the previous two years. Storing seeds for more than one year may eliminate rust from that source.

ASPARAGUS RUST *Puccinia asparagi*

Although considered scarce at present, this disease remains a threat to asparagus growing and has at times reached almost epidemic proportions in parts of Britain. It is occasional elsewhere in northern Europe.

Symptoms. Rust coloured powdery pustules, often in enormous numbers, develop on the feathery shoots or 'bowers' during summer, followed by darker brown streaking on stems, or more rarely, phylloclades ('needles'). Premature death of the shoots may follow. Yellow-orange cluster cups form on young shoots but are often overlooked.

Biology. The development of aeciospores, although common, occurs inconspicuously in yellow-orange aecia on the 'buds' in spring but both urediniospores and teliospores are also produced, the former causing the cinnamon-brown powdery covering on plants and the latter, which later persist and overwinter on the ground, being formed in the dark streak-like slits on the stems. Dew is important for summer spread of the disease which can result in few 'buds' being produced in the following spring.

Treatment. Avoid damp and poorly ventilated sites for beds. Cut back and burn the feathery shoots at the first signs of symptoms in summer in order to prevent the development of overwintering teliospores. As young asparagus is normally not cut until the third year, plant debris lying on the ground in young beds may enable teliospores to persist there undisturbed. These may infect the young buds on which aeciospores form, thus enabling an enormous disease potential to develop. Protect plants by spraying early in the season with mancozeb. If the rusty spore stage is seen early enough, dust with very fine sulphur. The first application of dust should be about three weeks after the last shoots have been cut, with repeat applications at monthly intervals. Sulphur dusting is claimed to be more effective in hot dry weather.

BLACKBERRY COMMON RUST *Phragmidium violaceum*
BLACKBERRY STEM RUST *Kuehneola uredinis* **Pl. 10**

Both diseases are common and widespread on wild and cultivated blackberries and on cultivated loganberries.

Symptoms. Common rust causes deep red to purple spots on the upper leaf surfaces and orange-yellow and/or black pustules on the undersides. Severe infections distort the leaves and cause premature leaf-drop. Orange slit-like lesions may also appear on the stems. Stem rust produces yellowish spots on the canes, and on the upper and lower sides of the leaves.

Biology. The orange-yellow common rust leaf pustules produce aeciospores and urediniospores; the dark ones produce teliospores. The slit-like lesions on the stems also produce aeciospores. The pustules on the upper leaf surfaces are aecia of stem rust while those beneath are either also aecia or produce urediniospores or the unusual light-coloured teliospores. Stem rust teliospores germinate on the leaves and the rust overwinters there as mycelium. Common rust teliospores remain dormant through the winter however and do not germinate until the following spring, when they infect young leaves and shoots.

Treatment. Collect and burn fallen leaves in late autumn and early winter, if practicable. Neither disease affects fruit production seriously but, if special protection is necessary, spray with Bordeaux mixture as the leaves unfold in spring.

CARNATION RUST *Uromyces dianthi* Pl. 10

Introduced into England around 1890 on plants imported from Europe. Normally much more severe on glasshouse than outdoor carnations and occasionally epidemic but usually little more than locally troublesome. Rare on other *Dianthus* spp.; the rust on sweet william (*D. barbatus*) is caused by a different fungus.

Symptoms. Small yellow blisters develop on leaves and burst during summer to become reddish-brown pustules. Similar symptoms may occur on stems, particularly of cuttings or young rooted plants. The disease usually starts near the base of plants and spreads upwards and when the attack is very severe the plants may appear distorted or stunted. It is often troublesome in glasshouses in winter (unless extra heating is supplied) as the disease is favoured by cool, damp conditions.

Biology. The brown pustules contain urediniospores and occasionally teliospores also. The alternate host of carnation rust, the spurge *Euphorbia gerardiana* does not occur in Britain, where the only natural means of spread and overwintering is by urediniospores.

Treatment. Some older cultivars of carnations are very susceptible but most modern types have some resistance or tolerance. It is essential, especially with glasshouse flowers, to water carefully and avoid splashing spores onto healthy leaves. Similarly, the humidity should not be high enough for dew to form on plants and adequate ventilation must therefore be provided. Cuttings should be taken only from healthy plants but when the disease is very slight, carefully snipping off odd infected leaves may give adequate control. Many different fungicides have been used successfully. Spray established plants at ten-day intervals with mancozeb, oxycarboxin or thiram from September to February but take care not to use directly onto blossoms as some discolouration may result. Soil drenches with oxycarboxin around established plants are also very successful. Spray cuttings similarly every ten days during the winter and start spraying plants at other times of the year as soon as symptoms appear. It may be wise not to grow carnations for two years on soil where diseased plants have been found.

CHRYSANTHEMUM RUST *Puccinia chrysanthemi* Pl. 10

Long known in Japan; first found in England in 1895, spreading from there throughout Europe and now fairly common.

Symptoms. Usually commonest late in the summer on indoor chrysanthemums as dirty brown pustules on the undersides of leaves. Yellowish-green spots appear correspondingly on the upper surfaces and severe attacks may cover and damage large areas of leaf. Defoliation and reduction in flower numbers can also result. The disease is relatively unusual on outdoor plants but annual chrysanthemums are sometimes attacked by other less important rust fungi.

Biology. The pustules produce urediniospores; teliospores and aeciospores are virtually unknown in Europe and it is as urediniospores or possibly as mycelium on old leaves that the disease overwinters. Its significance in many parts of the world is now eclipsed by that of the much more serious chrysanthemum white rust (see below).
Treatment. Many modern chrysanthemum cultivars have at least some resistance although a strict routine of hygiene is still essential. All infected plant material should be burnt immediately and, as a precaution, lower leaves stripped from all cuttings, both when initially taken and when transplanted. Care is also needed to avoid wetting the leaves when watering. Spraying with dilute Bordeaux mixture is claimed to give satisfactory protection but some cultivars are damaged by it and mancozeb, oxycarboxin or sulphur applied at fortnightly intervals from the first appearance of symptoms until the end of the season is probably better. The hot water treatment used for eelworm control (p. 89) will check rust disease also.

CHRYSANTHEMUM WHITE RUST

Puccinia horiana **Pl. 10**

This most serious disease was confined to China and Japan until 1963 when an outbreak occurred in England on imported plants. Since then, it has been found here many times and in many other European countries also although a vigorous eradication campaign has probably prevented its establishment in Britain.
Symptoms. Spots, varying from yellow to pale green, on the upper leaf surfaces on glasshouse chrysanthemums are often the most obvious first symptoms. There are usually corresponding dirty-buff and gradually whitening pustules on the undersides. The entire spots may eventually become brown and necrotic in the centre and the plants decline gradually.
Biology. Teliospores germinate to form basidiospores without being released, this change causing the overall white appearance of the pustules. These are the only spore types known and they spread the disease with astonishing speed. There are considerable differences in susceptibility between cultivars but the disease remains an ominous threat to commercial chrysanthemum growing.
Treatment. No control should be attempted and any known or suspected outbreak of chrysanthemum white rust must be reported to officials of the Ministry of Agriculture. The diseased plants will then be destroyed and efforts made to establish the source of the outbreak.

CINERARIA RUST *Puccinia lagenophorae*

Only known in Europe since 1961 but now very common in Britain on groundsel and related weeds of the genus *Senecio*, as well as on cinerarias (*Senecio cruenta*). The symptoms on cineraria are readily distinguished from those of the other rust infecting this and related hosts as cineraria rust forms distinct blisters on the leaves (including the upper surfaces) and stems on which vivid orange and yellowish-white aecial cups develop. No other rust attacking cineraria develops cluster cups nor affects the upper leaf surfaces. The symptoms are nonetheless not as dramatic as on groundsel on which dark brown or black teliospore pustules are also common and which may be virtually killed by the infection. The disease may be avoided by keeping cineraria beds clear of groundsel and by applying a monthly spray of mancozeb, thiram or oxycarboxin as an additional precaution.

GOOSEBERRY CLUSTER-CUP RUST *Puccinia caricina* var. *pringsheimiana*

Common and widespread but much more important in some years than others. Although most significant on gooseberry, the disease can also occur on black or more rarely, red currants.

Symptoms. Deep orange or red pustules develop on the lower leaves, fruits and, rarely, on shoots during spring and early summer. As the summer progresses, yellow-rimmed cluster cups develop on these pustules and as they do so the leaves may curl and swellings develop on the stems.

Biology. Aeciospores produced by the cluster cups are unable to re-infect gooseberries but, when carried by wind, do infect sedges, the alternate hosts. There, urediniospores and teliospores develop and the latter re-infect fruit bushes the following summer, having survived the winter. Dry weather in March is often the prelude to severe attacks as it delays the germination of teliospores and, when conditions become sufficiently moist later, the spores all germinate at a time when there is plenty of new foliage available to infect.

Treatment. Elimination of sedges from the vicinity of fruit bushes is essential. The disease has been serious at times in Norfolk where a mulch of sedges has sometimes been used on soft fruit. Copper-based fungicides are effective and a single spray applied about a fortnight before flowering is recommended. Do not use copper fungicides on the gooseberry cultivars 'Careless', 'Early Sulphur', 'Freedom', 'Golden Drop', 'Leveller', 'Lord Derby', 'Roaring Lion' and 'Yellow Rough' however as they may be phytotoxic. Mancozeb may be used instead.

HOLLYHOCK RUST *Puccinia malvacearum* Pl. 10

First recorded in South America in the middle of the 19th century and soon spread to Europe where it is now extremely common. Mainly attacks hollyhocks but can also occur in gardens on a number of malvas, on tree mallow and on sidalceas.

Symptoms. Raised orange-brown pustules develop on stems, bracts and particularly on the undersides of leaves, with corresponding small yellowish areas on the upper leaf surfaces. The pustules gradually darken and in severe attacks the leaves shrivel and characteristically hang down on the stem. Rarely almost complete defoliation may occur and the disease can sometimes reach almost epidemic proportions.

Biology. All of the pustules contain teliospores. Those formed early in the season can germinate immediately and spread the disease to nearby plants. Spores produced later in the year do not germinate until the following spring, surviving the winter in the pustules produced on the lower leaves and stem.

Treatment. Collect and burn diseased plant material in the autumn and repeat this operation in spring to help prevent the all-important first new infections as later control is very difficult. Also cut off all plants to ground level in autumn and remove the first new leaves in spring as a precaution against their becoming infected. Fortnightly spraying with oxycarboxin from early spring onwards may be successful and sulphur dust is also sometimes effective. Hollyhock leaves, being hairy, are not always easy to wet and a few drops of wetting agent may be added to fungicide sprays.

LEEK RUST *Puccinia allii (=Puccinia porri)* **Pl. 10**

Common and widespread and probably increasing in frequency in Britain. Most important on leeks but also affects onions, chives (especially in the South), garlic and other alliums.

Symptoms. Dusty reddish-orange slit-like pustules develop on the leaves, sheaths and stems during summer. In severe attacks the leaves may turn prematurely yellow and die, the bulb being reduced in size as a result.

Biology. On leeks only urediniospores are produced; on other hosts teliospores also occur while aeciospores are formed elsewhere in Europe but have never been found in Britain. It is now believed that the leek-infecting rust may be a distinct species from that attacking other host plants. In some areas, wild *Allium* species and crop debris can probably be important, however, as refuges for the survival of rust after leeks have been pulled.

Treatment. The disease normally declines with the cooler autumn weather and foliage developing late in the season usually remains healthy but may be at risk in mild autumns. It is often said to be worse on nitrate-rich soils and it is claimed that good supplies of potash will help to suppress it. Other and more reliable control measures are the destruction of infected plants, removal of potential *Allium* weed hosts (although these are infrequently important in Britain), the use of a long rotation (four to five years if possible) and good drainage. Spraying may be worthwhile if severe attacks develop and fortnightly applications of mancozeb, up to two weeks before pulling, are sometimes successful.

MAHONIA RUST *Cumminsiella mirabilissima* **Pl. 10**

A North American disease introduced into Britain in 1922 and now common and widespread throughout Europe. It causes angular, deep red-purple spots throughout the year on the upper leaf surfaces of *Mahonia aquifolium* and *M. bealii.* On the undersides are corresponding powdery brown pustules which produce urediniospores and teliospores. During May and June cluster cups may occasionally occur on greenish-black thickened areas under the leaves. Prune out and destroy diseased foliage, if necessary to ground level, and spray new shoots with Bordeaux mixture or oxycarboxin at 2–3 week intervals.

MINT RUST *Puccinia menthae* **Pl. 10**

Common, widespread and sometimes serious on garden mint, peppermint, marjoram, savory and several other less familiar mints and related genera.

Symptoms. Affected shoots and leaves are pale-coloured, swollen or otherwise distorted early in the season. Masses of rather indefinite dirty orange cups are produced on the stems and undersides of the affected leaves followed by first yellow and later black pustules on previously healthy parts. Large areas of leaf tissue may die and sometimes plants are defoliated.

Biology. On garden mint, a perennial mycelium is established and the fungus is thus able to survive the winter. On all hosts the aecial cups are followed by pale masses of urediniospores and darker teliospores, the latter being the means of overwintering on all plants except garden mint. Teliospores persist in the soil, and are believed to become lodged among bud scales as the new shoots emerge in spring. Several different races of *Puccinia menthae* are now known to occur.
Treatment. It is rare for a mint bed to be wholly infected but the disease is nonetheless troublesome. Rapid burning in the autumn, perhaps with a flame gun, to remove old debris and kill the spores by scorching the soil is often completely successful.

PELARGONIUM RUST *Puccinia pelargonii-zonalis* Pl. 10

Known in South Africa since the early years of the century. First recorded in Europe in 1962, reaching Britain in 1965 and now spreading rapidly throughout the rest of the world. Ivy-leaved and variegated pelargoniums are not affected but the disease can be serious on both pot and bedding zonal types.
Symptoms. More or less circular brown, typically rusty pustules surrounded by a necrotic patch, develop on the undersides of the leaves of affected plants and may occasionally occur on stipules also. When attack is severe, the leaves may fall and this can gradually result in a debilitated plant producing fewer flowers, fewer shoots and consequently few cuttings.
Biology. The pustules produce urediniospores (other types of spore being unknown in Britain) which can lie dormant on apparently healthy leaves or stipules until the onset of moist conditions prompts germination. They can also remain viable on dead leaves for up to three months.
Treatment. On indoor plants, remove and destroy diseased leaves as soon as they are noticed and take care that leaves do not remain wet for long periods. On outdoor plants, such hygiene is scarcely practicable but fortnightly sprays with mancozeb will afford good protection. A number of systemic fungicides, including benomyl, thiophanate-methyl, oxycarboxin and triforine are also claimed to be effective.

PLUM RUST *Tranzschelia discolor* Pl. 10

Common and widespread on plums and, less commonly, on apricots, peaches, nectarines and almonds. The alternate hosts are anemones on which considerable damage can occur in some areas.
Symptoms. Very vivid small yellow spots appear on the upper surface of the leaves from July onwards and corresponding brown powdery patches develop on the undersides. As the summer progresses, the patches progressively darken and by autumn are usually completely black. Severe attacks may result in total yellowing of the leaves and, in some cases defoliation which if repeated over a number of years, gradually weakens the trees. Diseased anemones develop an abnormally erect habit, with distortion of the leaves and reduction in the number of leaf lobes. The under surfaces of the leaves bear tiny pale yellow-brown cluster cups with whitish margins and the plants usually fail to flower.
Biology. The brown powdery patches on plum leaves are urediniospore pustules and the gradual darkening is due to their replacement by black

teliospores. The latter germinate in spring and infect the alternate hosts; cultivated *Anemone coronaria* and other anemone species. The resulting infection extends into the rootstock and can persist there, aeciospores from the cluster cups on the leaves subsequently reinfecting plum trees. Because the fungus perennates in anemones, diseased plants serve as a permanent reservoir of spores for infecting plums. There is some doubt concerning the significance of the anemone host as far as plum trees are concerned, since severe attacks may develop in plum orchards far removed from any anemones and the fungus can probably persist on plum trees as mycelium.

Treatment. Rust is not usually severe on plums in gardens although spraying the trees with mancozeb when the fruit is half grown and again after picking may occasionally be necessary. Although the spraying of diseased anemones with mancozeb may be partially successful, their continued presence, as sources of spores near to plum trees means that they are better uprooted and destroyed.

ROSE RUST *Phragmidium tuberculatum* Pl. 10

Common and widespread throughout Britain and northern Europe, although the precise identity of the rust fungus responsible is still disputed.

Symptoms. The first symptoms which arise in spring are bright orange pustules on leafstalks, branches, the undersides of leaves (especially on the veins) and any persisting fruit. More familiar, however, is the development of yellow-orange pustules on the undersides of the leaves during summer, and these become increasingly interspersed with black pustules as autumn approaches.

Biology. The first formed orange pustules produce aeciospores which, after germination and infection, give rise to the second yellow-orange pustule type in which urediniospores develop. The teliospores produced in the black pustules survive the winter on fallen leaves and germinate in spring to produce basidiospores which, spread by wind or rain splash, reinfect the bushes.

Treatment. Although several species and most cultivars of roses are susceptible, 'Allgold', 'Arthur Bell', 'Fragrant Cloud', 'Lilac Rose', 'Pink Favourite', 'Queen Elizabeth', 'Rose Gaujard', 'Sarabande' and 'Super Star' show some resistance in certain areas. The cultivars 'Fashion', 'Hector Deane' and 'The Doctor' are almost always very susceptible. Ideally, gardeners should collect up and burn rose leaves in autumn but anyone with more than two or three plants will rightly dismiss this as academic advice. Mancozeb, oxycarboxin and some other fungicides are all fairly reliable when sprayed fortnightly from April to September. Some gardeners prefer to use Bordeaux mixture (although it may disfigure some cultivars) in the early part of the season and mancozeb from June onwards. The effectiveness of fungicides against black spot (p. 270) and powdery mildew (p. 207) should be considered if these diseases are also troublesome.

SMUTS

(Plate 10)

Basidiomycete fungi (Order Ustilaginales), closely related to the rusts and most producing black, soot-like spore masses. Over 800 species exist, nearly half in the genus *Ustilago*, and have a worldwide distribution. They cause important diseases of cereals and grasses but relatively few are serious on garden plants. Sweet corn, leeks, onions, salsify and scorzonera are the only non-ornamental garden species attacked and very few smuts affect woody plants. The symptoms are unlikely to be mistaken for any other disease although the superficial growth of sooty moulds (p. 209) may at first sight seem similar. Infected organs may be distorted, as in sweet corn, but some smuts, particularly those of the genus *Entyloma*, which is most important on dahlias in gardens, cause little more than a leaf spotting.

Although related to the rusts, the life cycles of smuts are much less complicated. Smut infections occur on the young parts of plants and those described here either develop on seedlings from spores on the seed or in the soil, or on actively growing points such as shoots or flowers from spores blown or splashed from soil or plant debris. The spores are known as teliospores (also called chlamydospores or brandspores) and burst en masse from stems, leaves, flowers, seeds or rarely, from roots. They form in bodies termed smut balls, always contained within special pustular structures known as sori. These sori form from the mycelium in certain discrete parts of the host plant. On germination the teliospores do not infect directly and, as in the rusts, basidiospores (usually called sporidia in smuts) are often produced first and it is usually these that actually start the infections.

Some smut diseases, sweet corn smut for example, do not spread far through the plant from the original point of infection. Others, like anther smut of scillas, develop systemically and permeate almost the entire host tissues. Such systemic smuts can continue to infect new shoots annually as they are produced from some perennial infected organ, such as a rootstock.

The smut diseases important in gardens are generally difficult to control. Teliospores, once in the soil, can persist for several years and most fungicides offer little protection although Bordeaux mixture is useful in some cases. Destruction of the plants and choice of a fresh site for new stock is usually the only satisfactory measure.

CARNATION ANTHER SMUT *Ustilago violacea*

Common and probably widespread on both outdoor and glasshouse carnations and also on wild species of several caryophyllaceous genera. The flower stalks become stunted and the anthers distorted and filled with a purplish mass of spores. The fungus is probably systemic throughout the plant and possibly spreads internally from the lateral buds. Destroy diseased plants before the flower buds open, never take cuttings from such plants and thoroughly disinfect glasshouses where the disease has occurred. Avoid growing carnations in contaminated soil for at least five years. Weekly spraying with mancozeb may check established infections.

DAHLIA SMUT *Entyloma calendulae* f. *dahliae*

Originated in South Africa and now very common throughout Europe.

Symptoms. Circular or elliptical pale yellow-brown spots arise on the leaves, normally from July onwards; these gradually enlarge, darken and merge but usually retain a yellow margin. Darker areas within the lesions can sometimes be seen in a strong light. It appears first on the lower leaves, then spreads upwards and large areas of leaf tissue may ultimately die.

Biology. The causal fungus is a form of the species that produces calendula smut and spores produced in the lesions may germinate *in situ* to form sporidia which spread the disease to other leaves or plants. It persists as spores in the soil but transmission does not occur in seeds or tubers. There is some variation in cultivar susceptibility.

Treatment. Burn diseased foliage in autumn and remove any leaves adhering to the tubers before storing. Do not grow dahlias in contaminated soil for at least five years. Three or four fortnightly sprays of Bordeaux mixture may check the disease on growing plants, if applied from early in the season.

ONION SMUT *Urocystis cepulae*

Originally a North American disease, reaching Europe around 1880 and now occurs occasionally. Worse in cool seasons and Northern areas.

Symptoms. Dull streaking or spotting develops beneath the leaves and scales of young onions, chives, garlic, leeks and shallots. Affected leaves are swollen, twisted or otherwise distorted and the dark streaks eventually burst out as a black powdery mass. Some plants are killed; others survive to maturity but remain stunted or malformed.

Biology. Spores may persist in the soil for up to 15 years in the absence of host plants. When they germinate, they usually infect the growing points so that all new leaves in turn develop the disease. The initial infection is always on the first leaf but soon becomes more or less systemic.

Treatment. Because only the first leaf can be the site of initial infection, seedlings from a disease-free seed bed can safely be transplanted into contaminated soil. Care is needed however to avoid the transfer of infested soil (on tools for example), to clean sites. Slightly affected sets are a common source of the disease although the sale of these is illegal in Britain under the Sale of Diseased Plants Orders. Formaldehyde applied to the seed drill is sometimes effective if applied at the rate of 7 ml. formalin (=40% formaldehyde) to 1 litre water per 10 metres of drill. Apply it with a watering-can immediately after the seed is sown and close the drill afterwards; the seeds are not damaged unless the soil is very dry.

SWEET CORN SMUT *Ustilago maydis* Pl. 10

Long known and common throughout the warmer parts of Europe, where high temperatures favour spore germination. Assumed significance in Britain for the first time in the hot summers of 1975 and 1976 on sweet corn and on ornamental and forage maize.

Symptoms. Swelling and other, sometimes very extensive, malformation arises on cobs, inflorescences, stems and occasionally on leaves and the entire plant may be distorted. The swellings are often ashen or whitish and contain a dark powdery mass which later bursts out.

Biology. Spores released from diseased organs can either germinate directly or persist in soil and crop debris. The fungus does not develop systemically in host plants but produces localised lesions.

Treatment. Some cultivars are resistant but not to all fungal races, which complicates the problem and makes choice difficult. Destroy diseased plants and crop debris and avoid growing sweet corn on the same land for at least five years.

DOWNY MILDEWS

(Plate 11)

Phycomycete fungi (Family Peronosporaceae); all are obligate plant parasites and are closely related to the common pathogenic genera *Phytophthora* and *Pythium.* Unrelated to the powdery mildews, with which they are sometimes confused and, with a few exceptions, they are a very understudied group biologically. Few very important garden diseases are caused by downy mildews although that on lettuce is commonly troublesome in wet seasons. They produce off-white or faintly purplish mould in damp conditions, which, despite the name, may differ little from powdery mildew growth in general appearance. Seen under a lens, downy mildews appear as many individual spore-bearing heads whereas powdery mildews are denser and velvety with the individual heads hard to distinguish. When wiped off with the thumb, yellowing of the plant tissues is commonly seen under downy mildew growth. Spread of the diseases during the growing season takes place by production of asexual spores. Resistant oospores are formed by many downy mildew fungi and although in some they are probably the main means of overwinter survival, in others they appear to be functionless. It seems probable that each species of downy mildew is only able to infect one particular plant genus and that within these mildew species, further sub-divisions can be made of types capable of infecting only single plant species. Some downy mildews also exist as races, each with a further host restriction to particular ranges of cultivars.

Traditionally, copper-containing fungicides have been used for downy mildew control but at present the dithiocarbamate, mancozeb is the most effective chemical available for garden use. Most systemic fungicides available to gardeners are of little value.

CRUCIFER DOWNY MILDEW

Peronospora parasitica **Pl. 11**

Common and widespread on vegetable, ornamental and wild crucifers and found frequently on cabbages, cauliflowers, Brussels sprouts, radishes, stocks, swedes, turnips, wallflowers and watercress, among others. Sometimes a problem on bedding alyssums. This disease is often seen, together with white blister (p. 210), on the weed, shepherd's purse.

Symptoms. Most common on seedlings; yellowish specks develop on the upper surfaces of the leaves and cotyledons, with off-white patches of mould growth beneath in damp conditions. Severely diseased seedlings are stunted or killed but on mature plants, brown-yellow angular patches develop on the upper leaf surfaces with, in humid conditions, white mould beneath. The upper leaf surface is sometimes blistered around the patches and when attack is severe, the leaves turn yellowish and die. There may be pale brown discolouration of cauliflower curds, with black streaks and spots in the stem, although these symptoms can also arise from various other causes. Black internal spotting and streaking are also commonly found in radish.

Biology. Soil-borne; infects seedlings through the roots and the fungus sometimes develops systemically within. Conidia, produced on the mould, are rapidly spread by wind and carry the disease to neighbouring plants. Resistant oospores are sometimes produced and are probably the method of overwintering.

Treatment. Provide ventilation to seedlings in frames, boxes or glasshouses; do not allow water to drip on them and avoid close spacing, both of seedlings and young plants. Mancozeb sprays may be effective if applied fortnightly from the time when half of the seedlings have emerged. Four or five sprays should normally be adequate but must not be applied within a fortnight of harvest.

LETTUCE DOWNY MILDEW *Bremia lactucae* Pl. 11

Common and widespread on glasshouse and outdoor lettuces but different strains also affect other members of the Compositae, including centaureas, cinerarias, gaillardias, globe artichokes, helichrysums and several weed species. On lettuce it is most serious in damp conditions and appears either as a seedling disease in spring or as a disease of mature plants late in the season. Downy mildew on lettuce is often followed by grey mould attack (p. 236).

Symptoms. Pale green or yellowish areas develop on the upper leaf surfaces, with corresponding patches of delicate, downy whitish mould beneath in damp conditions. The lesions later become brown and angular as the tissues die. Plants may eventually become generally debilitated and stunted.

Biology. The first infections are initiated by conidia, or by oospores in the soil which originated from a previous diseased crop. Spread in the growing season is by further conidia produced on the mould growth and no wounds are necessary for the infection to occur. Several races of the fungus exist and they are not all able to infect all lettuce cultivars.

Treatment. Remove and destroy diseased plant debris and maintain as long a rotation as possible between lettuce crops. Spray fortnightly with mancozeb from the time when half of the seedlings have emerged but do not spray within a fortnight of harvest. In glasshouses take care to keep water off the leaves, maintain good ventilation and remove infected leaves as they appear.

ONION DOWNY MILDEW *Peronospora destructor*

Common and widespread on onions and shallots, especially in cool wet seasons and in wet areas, such as parts of the South and West of Britain.

Symptoms. Affected leaves turn yellow and die from the tip downwards but at this stage the disease can be confused with the many other problems which are discussed under onion leaf rot (p. 253). In moist conditions a fine off-white, but later purplish mould growth develops on dead parts. Bulbs are also infected and soften and shrivel in store and develop some mould growth, but this can be confused with the commoner symptom of neck rot (p. 238).

Biology. The foliage of autumn-sown plants may be infected when young by airborne spores, the fungus then growing down into the bulb where it remains dormant over winter. In spring, it produces spores which spread the disease to newly sown plants and this disease may therefore become more important as the growing of autumn-sown bulb onions increases in popularity. Semi-perennial onion varieties, such as Egyptian onions, commonly act as sources of the disease in gardens. Resistant oospores are sometimes produced in infected foliage and can survive in the soil for at least five years and also act as initial disease sources when they germinate. **Treatment.** The disease is very difficult to control. Remove and destroy affected plants as soon as they are noticed and do not replant the same site with onions for at least five years. Avoid damp, sheltered sites and maintain good weed control to ensure air flow through the crop. Do not sow onions in spring close to autumn-sown plants, which may carry hidden bulb infection. Some protection may be given by spraying fortnightly with mancozeb from the time when half of the seedlings have emerged, but not within a fortnight of pulling.

POWDERY MILDEWS

(Plate 11)

Ascomycete fungi (Family Erysiphaceae); all are obligate plant parasites and they cause some of the most familiar and serious garden diseases. Conidia are produced on a whitish mycelial coating to leaves, stems, buds and occasionally other above ground parts of plants to which the development of the spores gives a characteristic powdery appearance. Affected parts commonly become discoloured or distorted and the effect of powdery mildews is one of a general debilitation of the host plant through the slow decline of diseased tissues. There are well over one hundred species with a world-wide distribution but they are generally most serious in warm, dry climates. Although conidia are by far the commonest spore type, most powdery mildew fungi are also capable of producing ascopores which are borne among the hyphae in very small black bodies termed perithecia. Only seven powdery mildew genera are important in northern Europe; *Erysiphe*, *Microsphaera*, *Phyllactinea*, *Podosphaera*, *Sphaerotheca*, *Uncinula* and *Oidium*, the genus into which are placed those species with no known ascospore-producing state. The classification and naming of powdery mildew fungi is confused and has been frequently changed. The situation is further complicated because many species attack many types of plant and because more than one powdery mildew species may attack the same host plant. To avoid pointless repetition, relatively few powdery mildews are described and named here individually; those that are have certain unique features either of biology or importance. The remainder are considered jointly on p. 208.

Several fungicides are effective in controlling powdery mildews but they may need applying at least fortnightly during the summer in very dry seasons. Sulphur was used in the past but damages some plants and has been replaced in most instances by the systemic fungicides triforine, benomyl, thiophanate-methyl and carbendazim.

APPLE POWDERY MILDEW *Podosphaera leucotricha* **Pl. 11**
Very common and widespread and one of the most serious apple diseases. The same fungus occurs less frequently and less seriously on pear, quince and possibly on medlar.

Symptoms. A powdery white coating begins to develop on leaves, shoots and subsequently on flowers soon after leaf bud burst in spring. Blossoms wither and drop and leaves fall later as the symptoms spread rapidly to healthy foliage and shoots. A few leaves persisting at the end of an otherwise bare shoot are commonly seen on some cultivars. Very rarely a powdery coating may be seen on fruit but early infections which subsequently disappear commonly cause a web-like fruit russet.

Biology. The first infections in spring arise from fungus that has lain dormant over winter following infection in the previous season. Conidia are produced on these primary infections and are then carried by wind to spread the disease to secondary sites increasingly far from the original infected shoot. Such infections take place throughout the summer except when there is water actually lying on the leaf surfaces. Some buds may be killed by the disease but most survive to become the primary sources of the next year. Despite the very general development of mildew on shoots during summer the disease dies down in winter and the fungus in the buds is entirely responsible for the first infections in the following year. Early symptoms and effects vary slightly depending on whether the source bud was on a spur shoot or was terminal or lateral on a main shoot but the end result is more or less the same.

Treatment. There are basically three main ways to treat mildew; in winter, in spring and through the summer.

In winter remove all buds and shoots distorted by mildew and cut back any affected woody shoots to several buds below the limit of visible whitening. On small young trees, the cutting out of affected shoots can be continued throughout the season.

During the early pink bud stage in spring, carefully remove as much as possible of the affected leaves (the primary infections) but avoid showering spores onto healthy foliage. If done carefully and thoroughly it is possible, on young trees, virtually to eliminate mildew for the entire season in this way.

On large trees and as an added precaution on young trees, spraying should also begin at the early pink bud stage and continue fortnightly to late July. The best chemicals available to gardeners are the systemic fungicides benomyl, thiophanate-methyl or carbendazim which also have the merit of giving excellent control of scab (p. 228) and some control of red spider mite (p. 172). Sulphur is a traditional remedy but the cultivars 'Beauty of Bath', 'Cox's Orange Pippin' and 'Newton Wonder' among others, are damaged by it and it is probably better avoided.

CRUCIFER POWDERY MILDEW *Erysiphe cruciferarum*
Common and widespread, appearing as a thin powdery off-white coating to leaves, stems and seed pods of most crucifers; especially common and severe on swedes and turnips, sometimes on kales and increasingly so on closely spaced commercial Brussels sprouts, although still infrequent on this host in gardens. Powdery mildew of poppies is also probably caused by

this fungus. Badly affected leaves become yellowed and die and drop prematurely while the entire plant may wilt and roots of swedes and turnips may crack. The disease spreads rapidly by conidia in hot, dry weather and it became increasingly severe in the dry summers of the mid 1970's aided also by mild winters which it survives on crop debris. Dry light soils seem to favour this disease and early crops are very prone so sow turnips and swedes as late as possible. There is some variation in resistance among cultivars but none are sufficiently reliable to be recommended for garden use and no effective fungicides are available for small-scale application. Also see white blister (p. 210).

AMERICAN GOOSEBERRY MILDEW

Sphaerotheca mors-uvae

A North American disease, appearing in Europe about 1900 and spreading very rapidly. Now widespread but the intensity of attack varies considerably from year to year. In some recent seasons black currants have been more severely affected than gooseberries.

Symptoms. A powdery white coating appears on young shoots from April onwards; spreading rapidly to all new growth under moist, still conditions but the leaves are often least affected. The symptoms later intensify and stems and fruit develop a brown felty covering containing black dot-like bodies. The shoots are malformed and stunted and the fruit small and tasteless. On red and especially black currants, the symptoms are similar but the leaves are more severely affected. The disease occurs occasionally on other *Ribes* spp.

Biology. The mildew spreads during the season by conidia. The bodies produced later in the felt-like mycelium are perithecia within which ascospores develop. Some perithecia fall to the ground and discharge their spores in autumn; others remain over winter and discharge in the spring but it is not known how important are the overwintering spores in initiating new infections in the following year and mycelial threads surviving in the buds are probably the most important means of persistence. On black currant it is almost certain that ascospores from perithecia on fallen leaves initiate the new infections which are usually not seen until May.

Treatment. Avoid planting in damp shady situations, leave plenty of space between bushes, and control weeds. Cut out infected shoot tips in early autumn and maintain a free air circulation in the crop by winter pruning. Avoid excessive use of nitrogenous fertilisers. To prevent severe attacks on gooseberries, spray with sulphur starting just before the flowers open, again after fruit set and again two to three weeks later. On black currants start the sprays as the flowers open and continue fortnightly until early July. Sulphur damages some gooseberry cultivars however and should not be used on 'Careless', 'Early Sulphur', 'Golden Drop', 'Lord Derby', 'Leveller', 'Roaring Lion' or 'Yellow Rough'. Benomyl or thiophanate-methyl are safe alternatives for these cultivars. Spraying with a solution of washing soda is a traditional remedy for gooseberry mildew but is rarely very successful.

ROSE POWDERY MILDEW *Sphaerotheca pannosa* **Pl. 11**
Very common and widespread. One of the most familiar garden diseases. Occurs in almost all situations but roses in dry sheltered sites such as against walls are particularly prone.

Symptoms. Not usually seen before May. Powdery off-white patches or more extensive coatings develop on leaves, stems, buds or rarely flowers. Leaves may turn yellow and/or purple, and wither and drop prematurely while buds may fail to open. On stems, flower stalks and especially sepals, there may be a denser mat-like growth, sometimes localised on stems around the prickles.

Biology. The main initial spring infection and all spread during the season is by wind-blown conidia produced on the powdery mycelium. From late summer onwards ascospores are produced in dark coloured cleistothecia within the white mats of denser mycelium. In some parts of Europe these may survive the winter to initiate some infections in spring but there is no evidence that they do so in Britain, where the disease persists as mycelium or conidia on plants in glasshouses or in other sheltered sites.

Treatment. Choose resistant cultivars where possible. There is considerable variation in susceptibility but few cultivars can be relied upon at all times and on all sites; 'Super Star' and 'Frensham' for instance were once very resistant but are now attacked in most localities. The following lists give a general indication of some commonly grown cultivars that are particularly resistant or susceptible. Members of National rose or horticultural societies may be able to obtain more extensive lists.

Resistant large-flowered bush roses (Hybrid Teas): 'Alec's Red', 'Alexander', 'Blessings', 'Champs Elysées', 'Charlie's Aunt', 'Chicago Peace', 'Colour Wonder', 'Gail Borden', 'Honey Favourite', 'King's Ransom', 'Mme Louis Laprerièrre', 'Michèlle Meilland', 'My Choice', 'National Trust', 'Peace', 'Pink Favourite', 'Pink Peace', 'Prima Ballerina', 'Rose Gaujard', 'Troika', 'Uncle Walter', 'Yellow Pages'.

Susceptible large-flowered bush roses (Hybrid Teas): 'Betty Uprichard', 'Christian Dior', 'Crimson Glory', 'Eden Rose', 'Frau Karl Druschki', 'Golden Melody', 'Hugh Dickson', 'Josephine Bruce', 'Mme Butterfly', 'Peer Gynt', 'Picture', 'Spek's Yellow', 'Super Star'.

Resistant cluster-flowered bush roses (Floribundas): 'Allgold', 'Arthur Bell', 'City of Belfast', 'City of Leeds', 'Dickson's Flame', 'Escapade', 'Golden Slippers', 'Jan Spek', 'Korresia', 'Manx Queen', 'Marlena', 'Michelle', 'Molly McGredy', 'Moon Maiden', 'Orange Silk', 'Queen Elizabeth', 'Sea Pearl', 'Southampton'.

Susceptible cluster-flowered bush roses (Floribundas): 'Anne Cocker', 'Elizabeth of Glamis', 'Frensham', 'Iceberg', 'Lilli Marlene', 'Masquerade', 'Orange Sensation', 'Rosemary Rose', 'Woburn Abbey', 'Zambra', *Rosa gallica* 'Officinalis', *R. gallica* 'Versicolor'.

Because it is rarely possible to rely entirely on cultivar resistance, cultural and chemical methods should be practised also. Use mulches on dry sites, to retain moisture, and also restrict the use of nitrogenous fertilisers which promote susceptible soft growth. Apply chemical sprays fortnightly or three-weekly from April to September in all but the wettest seasons or most mild attacks, when less frequent sprays from May until August are adequate. Many chemicals give some control but if black spot (p. 270) and rose rust (p. 199) are also troublesome choose those proprietary products which include more than one chemical for this purpose. Dinocap was very effective against mildew but is no longer readily available, while benomyl and thiophanate-methyl are only moderately effective but not damaging. A carbendazium and maneb mixture is also available as a combined mildew and black spot control.

GENERAL POWDERY MILDEWS

In addition to the more individual diseases described above, there is a large and widespread group of powdery mildews, virtually indistinguishable by symptoms and all amenable to similar treatment. All occur most extensively in hot and dry seasons on closely spaced plants and may represent species of most of the common powdery mildew genera although each individual mildew species has a restricted host plant range. Garden plants on which one or more of these commonly occur are: acers (especially field maples), anemones, antirrhinums, aquilegias, asters (almost always affected in most gardens), begonias (especially serious on the cultivar 'Gloire de Lorraine'), calendulas, carnations, centaureas, chrysanthemums, cinerarias, clematis (often worst on large flowered and late flowering cultivars), cucurbits, cyclamens, delphiniums, digitalis, doronicums (almost invariable late in the season but usually too late to affect flowering), hawthorn, honeysuckle, hydrangeas (commonest on *H. macrophylla* in glasshouses, the mildew growth being accompanied by red-brown spots), Japanese spindle (originated in Japan and now very common in the South and West of England and elsewhere near the sea), laburnums (sometimes impairs flower formation), lawn grasses, lupins (may be devastating late in the season), marigolds, myosotis (often seriously affects flowering), parsnips, parsley and other kitchen herbs, peas, peaches, phlox, poppies, ranunculus, salsify, scabious, schizanthus, scorzonera, senecios, solidago, succulents (especially kalanchoes and sedums on which black spots occur surrounded by typical mildew growth), sweet peas, valerians, verbascums, vines and violas.

Symptoms. Almost identical on all hosts; a powdery white coating develops on leaves, stems and sometimes on other above ground parts. It is usually seen first on the leaves as discrete off-white patches which may later spread to cover the plant extensively. The leaves may turn yellowish, die and drop prematurely and the entire plant may droop.

Biology. Summer spread is by conidia; overwintering usually in crop debris either as conidia, mycelium or ascospore-producing bodies (usually perithecia). Some species may be seed transmitted.

Treatment. There is little variation in cultivar susceptibility although some pale-flowered delphiniums may be resistant to mildew. The best chemical treatments for garden use are probably benomyl, thiophanate-methyl or triforine sprayed fortnightly or three-weekly with the addition of a few drops of wetting agent. There is little that can be achieved in the way of general garden husbandry that is likely to have much impact on most mildew attacks. It is sometimes suggested that diseased parts of lightly infected shrubs such as hawthorn should be clipped out and burned but the showering of spores onto healthy leaves that this operation will cause may well do more harm. Diseased plant debris should however always be burned in autumn.

SOOTY MOULDS

(Plates 3, 4 and 11)

Black or dark brown soot-like deposits, commonly known as sooty moulds, often appear on the upper surfaces of leaves and on other parts of plants that are infested by sap-feeding pests, such as aphids (p. 104), adelgids (p. 120), whiteflies (p. 102), scale insects (p. 124) or mealybugs (p. 127). Many of these pests excrete a sticky, sugary fluid ('honeydew') which is derived from the sap on which they feed. Small droplets of honeydew accumulate on leaves, stems and fruits beneath the feeding sites of the pests and this honeydew, which can sometimes be heard pattering onto leaves, may form a varnish-like coating over exposed surfaces. Various non-pathogenic fungi, especially certain species of *Cladosporium*, then grow on the contaminated surfaces and produce the sooty deposits of fungal spores and mycelium.

Thick layers of sooty mould can build up fairly quickly and often cover all upper surfaces of affected leaves on shrubs and even on large trees. These symptoms are sometimes mistakenly thought to be the result of industrial atmospheric pollution but their true cause can usually be easily established by searching affected plants for signs of pests. Bay laurels, birches, camellias, ornamental citrus, lime trees, oaks, plums, roses, tomatoes, vines and willows are particularly susceptible but many other plants can be affected, both outdoors and under glass. Sooty moulds are especially troublesome on glasshouse and house plants since these are particularly likely to be attacked by sap-feeding pests and do not have the benefit of periodic rainfall, which washes some of the honeydew and sooty moulds off outdoor plants.

The fungi that produce sooty moulds do not cause direct damage to plant tissues but the black deposit cuts off light from the leaves, reducing photosynthetic activity and sometimes causing premature leaf-fall, with consequent weakening of the plants. The deposits also spoil the appearance of plants and contaminate ripening fruits, especially plums, grapes and tomatoes. Sooty blotch disease (p. 271) causes similar symptoms on apple, pear and plum fruits but is caused by a quite different fungus. Controlling the pests that cause the initial fouling of plants should lead to a general improvement although it may be some months before deposits disappear from older leaves. If possible, spray or sponge leaves with water to remove thick deposits. Affected fruit can be easily cleaned by washing or wiping and is usually quite edible since the moulds do not penetrate below the surface.

Honeydew and sooty moulds are sometimes a nuisance on cars, especially if they are parked regularly under limes, oaks or other large trees infested by aphids in summer. If it is impossible to avoid such situations, affected vehicles should be washed frequently to prevent damage to the paintwork.

WHITE BLISTERS

(Plate 11)

A small group of diseases caused by Phycomycete fungi of the genus *Albugo*; related to *Pythium*, *Phytophthora* and downy mildews. Only one species is of any consequence in Britain and northern Europe.

CRUCIFER WHITE BLISTER *Albugo candida*

Widespread but varies greatly in intensity from year to year. Most usually seen on the weed, Shepherd's purse but sometimes a problem on cultivated vegetable and ornamental crucifers and commonly occurs associated with crucifer downy mildew (p. 202). Small white lesions, at first smooth but later powdery as the spores are produced, make affected plants look as if they have been splashed on the above ground parts with white paint. Distortion of the affected organs or of the entire plant results if the fungus permeates the tissues. Spores are distributed by wind, insects or rain splash and germinate via a swimming swarm spore stage to infect through stomata. Resistant oospores are also produced and remain dormant in the soil for several months before they too germinate. Several races of this fungus exist but they are not all able to infect all crucifer species. Diseased plants should be destroyed and although further treatment is not usually necessary, severe attacks can sometimes be checked by spraying fortnightly with Bordeaux mixture or mancozeb up to one week before harvesting.

NEEDLE CASTS

(Plate 11)

The premature shedding of leaves is a fairly common secondary symptom of many plant diseases but the wholesale browning and drop of conifer needles, often with little or no obvious infection of the shoots, is a difficult symptom to diagnose. In gardens, it is seen most commonly soon after planting out Christmas trees (Norway spruce) which are dying because of damage to, or lack of, roots. Other types of root damage, as well as some diebacks, shoot and twig blights, leaf spots and especially winter cold damage are among other very common causes. There is additionally a group of diseases termed needle casts, often serious in forest plantations but in gardens only likely to be a problem on young trees growing close to mature plantings. All are caused by fungi (mostly of the Ascomycete order Phacidiales) and many species are common and widespread. Needle casts are most frequent on pines and larches but also occur on spruces and Douglas fir. On trees affected by needle casts, the needles commonly turn brown and fall in scattered groups or *en masse* from entire branches or even whole trees. On close examination with a lens, tiny black dot-like fungal fruiting bodies can usually be seen on the needles but these are absent from one common form of larch needle cast and small orange bodies are sometimes present instead in early summer on affected Douglas fir needles. It should also be noted that a number of rust fungi (p. 191) infect conifer needles and produce small, usually orange or white pustules. Most of the fungi responsible for needle casts also live harmlessly on fallen needles and on those killed by other causes and it is from these that the spores carry the disease. Because they can be saprophytic, however, the presence of fruiting bodies on needles need not indicate serious damage. Treatment in gardens is unlikely to be necessary but if elimination of other causes suggests a needle cast disease on small and valuable ornamentals, spraying with Bordeaux mixture in the following season may be worth a try. The timing of the sprays varies with different trees and the chemical may be damaging, especially in dry weather, so expert advice should be sought.

WILTS

(Plate 11)

This is a very common and widespread group of diseases all of which result in essentially similar symptoms. All, with the exception of Dutch elm disease (p. 212), are caused by normally soil-borne or occasionally seed-borne organisms and are therefore considered jointly. On herbaceous plants, the symptoms are often difficult to distinguish from root and foot rots and other stress factors, with which they may be associated. Host plants affected include fruit, vegetables, ornamentals and trees but the biology of the diseases is in all cases very similar. The most important garden plant species affected by wilts are acers, antirrhinums, asters (China and michaelmas daisies), beans, begonias, brassicas, carnations and other *Dianthus* spp., catalpas, cherries, chestnuts, chrysanthemums, cotinus, cyclamen, cucumbers, dahlias, delphiniums, elms, fuchsias, godetias, heleniums, limes, paeonies, peas (especially early in the season), potatoes, privet, quince rootstocks, raspberries, rhododendrons, rhubarb, robinias, roses, strawberries, sumach, sweet peas, tomatoes and wallflowers.

Symptoms. The only truly characteristic symptom is a brown or black discolouration seen in the conducting elements of the stem (whether herbaceous or woody) when cut through *well* above ground level. This discolouration can be traced both upwards in the plant and downwards towards the roots but if it is confined to the basal parts it is more likely to be caused by root damage than by a wilt. Accompanying effects may include epinasty (downbending) of the lower leaf stalks, wilting (often with, initially, some recovery at night), yellowing and later shrivelling of the leaves with the lower, or outer in the case of rosette plants, being affected first. Although many other factors, including root damage or cultural malpractices, such as inadequate or over-watering, can cause plants to wilt, these symptoms usually show on younger, not older leaves first. True wilt effects are sometimes confined to one side of the plant only and on raspberries, wilt disease is known as blue stripe since blue striping appears on one side of affected canes. Wilting of the leaves may sometimes occur very suddenly, especially during hot weather, and on trees it can be very dramatic when almost all the foliage droops simultaneously. Eventually plants become generally debilitated and may die.

Biology. The damage is often considered to result from the blockage of the water-conducting tissues of the stem, so starving the leaves of water. This blockage may occur because of cell collapse but is more usually because of gums and other materials causing physical obstruction. Although such mechanical blockage is a regular feature, it is now believed that the production of toxic substances by the pathogens in the conducting tissues is at least as important in causing the wilt effects. Many wilt organisms persist for several years in the soil; *V. albo-atrum* for example surviving as resistant mycelium, *V. dahliae* as small bodies termed microsclerotia and *F. oxysporum* as specialised spores known as chlamydospores. Wilt diseases are commonly associated with eelworm attack and wounds caused by these pests may provide infection sites, although on young plants at least, undamaged roots can also be affected.

Treatment. Wilt diseases are very difficult to tackle satisfactorily in gardens. Although many cultivars are resistant to wilts, few are available for garden use, although there are some notable exceptions which are usually so designated in catalogues. In glasshouses, do not plant any species, but especially not tomatoes, too early and into cold soil. Raising the temperature may help glasshouse plants to recover but the effectiveness of this treatment depends on the causal organism involved and this is impossible to determine without scientific tests. Increase the shading in glasshouses and apply no basal water but spray the foliage from above. When plants are lightly infected, pack the bases of the stems with damp peat, which may promote healthy new root growth. After removal of diseased plants, thoroughly disinfect glasshouses, all pots, boxes, benches, tools and other utensils and raise the next crop of plants in sterilised compost. In gardens, remove affected herbaceous plants together with as much as possible of the surrounding contaminated soil and avoid growing any of the above listed species on the same site for as long as possible. It should however be noted that carrots, parsnips and parsley are among the vegetables not affected while China asters and peas are both affected by specific wilt fungi and may safely be followed in a rotation by any other type of plant. On trees and shrubs it is worth trying a soil drench with spray strength benomyl or thiophanate-methyl around affected plants, repeating at fortnightly intervals until the symptoms subside or the treatment fails, when uprooting is the only solution.

DUTCH ELM DISEASE *Ceratocystis ulmi* Pl. 11

The most devastating plant disease that most people in Britain are ever likely to see. It also occurs less seriously throughout northern Europe, except in the most northerly areas. The disease was first recorded in Britain in 1927 and was serious for many years but then died down to occur sporadically and cause only restricted branch damage, but rarely tree death. It flared up again after the late 1960s when a new, more virulent, strain of the fungus was accidentally imported on logs from Canada and it has subsequently changed the landscape of much of England through killing many millions of trees. The disease is called 'Dutch' because of the extensive research formerly made on the problem in Holland.

Symptoms. The familiar yellowing of the foliage, usually from July onwards, is often followed very rapidly by branch and sometimes total tree death in the same season. In less severe attacks death may not occur until the following year but survival is rare once attack by the virulent strain of the fungus has occurred. Dark brown streaks may be visible when the bark and outer wood are peeled back from affected branches. Corresponding brown blotches may be seen in transverse section when branches are sawn through.

Biology. The fungus is spread to healthy trees by the elm bark beetles, *Scolytus scolytus* and *S. multistriatus* (see p. 171). The fungus in affected wood produces yeast-like cells which are transported within the water-conducting tissues. In common with other wilt diseases, the blocking of these conducting elements (so bringing about the dark streaks) and the production of a toxin, which is carried up to the leaves, result in the wilt symptoms. Under the bark of trees so weakened, the bark beetles tunnel and lay their eggs. The larvae resulting from these burrow further and so produce the characteristic fan-shaped galleries within which the spore-forming bodies of the fungus are produced. The main types of such bodies are small conidia-bearing structures and tiny, black, flask-shaped perithecia, which produce ascospores. In warm weather during summer, the mature beetles emerge from the galleries bearing fungal spores collected either by eating or by mere physical contact. These beetles fly to healthy trees and feed on the branches, eating out small channels in the crotches of twigs, into which the spores are introduced as they do so. The fungus thus gains access to the conducting tissues of trees to repeat the disease cycle and, once killed, the tree can remain a reservoir of infective beetles for about two years. Considerable disease is spread between closely growing trees, such as those in hedgerows, through common root systems and the beetles are not involved in this process.

Treatment. Control is barely practicable. All elms are susceptible, although smooth-leaved elm and wych elm seem slightly less so than others. In the early years of the recent epidemic in Britain, attempts were made to limit the spread by felling affected trees but this was soon recognised as of little value except in areas where the disease was not established. Here such felling is still important. Dead trees should however always be felled as, in the early stages, they provide breeding grounds for the beetles, and in the later stages become safety hazards as they decay. Unfortunately the felling and destruction of large trees, especially in urban situations, is usually a matter for experts and can be expensive; however, set against the possible damage that can result when trees fall, it is a wise investment. The timber of felled trees may safely be used but the bark must be stripped off and burned. In situations such as hedgerows where root transmission may be an important means of spread, healthy trees may be protected by digging a trench approximately 15 cm wide and not less than 60 cm deep midway between the trees and diseased neighbours. Great care is needed however, in urban situations to avoid damage to buried pipes and cables. The injection into healthy trees of systemic fungicides related to benomyl has been used as a means of protection against Dutch elm disease. The procedure has also been applied to eradicate the disease from trees in the very early stages of infection. Although it is possibly worthwhile with trees of exceptional value, it is of limited use as the procedure must be repeated annually and is by no means a complete protection. It can only be performed by experts with special equipment.

CANKERS, DIEBACKS, STEM and TWIG BLIGHTS

(Plate 12)

This section includes a wide variety of diseases affecting woody plants. The term canker is sometimes used to describe any disease condition in which there is sharply limited death of plant tissues resulting in a lesion. Under this definition however would be included diseases such as parsnip canker or tomato canker which in reality are forms of rot (p. 230). True cankers occur on woody plants and result from death of the cambium tissue in the inner bark, thus giving rise to an area where no new bark forms. Sometimes the lesion heals after one year's growth but commonly there is a repeated annual extension, often during the winter months while the host is dormant, and with some healing overgrowth during the summer.

Although a few viruses may give rise to canker symptoms (p. 215), their biology is very specialised and the causes of all the cankers described in this section are fungi or bacteria. Among the former, ascomycetes, and especially those of the genus *Nectria*, are important.

Cankers superficially indistinguishable from those of fungal or bacterial origin can arise through repeated spring or autumn frost damage but these are relatively unusual. More commonly, frost (p. 292), like mechanical wounding (p. 298), results in a lesion which heals after one year. Cup or dot-like fungal fruiting bodies or coloured, creamy bacterial slime on cankers are good indications of a microbial cause although not always conclusive. Several types of canker can serve as entry points for wood decay organisms (p. 248) and in such cases a toadstool or bracket-like fruiting body may appear. Small twig lesions can also be associated with certain leaf diseases or scabs.

When death of the cambium in a canker extends until the entire branch is girdled (such as commonly occurs on small twigs), the shoots beyond that point die. This is one form of dieback. In many other types of dieback, a gradual dying of stems or shoots from the tip downwards can occur in the absence of a canker lesion. Sometimes fungal fructifications occur on such branches but the causes are frequently less apparent. Wholesale dying back of entire shrubs and trees is more likely to be a secondary symptom of a root rot (p. 242) or other soil factor, such as waterlogging (p. 295) or drought (p. 291). Very sudden and complete death of entire branches can occur following wilt attack (p. 211) whereas certain environmental factors, such as frost or cold wind, can cause the death of shoot tips but usually there is no progressive killing of complete shoots. Attack by pests can also cause dying back but usually the pests themselves are present on the plants or evidence of their damage (such as boring holes) can be found at the junction of the live and dead tissues of the branches.

It is difficult to be precise over what is meant by a stem or twig blight as the word blight now has only a vague meaning scientifically. It is probably easiest to consider these conditions as diseases in which small stems or twigs are killed suddenly by the girdling action of very small cankers or by some very rapidly invading airborne organism, usually bacterial. Although the individual effects of such single infections are slight, the almost simultaneous appearance of disease over a large part of a tree or shrub can be very serious. The order cankers, diebacks, stem and twig blights is roughly one of increasing rapidity of action and of increasing difficulty of control. Slowly developing branch cankers should be pruned out and the wound treated with a sealant containing fungicide. Cankers, other than apple and pear canker or the bacterial canker of cherries and plums, on the main stems of garden trees are generally best tolerated until the tree shows obvious signs of decline or of decay from secondary infection. The cutting back of branches and twigs affected by diebacks and blights up to 30 cm beyond the visible limit of tissue death may save plants from some types of attack although in others a pruning or clipping out may need to be so drastic as to cause complete disfigurement and may compound the problem by providing more wounds through which fresh infections can occur. Chemical sprays are generally of little value against canker diseases and although they may arrest some branch and twig infections, the treatment of large trees is wholly impractiable.

APPLE and PEAR CANKER *Nectria galligena* f.sp. *mali* **Pl. 12**
Common and widespread and by far the most serious of several types of canker on these trees. It affects a number of other trees including poplars and hawthorn, but not ash, which is attacked by a different form of the fungus.

Symptoms. Elongated sunken branch lesions develop and are often centred on a leaf scar, small side branch or bud. The bark in the centre of the canker dies and may break away. Although branches may be girdled by cankers and die back beyond the lesion, some dieback of young twigs can be caused without any true canker being formed. In spring and summer small creamy pustules may appear on cankers but more usually masses of small rounded bright red bodies are seen in autumn and winter. On some cultivars cankers may have the effect of partial ringing and may temporarily result in an increased crop while occasionally a paper bark condition may occur (also see silver leaf disease p. 221). The canker fungus may also infect the fruits and form a brown rot, usually around the eye, while they are still on the tree and cause them to remain hanging over winter.

Biology. The creamy pustules produce conidia while the red bodies are ascospore-forming perithecia. Both spore types initiate infections after transport by wind or rain splash to small bark cracks, pruning cuts or, most importantly, the leaf scars formed during autumnal leaf fall. Cracks in lesions formed by the scab fungus (p. 228) are also common infection sites while diseased fruit hanging on trees can also be a source of disease.

Treatment. Some apple cultivars, 'Bramley's Seedling' and 'Newton Wonder' most notably, show resistance but all apples are prone to some degree of cankering. Some general cultural practices may help to lessen canker incidence; do not plant apples on wet and clayey sites, do not over-apply nitrogenous fertilisers and, if at all possible, grass down under the trees. Badly diseased trees should be cut down and burned but where attack is less severe, prune out all cankered branches, pare away the damaged tissue on large stems and treat all cuts with a wound sealant containing fungicide. Because poplars are attacked by the same canker fungus they should not be used as windbreaks around apple orchards and grey alder is a suitable alternative for this purpose. Although a spray with benomyl at the time of autumn leaf fall may lessen the number of leaf scar infections, this is only worthwhile on new trees if the garden has a history of cankering.

CLEMATIS DIEBACK *Ascochyta* sp. and other causes

A common and widespread problem but the causes are still imperfectly understood and may not always be the same.

Symptoms. Younger leaves droop suddenly, the upper parts of the leaf stalks blacken and affected leaves then wither and die, the entire process sometimes taking only a few days. Discoloured lesions may occur on the stem at or near ground level and dark patches also appear on some otherwise healthy leaves.

Biology. Very little is known about the biology of this condition. The stem lesions are caused by a fungus of the genus *Ascochyta*, which may originate from the soil, other plants or from the leaf patches. Infection possibly occurs in conditions of high humidity through small wounds caused by insects, wind damage or even stem ties but there is no extensive fungal development within the plant tissues.

Treatment. Especially difficult as the cause and biology are so incompletely known but it is important to avoid mechanical damage to clematis stems, particularly from securing ties. Sprays with benomyl are sometimes used to control powdery mildew on clematis and these probably help to suppress the *Ascochyta* on the leaves also. There appear to be some differences in cultivar susceptibility but insufficient is known to enable firm recommendations to be made. Following the death of a plant from dieback it would be wise to remove the soil to a depth of about 30 cm around the affected site and replace it with fresh soil before planting new stock.

CORAL SPOT *Nectria cinnabarina* Pl. 12

Exceedingly common and widespread; the fungus occurs mainly as a saprophyte on dead branches (it is very often seen on old pea sticks) but also as a parasite causing dieback on many woody plants including acers, aesculus, apples, beech, cercis, currants, elaeagnus, elms, figs, gooseberries, limes, magnolias, mulberries, pyracanthas and walnuts. It is rare on conifers.

Symptoms. Masses of pinhead-sized vivid salmon-pink cushion-like pustules occur at all times of the year on dead and dying twigs and branches. Sometimes, usually during spring, similarly-sized dark red bodies may occur with, or instead of, the pink pustules and on close examination these look much like minute raspberries. Large branches may wilt in summer if they are affected near to the base while sometimes a small canker may be produced which gives rise to girdling dieback.

Biology. The fungus probably never infects living tissues directly but commonly invades through dead parts or pruning cuts, especially in early spring, and also through the base of the stems when plants are growing in very damp conditions such as among dense grass. It commonly invades frost-damaged twigs on several types of tree including walnuts. Once inside the branches, the fungus invades the water-conducting elements and so causes the wilt symptoms. Spread of the pathogen occurs by conidia produced in the pink pustules or by ascospores from the dark red perithecia. There may be several strains of the fungus differing in virulence but this is uncertain at present.

Treatment. Eradication of the pathogen is very difficult because it is so commonly present on dead wood. Rigorous hygiene can help however; do not leave piles of dead branches in the vicinity of fruit trees or bushes and never leave dead branch stubs when pruning. Diseased soft fruit bushes are best uprooted entirely and burned but valuable ornamentals should be pruned free of affected wood to at least 15 cm beyond the visible symptoms, the cuts treated with a wound sealant containing fungicide, the affected debris burned and the remaining healthy parts of the plants sprayed immediately and then twice more at three-weekly intervals with thiophanate-methyl.

FIREBLIGHT *Erwinia amylovora* Pl. 12

This is a devastating problem in North America and was the first plant disease proved to have a bacterial cause. It was found in Kent in 1957 and has since spread northwards and westwards in Britain and now also occurs in Holland, Denmark, France, and Belgium and is likely to spread to other parts of northern Europe. It affects many rosaceous trees but is most serious on pears, apples, hawthorn, cotoneaster, pyracantha, sorbus, stranvaesia, amelanchier and chaenomeles although it has not been recorded in Britain on all the known host plants. It is a notifiable disease in England and Wales.

Symptoms. On pears it is most severe on vigorous trees; dead blossoms or dark-brown leaves hang from affected branches looking as if they have been scorched by fire. There may also be dark green-brown bark lesions while the fruits, if formed, are brown-black and wrinkled. All affected parts may exude a glistening white slime in warm damp conditions and if the bark is peeled from the edge of the lesions, there may be a red-brown, often mottled colouration beneath. The symptoms spread rapidly and mature trees may be killed within six months. The much less serious bacterial blossom blight is very similar in the early stages but infection usually does not progress beyond the spurs. On apple, the shoot tips at first wilt but remain green and exude drops of golden slime; later the leaves and shoots turn brown. On hawthorn, the leaves turn yellow, then brown and usually drop. On most other host plants the symptoms are similar to those on pear but on pyracantha, usually only the blossoms are affected.

Biology. The slime on affected parts contains the bacteria which are spread by insects or rain splash to the blossoms before moving down the blossom stalk into the fruiting spurs and branches. Host plants that produce blossom early are less severely affected because insufficient bacteria develop in time to cause much infection. Many pear cultivars which produce summer blossom are devastated however and for this reason the growing of the cultivar 'Laxton's Superb', which produces abundant summer blossom, is severely restricted by law in Britain. In host plants other than pears, infection through the shoots rather than blossoms is the normal process. Spread across country may be by bees or other insects, by transport of diseased plants or other means.

Treatment. In England and Wales, as fireblight is a notifiable disease, any known or suspected outbreak must by law be reported to the Ministry of

Agriculture. Since 1968 the uprooting and burning of affected trees has usually only been required in areas where the disease is not yet established and although detailed procedures have now been worked out by which fireblight can be fairly successfully controlled they must be carried out under expert supervision. Gardeners should be alert to any suspicious symptoms on fruit trees, ornamentals and particularly hawthorn hedges and should not hesitate in calling in a Ministry adviser. The continued planting of new hawthorn hedges, especially in commercial fruit growing areas, is to be discouraged.

GOOSEBERRY GREY MOULD DIEBACK

Botrytis cinerea

The grey mould fungus causes dieback on many plants but is probably most serious on gooseberries, although similar symptoms occur on currants and raspberries also. The leaves first wilt then become brown and shrivelled and, as they do so, the bark cracks and in damp conditions fluffy mould growth develops. Ultimately entire bushes may die, branch by branch. If the symptoms are detected sufficiently early, it may be possible to save plants by cutting out and burning the affected parts but later, cure is impossible and the complete bush must be dug up and destroyed.

PLUM and CHERRY BACTERIAL CANKER

Pseudomonas mors-prunorum **Pl. 12**

Common, widespread and may be very serious on cherries and plums but is less important on apricots, peaches and ornamental *Prunus* species.

Symptoms. These are of two distinct types. Cankers usually occur on the branches or crotches of cherries or on the main stems of plums. At first they appear as shallow depressions bearing (especially on cherries) blobs of amber-coloured gum but later enlarge and may exude quite copiously although on plum stems they may merely form elongate depressions, sometimes confined to one side only. Affected branches may die back after yellowing or stunting of the leaves. The second symptom is the development of dark brown more or less circular leaf spots in late spring which may ultimately merge and form patches of dead tissue which may drop out and leave a 'shot hole'.

Biology. Cankers are initiated in autumn or winter by bacteria which are splashed from the leaves and enter the stem tissues, usually through leaf scars. The lesions extend rapidly in the spring but then activity usually declines and the bacteria die out. No new cankers form during spring or summer when the trees are resistant to this type of infection but at this time the foliage is attacked instead to cause the leaf spots on which more bacteria form.

Treatment. No plum or cherry cultivars are resistant and a few, including 'Victoria' and 'Early Laxton' plums, are very susceptible. Control of this disease is very difficult in gardens although if care is taken when tying trees (especially plums) to support stakes this will lessen any bark damage through which initial infection could arise. The severity of the disease can be appreciably lessened by high working onto resistant rootstocks, such as the myrobalan type plum stocks or F12/1 cherry stock. Some control of the leaf spotting can be achieved by spraying in spring with Bordeaux mixture and may be worthwhile on ornamental *Prunus* spp. Spraying of cherries with Bordeaux mixture in mid-August, again two weeks later and finally in early October may be successful in reducing the number of bacteria present during the susceptible leaf-fall stage of tree growth. This is a very difficult operation to perform satisfactorily however; not only are cherry trees often large and not amenable to spraying but Bordeaux mixture can be phytotoxic and may damage the plants significantly.

RASPBERRY CANE BLIGHT *Leptosphaeria coniothyrium*

Common in Britain but also occurs elsewhere in northern Europe. The disease does not affect black currants, loganberries or other hybrids but is particularly serious on the raspberry cultivar 'Lloyd George' although 'Norfolk Giant' and others are also susceptible.

Symptoms. Leaves on the fruiting canes shrivel and die and the canes themselves bear dark patches just above ground level on which the bark cracks and masses of small pin-head sized bodies develop. The canes also become markedly brittle and may snap at the position of the lesion.

Biology. The fungus infects the canes from the soil and both conidia and ascospores may be produced on the lesions; infection, as with spur blight, may occur through areas damaged by the raspberry cane midge (p. 146). The disease is readily spread on affected canes, spores from which can contaminate clean soil, or in soil adhering to stools.

Treatment. Cane blight can often be avoided by handling canes with care to prevent damage but when attack has occurred, cut back diseased canes to below soil level and burn them, taking care to disinfect the secateurs afterwards. Do not transplant stools from a site where the disease has occurred and do not plant strawberries near to infected raspberry canes as *L. coniothyrium* can cause a troublesome root disease of strawberries. Where cane blight attack is linked solely with cane midge damage, control can be obtained by applying an insecticide such as fenitrothion in early May and again about two weeks later.

RASPBERRY SPUR BLIGHT *Didymella applanata*

Common and widespread on raspberries and loganberries but usually only serious in northern areas and in Britain most frequent in Scotland.

Symptoms. Although large irregular brown blotches may form on the leaves early in the summer these are seen infrequently but by August purple lesions appear on the canes and gradually turn brown-black and then whitish. Ultimately 10 cm or more lengths of cane can be affected and are sometimes girdled. As the winter progresses, the cane lesions become less distinct, turn silvery and are dotted with tiny black bodies. Canes rarely die as a result of spur blight but since buds on affected nodes are killed, the number of fruiting spurs and therefore the fruit yield are reduced in the following season. As with cane blight (above), spur blight may follow attack by cane midge (p. 146) although the insect is less significant for this disease.

Biology. The silvery sheen on the lesions is due to the shrinkage of the inner tissues and the admission of air between these and the outer bark. The black bodies are of two types: pycnidia which produce conidia, and perithecia which discharge ascospores in spring when the initial infections occur. Either type of spore can initiate such infection, normally via the leaf stalks and buds. Ascospore release and germination is favoured by wet conditions and the disease is therefore worse in seasons with a damp spring although summer drought can accentuate the problem as the fruits produced on diseased canes tend to dry and shrivel under such conditions.

Treatment. Cut out and burn affected canes and maintain normal cane thinning early in spring to prevent overcrowding. Spray established infections (or healthy canes when the disease is known to be prevalent in the area) with benomyl or thiophanate-methyl. Apply the first spray when the canes are about 15 cm high and repeat four times at fortnightly intervals. The new raspberry cultivars 'Malling Admiral' and 'Leo' have some resistance to spur blight.

ROSE CANKERS

Several cankers and associated diebacks are widespread on roses but stem canker (*Leptosphaeria coniothyrium*) and grey mould dieback (*Botrytis cinerea*) are the commonest and most serious.

Symptoms. STEM CANKER: brown, cracked and sunken lesions often with a reddish border, develop on stems. The lesions increase in size and eventually form large, irregular cankers which may girdle the stems and cause a dieback. Tiny black bodies usually develop on the canker surface. Stem canker can be a problem following budding when the disease spreads both up and down from the union.

BROWN CANKER: numerous small rounded reddish stem spots which later form off-white lesions. These may develop into light brown cankers, often with purplish margins and on which minute black pointed bodies may arise. The stems are commonly girdled and, depending on the time of year that this occurs, the upper parts of stems may die or produce knobbly gall-like outgrowths.

BRAND CANKER: reddish stem spots which enlarge, darken and develop small pale brown centres on which small black dot-like bodies may form. In spring, the damaged areas may appear black and eventually the lesions may merge, girdle the stem, and cause a dieback.

CLATHRIDIUM CANKER: small brown bark depressions with purple margins, usually around a small wound. Occasionally they girdle the stem to cause dieback but more usually remain confined to one side. The margins of the lesions characteristically remain smooth and, unlike stem cankers, never become ragged although small black bodies commonly form on damaged tissue.

GREY MOULD DIEBACK: most commonly a dying back of stems from the apex, old flower or fruit stalk, dead branch stub or similar origin. The symptoms are common on stems after the tip has been damaged by cold or frost. Fluffy grey mould growth may be present but is not invariably so.

BRIAR SCAB: masses of black crusty bodies on the stem; frequently around thorns.

Biology. Grey mould biology is described in detail elsewhere (p. 232) but this and all the other rose canker fungi infect through small wounds, dormant buds, pruning cuts or similar points of weakness. Conidia and, in some instances, ascospores are produced in the dark bodies on cankers and may bring about significant spread of disease during the growing season.

Treatment. Remove dead flower heads, buds and damaged shoot tips as a matter of routine. Taking care not to leave stumps when pruning will help eliminate potential infection sites. Cut out and burn any cankered stems and remove entire bushes if the disease is extensive but if the damage is slight, spray three times at three-weekly intervals with thiophanate-methyl after removal of the diseased parts, taking care to spray onto all cut surfaces.

SILVER LEAF *Chondrostereum purpureum*

Very common and widespread, mainly on rosaceous trees and especially on plums, of which it is the most serious disease. Other common hosts are almonds, apples, apricots, cherries, hawthorns and roses while among plants of other families affected are currants, gooseberries, laburnums, poplars and willows, although not all develop foliage symptoms. It is infrequent on pears. This disease is caused by a close relative of many wood-rotting fungi but, unlike them, it does not induce decay.

Symptoms. Leaves develop a silvery sheen, usually at first confined to a single branch but soon spreading. Later, the leaf tissues may split and browning may occur at the margins and around the mid-rib. Affected branches have a dark brown discolouration in the wood and usually die back and, from late summer onwards after such branch death, small bracket-shaped or flat crust-like fructifications with a lilac-purple spore surface develop on the bark. The upper surface of the bracket or the under surface of flattened forms, is brown and hairy and the fructifications are soft and leathery when wet; shrivelled and crisp when dry. Spread of the disease from affected branches to the rest of the tree may occur but is not inevitable. Silver leaf is common on apples following top grafting and is often accompanied by papery peeling away of the bark, although this symptom can also accompany apple canker (p. 215) or arise as a result of poor soil texture. A common and superficially similar symptom to silver leaf is that of a nutritional disorder known as false silver leaf. It induces no staining in the wood however and may be treated by mulching the trees and giving fertiliser in the following season.

Biology. Basidiospores from the fructifications infect through wounds in the wood, normally from September to May. Toxic substances produced by the fungus are carried upwards to the leaves where they cause the leaf tissues to separate. Air entering the spaces so formed brings about the silver effect but there is no fungus present in the leaves.

Treatment. Natural recovery is quite common and it is best to wait and see for some time after the appearance of silvering. The leaves are not a source of disease and need not be destroyed but once branches begin to die, they should be cut back beyond the limit of any brown stain in the wood, flush with the parent branch or stem, and the wound treated with a sealant. If the entire tree is silvered, especially if silvering appears on the suckers, the main stem and roots will be affected and all should be uprooted and burned. Piles of logs and dead branches of any type should not be stored in orchards. Although all plum cultivars are liable to be affected, 'Victoria' is the most susceptible while damsons and greengages are usually fairly resistant.

Gardeners are commonly apprehensive regarding the legal status of silver leaf disease. In the Silver Leaf Order, 1923 it was stated that all dead wood of plums and apples should be burned on the premises before July

15th in each year and where such dead wood was in the trunk and extended to the ground, the whole tree, including the roots should also be burned. Moreover, wood of any kind bearing fructifications of the silver leaf fungus was required to be destroyed. While such actions are thoroughly to be recommended however, at the present time the legal requirements are no longer enforced.

WILLOW ANTHRACNOSE *Marssonina salicicola*

Several fungi commonly cause small cankers and/or diebacks on willow stems, sometimes associated with leaf spots, but by far the most important in gardens is the anthracnose fungus *Marssonina salicicola*. It may seriously disfigure weeping willows and is almost epidemic in wet seasons.

Symptoms. Most obvious are small ashen or pale brown stem lesions, red-brown spotting on the leaves and a gradual defoliation and dying back of the shoot tips, sometimes to the extent that weeping trees cease to weep as their shoot length is reduced.

Biology. *M. salicicola* produces conidia on the stem and leaf lesions and although these are the means of disease spread, the biology of this condition is imperfectly known.

Treatment. Virtually impossible on large trees as the lesions and damaged twigs are usually so numerous that pruning out the affected parts is impracticable. On small trees in gardens, Bordeaux mixture sprays applied every three weeks from just before bud burst until early July (avoiding very hot spells) may prevent the disease from becoming established. Although not the best chemical treatment, it is the only one available for gardens.

GALLS, LEAF CURLS and WITCHES' BROOMS

(Plate 12)

Many malformations are caused by a disturbance of the normal growth of plant organs, usually through some disruption of the plant's hormone systems. Galls are swellings and other abnormal growths that arise from localised tissue proliferation and may occur on roots, stems, leaves or, more rarely, on flowers or fruit. Those described in this section are caused by several quite unrelated types of fungi and bacteria but they are in many respects very similar to the galls induced by some eelworms (p. 84), mites (p. 172) and insects (p. 158). The causes of two of the most serious gall diseases, clubroot of crucifers and wart of potatoes, are curious organisms, generally considered to be distantly related to fungi but lacking mycelium. Witches' brooms are abnormal proliferations of shoots on woody plants. They may be broom-shaped but are often more irregular, sometimes resembling birds' nests. Most are caused by fungi although viruses, mycoplasmas and other sub-microscopic organisms induce witches' broom symptoms on some plants while the exact causes of many are unknown.

Most stem galls and witches' brooms are of little consequence although they do disfigure ornamentals and in such cases can often be pruned out. Root and tuber galls are sometimes very serious in weakening affected plants and are caused by organisms with very long persistence in the soil.

Control of them is extremely difficult and the maintenance of existing disease-free land by strict hygiene is essential.

Most leaf curls are caused by Ascomycete fungi of the genus *Taphrina* and result from unequal expansion or growth of the leaf tissues although superficially similar conditions may be caused by certain viruses, mites and insects and some other leaf diseases such as scabs can, when severe, also cause puckering of leaves. The only serious leaf curl disease is that of peach and this can usually be controlled by fungicide sprays.

CLUBROOT *Plasmodiophora brassicae* Pl. 12

Very common and widespread. Clubroot is probably the most problematic disease to deal with in gardens. It affects all crucifers but is rarely a problem on radishes and in gardens it is most frequently seen on Brussels sprouts, cabbages, cauliflowers, swedes, turnips, stocks and wallflowers and can be particularly damaging on Chinese cabbage. Contrary to common belief, it does not cause disease symptoms on plants such as lettuce, beetroot and spinach which are sometimes confused with crucifers. It is generally worse on acid, poorly-drained soils and usually less serious in hot, dry seasons and on spring-maturing crops.

Symptoms. Sometimes the above-ground parts of affected plants wilt on hot days but may, in the early stages of the disease, then recover at night. In severe attacks plants may be stunted, take on a red-purple tint to the foliage and occasionally topple over or die. The roots are swollen and distorted, either in the form of a single large gall (the club symptom) or, when the lateral roots are affected, as clusters of galls reminiscent of dahlia tubers (the finger and toe symptoms). Knobbly swellings occur at the bases of naturally swollen, bulbous roots such as those of swedes and turnips. In the later stages the galls are often affected by soft rot organisms and decay to an evil-smelling mass. Somewhat similar galls may be caused by the turnip gall weevil (p. 169) but these, when cut through, are seen to be hollow and may contain a weevil larva. The later stages of cabbage root fly attack (p. 150) are sometimes superficially similar but also usually contain larvae or evidence of their burrowing activity. The small hard swellings on swedes and turnips of unknown cause known as hybridisation nodules (p. 276) may be very difficult to differentiate from clubroot, while hormone herbicide injury (p. 301) to stem bases can also be confusing.

Biology. The causal organism persists in the soil as resting spores which can probably survive in the absence of host plants for twenty or more years. Ultimately, these spores germinate (possibly under chemical stimulation from the host plant roots) to produce swimming swarm spores which invade intact roots, usually through the root hairs. Further swarm spores of a different type are produced within the root hairs and, after liberation, spread the infection to other parts of the roots which then swell and become distorted. More resting spores form within the swellings and are released into the soil when the galls decay. Although this disease is less severe on alkaline, well drained sites, the reasons for this are not known. The pathogen is most commonly transferred to disease-free sites on infected transplants or in soil on plants, boots or tools.

Treatment. Extremely difficult. There is almost no resistance to clubroot in garden crucifers other than radishes and the need to keep this disease out of uncontaminated soil cannot be overstressed. Certain measures can be adopted to this end. Never obtain brassica plants from a source not known to be disease-free; in practice this means if possible raise them from seed in sterilised compost rather than buy them. Scrub boots and tools thoroughly with very hot soapy water after use on contaminated land. Once a garden has been contaminated, there is no realistic means of eradicating the disease from the soil although certain procedures may help to lessen its effects. Improvement of the drainage and liming to raise the pH to about 7.5 may lessen the severity although care is needed not to over-lime if potatoes are to be grown on the same land as this may encourage common scab (p. 229). It is wise to maintain as long a rotation as possible between cruciferous crops although the three to four years practicable in most gardens is unlikely to have much effect on badly contaminated land. Earthing up diseased plants may stimulate new roots to form and so hold off the worst effects of the disease until after the crop matures. At the end of each crop, carefully dig up all diseased plants and as much as possible of the root system before it decays. These plants must be destroyed, ideally by drying and burning but, failing that, by burial in a deep hole in a remote corner of the garden.

Transplants may be protected by dipping the roots in a 10% aqueous suspension of pure calomel (mercurous chloride) or a 2% suspension of thiophanate-methyl or benomyl before planting out. Half a litre of suspension will be sufficient for about 200 plants which should be swirled in the liquid in bunches of about twelve at a time. Better adherence is achieved with calomel if the fungicide is made up in 1% cellulose wallpaper paste instead of water. Alternatively, if only a few plants are to be grown, raise each in an individual pot (of about 12 cm diameter) of sterilised compost or soil and plant it out in the complete pot ball; roots growing beyond the ball develop small galls but the plants are not seriously affected. There is no effective chemical treatment for direct-sown plants and although the application of calomel dust to the drill is often recommended the results are usually disappointing. In a large and badly contaminated garden the granular soil sterilant chemical dazomet may be tried in accordance with the manufacturer's directions. It will not eradicate the disease but, if applied with care, may diminish significantly the numbers of spores present near to the surface. Proprietary phenolic emulsions drenched onto the soil may have similar, localized, partial-sterilant effects. Deep digging is still likely to bring new, unaffected spores to the surface however. There are many traditional remedies for clubroot, including applications of rhubarb, manure and soot, or mothballs and egg-shells to planting holes; there is no proven scientific basis for any of these but they are probably worth trying if all else fails.

CROWN GALL *Agrobacterium radiobacter* var. *tumefaciens* **Pl. 12**

Very common and widespread on many woody and herbaceous host plants. This is by far the commonest gall-forming disease and is probably most serious on fruit trees. Among the plants on which symptoms are most frequently seen are apples, beetroot, begonias, cherries, chrysanthemums (marguerites), currants, dahlias, elms, euonymus, gooseberries, grapevines, hawthorns, hollyhocks, loganberries and blackberries, lupins, mari-

golds, marrows, peaches, pears, pelargoniums, phlox, plums, poplars, privet, quinces, raspberries, rhododendrons, roses, runner beans, swedes, sweet peas, tomatoes, wallflowers, walnuts, willows and many wild plants.
Symptoms. These are very variable and it is almost impossible to be certain of differentiating crown gall from all other types of gall. Usually irregular but sometimes more or less spherical, knobbly swellings can arise on almost any part of affected plants but occur most typically at the junction of root and stem. They are common and often very large (1 m or more in diameter) on the trunks and branches of trees and are also frequently seen on woody stocks produced by layering at the point where the rooted layer is severed from the stool. On shrubs and trees, galls are usually very hard but on herbaceous plants they are commonly soft and fleshy and, when old, may decay through the action of soft rot bacteria. On some cane fruits, elongate masses of small round galls may burst through the cane surface. The root-forming masses known as burr knots on the branches of certain apples and other plants are superficially similar to crown gall but are not caused by a pathogen.
Biology. Imperfectly understood but several strains of this bacterium exist and they are not all able to infect all host plants. The initial infection almost certainly arises when soil-inhabiting bacteria are blown or splashed on to above-ground parts and penetrate through small wounds. The bacteria may possibly move within affected plants to establish secondary galls some distance from the initial infection. Despite the often dramatic appearance, the effects of crown gall on the vigour of the host plant are rarely serious.
Treatment. Extremely difficult but rarely necessary. Since most damage is to fruit trees, these should not be grown on land which has supported diseased plants. Handle planting stock, especially of fruit trees, with care to avoid wounding, sever apple stocks from the stool with a clean cut and cut out and burn disfiguring galls on ornamentals. The application of sulphur to contaminated soil is sometimes claimed to be effective but the relatively minor importance of the disease in gardens probably does not justify the effort and expense.

PEACH LEAF CURL *Taphrina deformans* Pl. 12

Common and widespread on peaches, almonds and nectarines but rarely on apricots and infrequent on trees in conservatories or other enclosed sites. Worst following cold wet springs and particularly prevalent on trees growing in cool, damp situations such as close to expanses of water. Similar diseases occur on cherries, pears, alder, poplar, elms and oaks.
Symptoms. Soon after bud burst in spring, the young leaves thicken, curl and twist, becoming yellow with reddish areas. The puckering and reddening increases and a pale bloom covers the affected leaves, which later turn dirty brown and drop prematurely. Young shoots and more rarely flowers and fruit may similarly become twisted and distorted and after repeated attacks trees lose their vigour and fruit production declines. Certain aphids also cause curling of peach leaves but the presence of the insects or their cast skins on affected plants readily distinguishes this condition.
Biology. The bloom on the leaves results from the production of ascospores which are carried by wind and rain to the surfaces of the shoots where they germinate in autumn and produce yeast-like colonies. These survive

the winter among the bud scales and in the bark, spores from them infecting the young leaves in cold wet conditions in spring. Hot dry weather in the summer may check disease development.

Treatment. If possible, collect and burn affected leaves early in the season before the ascospore bloom develops. There is no advantage in destroying the leaves later in the season nor in spraying them with fungicide. Fungicidal sprays should however be directed towards eradicating the yeast-like colonies and their spores: spray with Bordeaux mixture after autumn leaf fall and again as the buds swell in late February or early March.

MINOR LEAF CURLS *Taphrina* spp.

These are common and widespread on various host plants and all are caused by species of *Taphrina*. *T. minor* causes a leaf curl similar to peach leaf curl on cherries; *T. bullata*, small brown leaf blisters on pears similar to those of the pear leaf blister mite (p. 178); *T. tosquinetii* causes severe distortion of the leaves and young shoots of alder; *T. sadebeckii*, yellow leaf blisters on the same host; *T. aurea*, bright yellow blisters on the undersides of poplar leaves; *T. ulmi*, green blisters which later turn brown on elm leaves and *T. caerulescens*, pink-purple leaf blisters with grey then brown discolouration to the under leaf surface on oaks. The biology of all these is, as far as is known, probably similar to that of peach leaf curl and although none are normally serious, they may be similarly treated in severe cases if on young trees.

POTATO WART *Synchytrium endobioticum* Pl. 12

Widespread; commonest in Britain in northern areas but only a few cases are now recorded each year; mainly in gardens. This disease was devastating when first recorded at the beginning of the century but it is now generally of little practical significance since legislation has limited the planting of susceptible cultivars. It is however a notifiable disease in Britain and comparable restrictive legislation exists in other parts of northern Europe (see below).

Symptoms. Often undetectable until the tubers are dug, but occasionally green-yellow cauliflower like growths may occur on stem bases or other above-ground parts close to soil level. The tubers become entirely warty and knobbly or develop whitish warty outgrowths which later blacken and decay. These may be confused with certain symptoms of gangrene (p. 240) or with the canker form of powdery scab (p. 230) although the latter causes smooth not warty outgrowths and can also affect roots, which wart never does. Symptoms are more severe in wet conditions and in dry seasons may be so slight as to be overlooked although outgrowths can arise on tubers after some time in store.

Biology. The causal organism, like that inducing clubroot, produces no mycelium but nonetheless has a complicated life history. Warted tubers contain resistant spores which are released into the soil when the tissues decay. They can persist for thirty or more years in the absence of potatoes but eventually germinate to produce swimming swarm spores which infect the tubers. This infection usually takes place through the eyes, although young tubers may be susceptible all over. More swarm spores may be produced in diseased tubers during the summer and give rise to further infections before resistant spores are produced again. The disease is commonly spread in contaminated soil adhering to boots and garden implements as well as in diseased tubers, especially if these are used as seed. Several races of the organism are known and some, particularly from outside Europe, can infect cultivars immune from the common European race. Many older cultivars are susceptible to this European race but newer ones are generally immune and in Britain all new cultivar introductions are now required by law to be so.

Treatment. Once contaminated, it is almost impossible to free land from wart disease and in Britain, under legislative orders, the discovery of wart disease must by law be reported to Ministry of Agriculture officials. A notice may then be issued prohibiting the growing of potatoes on the contaminated land while only officially approved immune cultivars may be grown in a surrounding safety zone. The Wart Disease of Potatoes (Great Britain) Order, 1973 prohibited the growing of any non-immune potato cultivars in private gardens but this restriction was lifted in 1974 and any potato, immune or not, may now be grown in gardens if the land is free from wart.

WITCHES' BROOMS — Pl. 12

These descriptively named conditions are common and widespread on several woody host plants and arise from several different fungal, viral, pest or unknown causes. Any other factor such as frost, drought or browsing by animals that repeatedly damages shoot tips may also give rise to witches' broom-like symptoms. Witches' brooms are most commonly seen on birches but also fairly frequently on cherries, hornbeams, plums, ornamental *Prunus* spp., several types of conifer and, in parts of Europe, robinias.

Symptoms. Similar on all host species; large clusters of closely growing, many-branched twigs form in the crowns of trees and often bear abnormal foliage, the needles on conifer brooms for instance being markedly short. At a distance they are often mistaken for large birds' nests. Brooms increase in size and may occasionally become enormous, taking over most of the crown.

Biology. The mode of development of brooms is not fully understood. Known fungal causes are *Taphrina turgida* on birches, *T. insititiae* on plums, *T. cerasi* on cherries and ornamental *Prunus* species and *T. carpini* on hornbeams. All are present as perennial mycelium within the brooms and produce ascospores on the abnormal leaves but the initial mode of infection is uncertain. On robinia the cause is a mycoplasma (see p. 278). On conifers the causes in most cases are unknown (apart from the rust brooms on firs) but are probably due to some factor causing mutations in the buds. Some witches brooms can themselves be propagated by cuttings and have been used to produce dwarf cultivars of some species. Apparently no brooms have much effect on the trees' vigour.

Treatment. Only necessary for aesthetic reasons on ornamental species although as brooms on fruit trees do not bear fruit some slight crop loss may occur. Cut out and burn the affected parts in winter.

SCABS

(Plate 13)

A small and ill-defined group of diseases which is limited in this section to three affecting fruit, swollen vegetable roots or potato tubers. Stem lesions and corm lesions, sometimes termed scabs, are treated as stem rots (p. 252) and corm rots (p. 231) respectively. Scabs are characterised by swollen, rough, usually corky lesions and although often merely disfiguring, apple scab is, for this reason, a serious problem in commercial production where the appearance of the fruit is an overriding consideration. Soil-borne scabs are caused by bacteria or fungus-like organisms and are very difficult to treat. Fruit scabs are caused by species of the ascomycete fungus *Venturia* and sprays of benomyl and related chemicals and captan usually give satisfactory control of them.

APPLE SCAB *Venturia inaequalis* Pl. 13

Very common and widespread. Commercially, scab vies with powdery mildew as the most serious apple disease but as its effects are often only fruit blemishes, much can be tolerated in gardens although scab lesions on twigs often provide sites of infection for apple canker (p. 215). Very similar diseases affect pears and cherries.

Symptoms. LEAVES: more or less rounded greenish-brown blotches develop, especially on the leaves of the flowering spurs. The centres of the spots become blackened then grey and necrotic and some blistering of the leaf may occur. Eventually the leaves may be extensively covered with lesions and can drop prematurely. Similar symptoms can also occur on the sepals. TWIGS: blistered swellings arise which burst in spring to produce green-brown pustules. FRUIT: at first dark spots appear but these later become greenish and sometimes cracked and corky; they develop on fruit of all ages and are often very numerous. In store, small sunken, circular spots form but no fruit rotting develops with scab although it may occur if other organisms invade the lesions. Infection also occasionally develops on flowers. Although virus-like agents may cause somewhat similar fruit symptoms, the combination of these with leaf lesions is peculiar to scab.

Biology. The fungus overwinters primarily on fallen leaves and produces ascospores in perithecia on them in spring. These spores infect young leaves on which spots develop and conidia form. On trees severely affected with the disease, overwintering of the fungus can also occur in twig lesions which similarly produce conidia in the following year and these seem to be of increasing importance as the season progresses if no control measures are employed. The conidia are blown or splashed to leaves and to growing fruit on which further conidia form and these spread the disease from the initial point on the fruit to other parts of the same fruit, so giving the appearance of one large and many smaller lesions. It is improbable that much new infection actually takes place in store but latent infections producing pinpoint lesions may then become apparent. Wet and overcast weather, especially around blossom time, favours scab infection.

Treatment. Most of the best dessert apples are highly susceptible and 'Bramley's Seedling', once recommended as resistant, can also be seriously affected. A number of treatments are possible however. If at all practicable, fallen leaves should be collected from affected trees and burned; the over-wintering stage of the fungus is thus removed and the life cycle broken. A detailed and complex technology has been developed around the timing of fungicide sprays for scab control in commercial orchards so that expensive treatments are not applied unnecessarily. In gardens, less critical standards are required and benomyl or thiophanate-methyl sprayed fortnightly from the time of bud burst onwards are usually effective. Continue the sprays until blossom drop if no wood scab infection is present. If twigs are affected however, the sprays must be continued through until harvest time. Rigorous application of this treatment should eliminate wood scab by the end of the third season when the shorter spray period can be resorted to. Because strains of the scab fungus tolerant to benomyl and thiophanate-methyl have developed, it is wise to spray in alternate seasons with captan. This fungicide should be applied first when the flower buds are still tightly closed, secondly when the opening buds are pink tinged, thirdly when most petals have fallen and fourthly three weeks later. Wood scab is indicative of neglected trees and cutting out scabbed twigs is a very valuable additional control measure, if practicable, especially as it helps to reduce the danger of canker infection.

COMMON SCAB

Streptomyces scabies and other *Streptomyces* spp. **Pl. 13**

Very common, especially after hot dry summers, and widespread throughout Britain and northern Europe. It is most severe on light, sandy, alkaline soils and serious attacks often occur after old grassland is newly broken. Scab is most serious on potatoes but also affects beetroot, radish, swedes and turnips. The remarks below refer specifically to potato tubers but are equally applicable to the swollen roots of these other host plants.

Symptoms. Scabby spots of corky tissue with more or less angular margins appear scattered over, or sometimes almost covering the tuber. The lesions may be superficial or take the form of deep pitting, when the surface of the tuber appears cratered or pock-marked. The damage is very similar to that produced by powdery scab (p. 230) which is more prevalent on heavier and wetter soils but generally common scab is the more frequently seen disease. The symptoms may also appear on roots and stolons but are rarely noticed. The yield of the plants is seldom reduced but the additional peeling necessary results in excessive waste.

Biology. Common scab is one of the few plant diseases caused by an Actinomycete, a group of organisms usually considered to be related to bacteria but, unlike them and like fungi, producing mycelium. Spores or hyphae from the soil infect through stomata and lenticels; the infection starting at the time of tuber formation or enlargement, this being dependent on the moisture content and lime status of the soil. More spores are produced in the scabs and are released into the soil where the organism persists more or less indefinitely as a normal member of the soil microflora. Since the organism is so widespread and the disease dependent on soil conditions, the planting of affected 'seed' usually presents little danger of transmitting additional infection to the resulting crop unless the eyes are infected and this does not usually occur to any extent.

Treatment. The use of cultivars which are relatively resistant to scab is the most satisfactory means of control. These include 'Arran Pilot', 'King Edward', and 'Pentland Crown'. Others including 'Desirée', 'Majestic' and 'Maris Piper' are very susceptible. Apply green organic matter, such as lawn mowings, to light soils with humus deficiency. On a small scale, lawn mowings should be applied at the rate of about three buckets-full per square metre and well dug in. Do not apply lime to scab-infested land; a common cause of increasing scab incidence on potatoes is the application of excessive lime for clubroot suppression in a preceding brassica crop. Do not throw scabbed potatoes or peelings onto a compost heap and reject any diseased tubers. On light, sandy land where scab may be expected, its occurrence may be lessened by watering potatoes just when the tubers are beginning to form and at other times when the soil is becoming dry.

POTATO POWDERY SCAB *Spongospora subterranea* var. *subterranea* **Pl. 13**

Common and widespread although generally less of a problem than common scab, unlike which, it is most serious in wet seasons or on heavy soils. The disease also affects tomato roots.

Symptoms. Although it occurs on the stolons and roots (on which the very small tissue proliferations often superficially resemble the cysts of potato cyst eelworm (p. 89), it is only important on tubers. The tuber symptoms are often very similar to those of common scab (p. 229) although usually more rounded in outline. When small, the scabs may also very occasionally be confused with the symptoms of skin spot (p. 268) but dry brownish powder forms within each lesion. Sometimes powdery scab develops as a canker type of malformation which can often be mistaken for a symptom of the much more serious wart disease (p. 226).

Biology. Closely related to the organism causing clubroot and has a similar life history. The powder within the scab lesions comprises masses of spore balls which, when released into the soil, can probably survive for ten or more years. Ultimately the spores germinate to produce swimming swarm spores which infect host root hairs and produce further swarm spores within. These, when released, spread the infection through wounds, eyes and young lenticels, to produce new lesions. The wart-like symptoms arise when wet soil conditions promote new growth following a dry period. The increased moisture also favours the activity of the scab organism which then attacks the susceptible newly formed tuber tissue and causes the misshapen appearance of extensive scab pustules. The powdery scab organism has a secondary importance as the vector of a virus.

Treatment. Difficult. Maintain as long a rotation as possible between potato crops; improve drainage, do not compost diseased tubers or peelings and reject scabby seed tubers.

BULB AND CORM ROTS

(Plate 13)

Although they are very different structures botanically, bulbs and corms are storage and perennation organs requiring similar cultural treatment and are commonly considered together. All are fleshy structures and are therefore particularly prone to rotting, either in the ground, as a result of which the plants fail to emerge or are stunted, or in store. Among the most important causal fungi are species of *Fusarium* and *Sclerotinia*, as well as certain bacteria. Similar conditions, sometimes associated with fungal or bacterial action, can be caused by eelworms (p. 84) while woodlice, slugs, mites and many insect pests may cause damage which facilitates infection by rotting organisms. Rot can sometimes be detected at planting time and elimination of diseases by rogueing at this stage is a major means of control. Routine soaking of bulbs or corms in fungicides, such as benomyl or thiophanate-methyl before planting or storage, has helped to diminish significantly the importance of many rots. The only common bulb rots not considered in this general account are bacterial soft rot, which affects many different types of plant, and onion neck rot, both of which are considered in the section on Fruit and Vegetable Rots (p. 233). Rotting of the roots of bulbous plants is also common but often does not spread into the storage organ itself and descriptions of these root rots will be found in the section on Root and Foot Rots of Herbaceous Plants (p. 242).

Symptoms. Only the commonest symptom types on the most frequently affected host plants can be described and examples of some of these are shown on Plate 13. On growing plants – emergence is usually patchy within an affected bed, some plants appearing normal, some stunted and some failing totally. Plants that do emerge commonly develop a spotting and then a more general yellow colouration to the foliage which may later turn brown and die back. Sometimes the foliage merely dries and shrivels but some bulb and corm rots result in a soft decay of the leaf bases. When dug up the bulb or corm may also be either soft and wet or dry and crumbly but almost invariably the tissues will be discoloured, often with brown or black streaks. Millepedes and maggots may sometimes be found tunnelling into the damaged areas but they are not directly responsible for the decay. In store – similar symptoms appear to those described above but mould growth (white, grey and fluffy, or green-blue) may be expected also in many cases.

Biology. Most of the fungi and bacteria that cause bulb and corm rots are soil inhabiting and the initial infection of healthy stock arises from the soil, commonly through small wounds. Subsequently the organisms may spread to daughter bulbs or to others adjacent to them in store.

General Treatment. A number of general measures may be taken to prevent or treat most bulb and corm rots. Bulbs and corms must always be handled with great care to minimise mechanical injury which will predispose them to infection. Such careful handling is particularly important when they are lifted prior to storage while another common cause of damage at this time is allowing them exposure to direct sun. Any bulbs or corms seen to be damaged either before storage or before planting must be destroyed while storage under cool, dry, well-ventilated conditions is least likely to lead to losses by rotting. Dipping bulbs and corms for 15–30 minutes in a suspension of benomyl or thiophanate-methyl before planting is a good routine treatment and will protect them from a number of rotting conditions. Any growing plants showing symptoms should be carefully dug up, together with a spadeful of surrounding soil, and destroyed. It is wise to leave a contaminated site free of bulbs or corms for about three years before replanting with fresh stock.

FLOWER AND BUD ROTS

(Plate 13)

Flowers and buds contain some of the most delicate of plant tissues and they are therefore particularly prone to attack by rotting organisms. Damage can be serious as on both ornamental species and fruit, the end products of cultivation (flowers and fruits) are lost. These diseases almost invariably arise from fast-growing airborne fungi or bacteria, of which the grey mould fungus *Botrytis cinerea* is the commonest, and symptoms sometimes spread from the flowers and buds to the shoots and stems, so giving rise to a dieback. Routine removal of dead and diseased heads will help minimise potential sources of disease but chemical control is sometimes difficult as certain flowers may be sensitive to a number of the more traditional fungicides, although many modern products are safer. Apart from grey mould, however, only rhododendron bud blast, chrysanthemum ray blight and rhododendron petal blight are sufficiently common to justify a separate description.

GREY MOULD *Botrytis cinerea* **Pl. 13**

Very common and widespread on the flowers and buds of many host plants; sometimes associated with stem and leaf rots or other damage by the same fungus. The symptoms are varied but are usually associated with grey mould growth on the diseased tissues. There may be rotting of buds, flowers or flower stalks or petal spotting. The fungus spreads rapidly by means of airborne conidia produced on the mould and persists in the soil as sclerotia or saprophytically on plant debris. Grey mould control is basically synonymous with good hygiene; maintain good ventilation and raise the temperature in glasshouses; avoid overcrowded, damp and shaded situations outdoors; remove buds or flowers that have for any reason become moribund as they may easily be colonised by the grey mould which can then spread to affect more healthy organs; carefully remove affected flowers and buds (and maintain routine 'dead-heading') and spray plants with benomyl or thiophanate-methyl, repeating if the disease reappears. Also see pp. 218, 236–7. Chrysanthemum ray blight (see below) can easily be confused with grey mould damage.

CHRYSANTHEMUM RAY BLIGHT
Didymella chrysanthemi **Pl. 13**

Affects all above-ground parts but is most severe on the shoots and on the flowers which develop reddish petal spots on light coloured cultivars and brownish spots on dark coloured types. Control is not easy but it is important to remove and destroy diseased plants promptly and avoid high humidity in glasshouses. Where the disease is suspected or prevalent, dip unrooted cuttings in a benomyl suspension.

RHODODENDRON BUD BLAST
Pycnostysanus azaleae **Pl. 13**

Common and widespread.

Symptoms. Brown discolouration of the young flower buds develops in autumn and spreads during the winter until the entire bud becomes dry, and eventually dies but does not drop. Tiny, stiff, black pinhead-like structures emerge from the affected buds in spring.
Biology. The pinhead structures are coremia; conidia-bearing fungal organs. Bud blast attack is often associated with infestations of the rhododendron leaf-hopper insect (p. 99) but the exact inter-relationship is uncertain.
Treatment. The best treatment is to remove and destroy all affected buds and spray with mancozeb or Bordeaux mixture with a wetting agent just before flowering and at monthly intervals thereafter when the attack is severe. Control the leaf-hopper with malathion sprays at three weekly intervals, starting in mid-June, if feasible.

RHODODENDRON PETAL BLIGHT

Ovulinia azaleae **Pl. 13**

Occasionally causes the blooms to become limp and slimy and remain hanging on the plant covered with a white coating on which conidia form. If only a few flowers are affected remove and destroy them. If the disease occurred the previous year, spray weekly with mancozeb as the flowers open and while they are in bloom.

FRUIT AND VEGETABLE ROTS

(Plate 14)

Almost all fruit and vegetables are, like the ornamental bulbs and corms described on p. 231, plant storage organs and, as such contain fleshy tissues that are very prone to infection by a wide range of decay-causing fungi and bacteria. Infection and subsequent rotting can occur either in the ground or in storage and, as wounds are commonly necessary for infection to take place, careful handling at harvest time and the control of wound-forming agents, such as pests, can minimise many storage rot problems. In glasshouses, carefully control humidity and temperature to reduce damage on cucumbers, tomatoes and other fleshy produce and support low-growing fruit of such crops clear of the soil to minimise the risk of infection by soil-inhabiting pathogens. In general, the prompt removal and destruction of any rotting fruits and vegetables is desirable to lessen the chance of further disease spread although some rots in which infection takes place on the growing plants are not able to spread to neighbouring healthy produce in store. Indeed care with such cultural practices and good hygiene are often the only preventative measures that can be adopted in gardens because the fruit and vegetables themselves are destined for consumption and chemical treatments applied to them prior to storage are potentially hazardous. There are however a few instances where the application of fungicide to a growing crop can lessen the likelihood of damage on the stored produce and these are indicated in the text.

BACTERIAL SOFT ROT

Erwinia carotovora and other bacteria **Pl. 14**

Very common and widespread everywhere in garden or store on many vegetables but especially troublesome on brassicas (particularly turnips and swedes), celery, cucumbers and other cucurbits, leeks, lettuce, onions, parsnips, potatoes and tomatoes; also on ornamentals, including cyclamen, hyacinths, irises, muscaris and zantedeschias.

Symptoms. Soft rot often follows damage from other causes such as slugs, carrot fly or other pests and diseases. The symptoms usually begin as a small water-soaked lesion around a wound but this stage of the disease is seldom noticed. The lesion enlarges rapidly and the tissues of stems, leaf bases and/or storage organs disintegrate to become an evil smelling soft and slimy mass of usually brownish putrefaction. The leaves may rot in patches and discoloured areas appear on less severely affected organs such as cauliflower curds. Storage organs, such as swedes, turnips and sometimes tomatoes and other vegetables and ornamentals, may persist as a shell of outer tissues with the centre totally disintegrated. On tomatoes, the stems may be affected and the pith becomes yellow-brown and disintegrates while the lower parts of stems turn slimy. Symptoms superficially similar to those of soft rot can occur from other causes on cucumbers and other cucurbits and on parsnips.

Biology. *E. carotovora* is the most important of several soft-rotting bacteria. It is a motile, soil-inhabiting bacterium that is never transmitted on seed but infects through wounds and, by means of enzymes, brings about the destruction of the layer by which the cells of plant tissues are held together. Numerous different strains exist and not all are capable of infecting every host species. Several factors increase the severity of soft rot including poor drainage, especially if combined with high applications of farmyard manure; potassium deficiency or, conversely, nitrogen abundance.

Treatment. Soft rot attacks may be minimised in a number of ways: maintain as long a rotation as possible between susceptible crops; control wound-forming pests and diseases; avoid potassium-nitrogen imbalance and impeded drainage and do not over-apply manure, especially to waterlogged soils; although, contrary to common belief, manure itself does not contain the soft rot bacteria. Chemical control of the disease is seldom practicable but gouging out the affected tissue on lightly diseased bulbs or corms, followed by dusting with dry powdered Bordeaux mixture, is worth trying on valuable plants. Following a soft rot attack, the affected produce should be buried deeply and never composted.

BITTER ROTS *Glomerella cingulata, Pezicula alba* and *P. malicorticis* **Pl. 14**

One or more forms of bitter rot and the associated canker lesions are common and widespread on various fruit trees.

Symptoms. Bitter rot – common on apples, quinces and occasionally on pears. Round, brown, saucer-like depressions develop, sometimes while the fruit is still on the tree but usually more serious in store. The depressions may bear concentric rings of either off-white to yellow-brown glistening pustules or darker pustules oozing minute pink, worm-like tendrils. On cherries, only dark pustules occur and the entire fruit shrivels while on grapes the disease usually only occurs under glasshouse conditions and only pale pustules form. Perennial canker – sometimes small cankers or elliptical sunken branch lesions up to 30 cm long develop at the base of spurs, particularly on old neglected trees.

Biology. *P. malicorticis* and *P. alba* are the commonest and most serious causes of bitter rot on apples in Britain although *G. cingulata* is most frequent on pears and quinces and alone affects cherries, grapes and peaches. The fruits are usually infected when air-borne conidia germinate and invade through the lenticels; they become increasingly susceptible as the season progresses. *P. malicorticis* and *P. alba* rots are virtually indistinguishable by eye and produce conidia on pale pustules while *G. cingulata* produces them in characteristic pink slimy tendrils. Perennial canker is not a serious disease in Europe; its main cause is *P. malicorticis* although *P. alba* causes minor cankers on and death of spurs. Ascospores of both may be produced on diseased wood but are most unlikely to be a major source of the disease for attacking the fruit.

Treatment. Very little can be done to limit bitter rot attack in gardens although affected fruits should be removed and destroyed as soon as they are noticed; this can be done most effectively by examining stored apples regularly. If the disease is a problem on grapes, it can sometimes be checked by improving ventilation and removing affected fruit and the following season's blossom should not be syringed as this may encourage infection as well as pollination.

BROWN ROT *Sclerotinia fructigena* and *Sclerotinia laxa* Pl. 14

Very common and widespread. Probably the most serious fruit rot in gardens and often present with the associated symptoms of blossom wilt, spur blight and wither tip.

Symptoms. Brown rot – on apples, pears, plums, cherries, peaches, almonds, nectarines, apricots, quinces and rarely on medlars. Soft brown patches appear on the fruit, sometimes around a wound, either while they are on the tree or in store, and these enlarge and extend to other fruit in contact. Dirty white or yellowish cottony pustules develop on the patches, usually arranged concentrically while sometimes, particularly in store, affected apples may turn completely black and develop no pustules. The fruits may ultimately shrivel and, if still attached to the tree, remain hanging there throughout the winter. Blossom wilt – on apples, pears, plums, cherries, nectarines, peaches and apricots; also on ornamental *Prunus* spp. Flowers and later spur leaves wilt, usually about a fortnight after coming into blossom. Small cankers may develop on those spurs that bear either brown rotted fruit or wilted blossoms, and extend into the branches which are sometimes girdled and killed. Spur blight – on plums and some ornamental *Prunus* spp.; causes withered leaves on the foliar spur, often with a small canker at the base. Wither tip – on plums, almonds or rarely cherries; causes withered leaves and drooping of the tip of the terminal shoot with brown lesions near the base of the lowest affected leaves. It is often accompanied by aphid infestations.

Biology. The first infection of the fruit occurs when wind-blown or insect-borne conidia land on a wound or puncture, such as those caused by birds, earwigs, caterpillars, wasps, frost or hail. Mycelium then spreads rapidly through the tissues and into neighbouring healthy fruit, more conidia being produced on the cottony pustules. Mycelium also spreads down into the spur or branch to form the canker. Blossom wilt, spur blight and wither tip similarly arise when conidia of *S. laxa* infect flowers or leaves and then the mycelium extends down into the spurs or branches to form cankers. The fungus overwinters in cankers and also in mummied fruit which continue to produce conidia while hanging on the trees. In parts of Europe, although not in Britain, ascospore-producing apothecia develop on fallen fruit during the winter.

Treatment. There are some slight variations in cultivar susceptibility to brown rot and 'Bramley's Seedling' apple is resistant to blossom wilt. A number of measures will limit the severity of the problems: remove and destroy apple mummies and cut out and burn cankers and diseased spurs in winter, treating any cuts with a wound sealant containing fungicide. Remove diseased or damaged fruit from the trees, take care not to put any into store and avoid pulling the stalks from fruit intended for storage. A spray with benomyl or thiophanate-methyl in mid-August and again two to three weeks later will help to reduce brown rot on fruit intended for store and a similar spray when the flowers are open and again one week later will help to control the blossom wilt. Careful hygiene and handling are much more effective however in gardens than are chemical treatments.

GREY MOULD ROT *Botrytis cinerea* Pl. 14

A ubiquitous pathogen; the cause of many different symptoms on a very wide range of host plants. Descriptions of grey mould flower and bud rot will be found on p. 232 and of grey mould dieback of woody plants on p. 218. This description is of grey mould rot symptoms only.

Symptoms. Distinctive fluffy grey mould with a powdery surface covering appears on affected organs and a soft, usually brown rot develops beneath. A grey cloud of spores may be liberated when affected produce is disturbed and scattered black bodies may be present among the mould growth; in the later stages these bodies may occur alone, the mould itself having disappeared. It is common as a rot on apples, and less so on other orchard fruit, on grapevine (very serious under glass and in the open), strawberries (the commonest and most serious rot), figs, blackberries, raspberries, gooseberries, beans, brassicas, celery (in storage), carrot (in storage), cucumber and other cucurbits, lettuce (a very serious problem, considered in detail on p. 252), tomato, peas (sometimes causing 'chalky' peas) and potatoes (but easily confused with several other rots). On apples it may also commonly cause a symptom known as dry eye rot in which a brown sunken area appears around the calyx of the growing fruit. This may ultimately lead to the normal grey mould rot in store. Grey mould is always worse under cool, damp, overcrowded conditions.

Biology. Despite its importance and widespread occurrence, this is a weak pathogen, often attacking through some form of wound and frequent after frost damage or on stressed plants. It is common everywhere on dead or dying plant material and spreads by the numerous conidia produced on the grey mould. On beans, peas, strawberries and some other host plants, infection initially occurs through the petals and only develops later in the fruit. On other plants, such as carrots, the fungus may be present on the leaf bases, from which it spreads after roots are put into store. The small black bodies frequently formed among the older mycelium are sclerotia. These can give rise, on germination, to apothecia in which ascospores form, but in Britain they usually produce conidia once more. The sclerotia may help the fungus to overwinter although mycelium can continue to grow at low temperatures.

Treatment. Always avoid damp and overcrowded situations for both growing and stored fruit and vegetables and reduce the humidity in glasshouses at the first sign of symptoms by increasing both ventilation and heat if possible. The key to satisfactory prevention of grey mould attacks, especially in glasshouses, is good hygiene. As the fungus can exist saprophytically, it will grow on any dead or moribund plant remains which must therefore be cleared away promptly. Chemical treatments are not worthwhile or practicable on some crops in gardens but the following are sensible precautions. Spray blackberries, gooseberries and raspberries with benomyl or thiophanate-methyl just after the start of flowering and repeat at least three times at ten day intervals; spray strawberries with benomyl or thiophanate-methyl when the flowers open and repeat this treatment at ten day intervals until the fruit are at the white stage; spray beans with benomyl or thiophanate-methyl once when the flowers are fully open; spray lettuce with benomyl or thiophanate-methyl after planting or thinning and repeat at fortnightly intervals; spray cucumbers fortnightly or three-weekly with benomyl or thiophanate-methyl beginning as the flowers open. Although for many of these diseases, sprays with benomyl or thiophanate-methyl are the most effective treatments, strains of grey mould tolerant to these fungicides have become established in some parts of the country and it is unfortunate that the best alternative chemical, dichlofluanid, is no longer available to gardeners.

LEATHERY FRUIT ROTS *Phytophthora cactorum* and *Phytophthora syringae*

Common, widespread and serious on some apple cultivars and occasional on strawberries. Less frequent on pears.

Symptoms. Affected apples become leathery and crack to reveal a white colouration. On pears, either dark brown lesions with well-defined borders or lesions covered with glistening white pustules develop. Strawberry fruit become leathery, brown and shrivelled and the fruit stalks shrivel and die.

Biology. The causes are soil-borne fungi; only serious on wind-fall apples and pears and when fruits hang near to the ground, especially over bare soil. The spores are splashed upwards by rain and the disease is therefore worse in wet seasons or following severe storms at harvest time. These spores germinate to produce swimming swarm spores which then infect the fruit.

Treatment. In orchards use routine fungicide sprays to control scab (p. 228) as these help to suppress leathery rot also. Support low hanging branches, maintain grass cover under trees if possible and use straw liberally between strawberries. Three fortnightly applications of sulphur dust, beginning in early May, sometimes give some control in strawberries, especially if generous applications of potash fertilisers are also used on the crop.

MINOR ROTS OF STORED FRUIT Pl. 14

A number of rotting conditions appear commonly on apples and other fruits in store even when the produce has seemed healthy at harvest time. Only one very general recommendation may be made: remove and destroy any affected fruits as soon as they are seen. Many of these diseases will spread rapidly in store but prompt hygiene can save much fruit from decay. Always store fruit in well ventilated cool situations and avoid contact between individual fruits.

ONION NECK ROT *Botrytis allii* Pl. 14

Very common and widespread. The commonest disease of stored onions throughout Europe.

Symptoms. Only seen after about 10–12 weeks in store as a softening of the bulb scales followed by the development of a brown, sunken lesion around the neck. The rot spreads from the lesion throughout the onion tissues and fluffy masses of grey mould and small black bodies often develop on badly affected bulbs.

Biology. It was long thought that infection arose from conidia landing on the bulbs at harvest time but it is now known that most infection is seed-borne, a high percentage of onion seed being contaminated in most years although some disease may also originate from crop debris. Mycelium from the germinated spores invades the emerging cotyledons and more spores develop on the dying green tissues and spread the disease to other plants but there are no obvious symptoms at this stage. The bases of the older leaves soon become infected, then the necks, and although there is no bulb to bulb spread in store, the symptoms do not appear simultaneously on all onions so giving the appearance that spread is taking place.

Treatment. Control is relatively straightforward; gardeners should dust all onion seed with benomyl before sowing as only seed for commercial use is sold already treated. Soaking or dusting onion sets with benomyl would probably also be effective but this is not yet proven. Maintain a three or four year rotation between onion crops and do not dump old onions in gardens.

PARSNIP CANKER *Itersonilia pastinacae, Mycocentrospora acerina* and *Phoma* sp. and other factors

Widespread and fairly common, especially in wet seasons. This is a complex disease, the causes of which have only recently been elucidated.

Symptoms. Three main types. Black canker: small, ill-defined dark lesions develop on the root, often at the bases of the lateral roots, and extend to form a brown or purple-black rot. Small black bodies may develop on the lesion or necrotic spots with pale green halos may appear on the leaves but these two symptoms do not occur together. Purple canker: arises on black fen soils and is manifest as purple lesions with brownish water-soaked margins. Orange brown canker: a brown roughening of the skin arises around the shoulder of the root.

Biology. Black canker is caused mainly by *I. pastinacae.* This fungus also forms the leaf spots from which spores are washed down to the soil to infect the roots through wounds, such as those caused by carrot fly (p. 149).

Infection commonly starts where the fine rootlets join the main root, although the fungus can also be seed-borne. *Phoma* sp., is a less common cause of black canker and develops spores in black pycnidia on the lesions. *M. acerina* causes the brighter purple lesions and is very common on highly organic soils. The same fungus causes carrot liquorice rot and celery crown rot, among other diseases. The causes of orange brown canker are not known but it is believed that several soil-inhabiting pathogens are responsible.

Treatment. The cultivar 'Avonresister' is highly resistant to all forms of canker and should be grown where the diseases are troublesome. Other measures which may help are the maintenance of good drainage, rotations of four years and the eradication of any wild parsnips in the vicinity as these are potential hosts for harbouring the disease. Attempts should also be made to control carrot fly. Parsnips with smaller roots are less prone to canker and close spacing and the delaying of sowing until the end of April or early May will produce this effect. Earthing up in summer may prevent the spores of *I. pastinacae* reaching the roots and is sometimes a successful preventative treatment.

POTATO ROTS

Potato tubers are prone to several different types of rotting of which three are described here. The identification of potato tuber damage is not easy for rots may follow attack by other diseases (particularly blight p. 214), pests or disorders. They may also be affected by more general rotting conditions, such as bacterial soft rot (p. 234) and grey mould (p. 232).

POTATO DRY ROT *Fusarium* spp. **Pl. 14**

Very common and widespread but only occurs in stored tubers, never on growing plants although it is a common cause of emergence failure after planting seed thought to be sound.

Symptoms. Large tubers tend to be more susceptible than small ones. Dark brown external lesions appear on the tubers, enlarge rapidly and become sunken and shrunken, with concentric wrinkles. When cut through, the flesh around the lesions is seen to be pale brown, usually containing cavities lined with a fluffy white, blue or pale pink mould while a white mould may also appear externally. The rot may progress to affect the entire tuber or remain restricted. In moist conditions there is less wrinkling and shrinkage and bacterial soft rot may follow dry rot.

Biology. The commonest cause of dry rot is *Fusarium solani* var. *coeruleum.* The fungi are present in the soil which adheres to harvested tubers and can survive in gardens for at least nine years in the absence of potatoes. Infection only takes place when tubers are damaged before storing and the disease is most serious when potatoes are stored at relatively high temperatures. Tubers are less susceptible if grown with adequate fertiliser applications and in general, susceptibility is least when mature potatoes are first lifted and is highest in the spring after winter in store. The disease does not spread in store, even by contact, unless the tubers are damaged. It is worst on early cultivars but 'Home Guard', together with the maincrop cultivars

'Arran Banner', 'Pentland Crown' and, to a lesser extent, 'King Edward' are fairly resistant. 'Arran Comet', 'Arran Pilot', and sometimes 'Majestic' are very susceptible while many of the older cultivars still popular in gardens, are also susceptible.
Treatment. Buy ample seed, particularly of known susceptible cultivars, to allow for some loss. Do not use diseased tubers as seed, even if they sprout: the resulting plants are much less likely to survive than healthy stock and the progeny tubers are more likely to rot if they become damaged. Do not store immature tubers, which are highly susceptible to infection, and remove the haulm about two weeks before lifting potatoes for store as at this time the tubers are more resistant. Potatoes intended for store must be handled carefully at all times and diseased tubers should be buried deeply well away from land on which potatoes are grown. No chemical treatments are suitable for garden use.

POTATO GANGRENE *Phoma* spp. Pl. 14

Common and widespread in some European countries. Especially serious on seed potatoes in store.
Symptoms. Can be observed first several weeks after lifting. Small, but enlarging 'thumb print' lesions with well defined edges develop on the tubers and may enlarge to cover the entire tuber or remain restricted and shrivelled. The rot associated with the lesions is at first pale pinkish and watery but later becomes purple-black with cavities and black dot-like bodies may appear on the cavity walls. Crops grown from diseased seed may emerge late, show gaps and produce proportionately more small tubers but these effects are most likely to be seen when general growing conditions are poor. Gangrene may be confused with dry rot (p. 239) but there are no coloured patches of mould growth, such as are sometimes seen with that disease. Dry rot usually causes concentric wrinkling of the skin; with gangrene it is irregularly wrinkled, if at all, but expert identification may be needed as both diseases can occur together.
Biology. The usual cause in western Europe is *Phoma exigua* var. *foveata*. The black, dot-like pycnidia on the potato haulm produce conidia which may be washed into the soil and infect either healthy tubers or those bruised or injured during lifting. Diseased seed, when planted, gives rise to diseased plants to repeat the cycle.
Treatment. In commercial practice, controlled temperature and humidity in the store, together with chemical treatment at lifting, is used to attempt to control gangrene. No chemical is suitable for garden use, however, and, although saving one's own potato seed is generally unwise because of virus problems (p. 277), gardeners doing so should take great care to avoid damage at lifting while the examination of stored tubers and removal of any suspect is essential if gangrene is not to become a problem.

POTATO PINK ROT *Phytophthora erythroseptica* Pl. 14

Fairly common and widespread but infrequently a serious problem.
Symptoms. May occasionally be seen on the haulm. These include leaf yellowing and wilting of the plant late in the season. The principal symptoms however are obvious on the tuber, initially at the stem end, and are

usually noticed at harvest as wet rots, the largest tubers commonly being more affected. The tissues have a rubbery consistency and internally are of an off-white colour. This colour usually becomes rather pink in about half and hour and finally black. Such tubers eventually decay. In the soil at harvest time, affected tubers resemble those with blackleg symptoms but in the latter disease they disintegrate rapidly whereas tubers with pink rot usually maintain their consistency.

Biology. The disease is worst after warm summers on fairly heavy land and in wet parts of gardens. The fungus can survive in the soil for several years as resistant oospores; these ultimately germinate and give rise to swarm spores which infect the tubers, sometimes directly but more usually via the stolon. More oospores are produced in the roots, stolons or stem bases (but infrequently in the tubers) and are released into the soil when the plant decays. The disease can also be spread in storage by contact of tuber eyes with a diseased tuber. It may also be introduced into the soil by planting infected tubers that have few obvious symptoms.

Treatment. Destroy or bury deeply all diseased plant material away from land on which potatoes are grown. Maintain a three or four year rotation between potato crops, if possible, and drain waterlogged land.

VIOLET ROOT ROT *Helicobasidium purpureum* Pl. 14

Common throughout Europe but less serious in cooler, northern areas; rare in Scotland. It is most important as a rot of beetroot, carrot, parsnip, potato, swede and turnip but also causes a serious root rot of asparagus, celery, seakale and occasionally many other vegetables, as well as many ornamental and weed species. The disease is sometimes serious in clamped vegetables.

Symptoms. Similar on several species; above ground, plants may appear feeble, stunted and yellowed whereas the roots, rhizomes, tubers, bulbs or corms and sometimes the crown and stem bases are covered in ramifying purplish strands containing dark spots and/or a felty mass to which soil adheres. Root tissues are affected by brownish rot, often associated with secondary bacterial soft rot, while large dark velvety bodies may occur among the mycelium and in surrounding soil.

Biology. The velvety black bodies (sclerotia) may persist for many years in the soil before they germinate and give rise to mycelium which infects plants. Persistence of the fungus on living or dead roots of the many wild host plant species is probably also important. Disease spread from plant to plant by mycelial growth during the season is slow and the symptoms, even from early infections, may not appear until autumn. Acid soils and temperatures of around 15°C (59°F) favour disease development and all host plants are uniformly susceptible although the carrot cultivar 'Chantenay Red Core' is claimed to have some tolerance.

Treatment. Burn diseased roots or bury them well away from plant beds. Remove all residual crop plants at the end of the season and suppress rampant weed growth, on which the disease might persist. Maintain high soil fertility with balanced fertiliser applications and try not to allow the soil, even in patches, to become waterlogged. Following severe attacks, do not grow root crops on affected land for three or four years. Crops that are probably safe to plant during this period are Brussels sprouts, cabbages, cauliflowers, peas and sweet corn. No chemical treatments are very effective and none is suitable for garden use.

ROOT AND FOOT ROTS (Herbaceous Plants)

(Plate 15)

This section includes many of what are probably the commonest garden disease problems. They are very frequent on seedlings when they are known collectively as damping-off, but are often troublesome on cuttings and on mature plants also. Root and foot rots are caused by a wide variety of fungi, usually soil-borne, and commonly including species of the Phycomycete genera *Phytophthora* and *Pythium*, although several types of fungi may act together and it is often impossible, without scientific tests, to relate particularly symptoms to specific pathogens. For this reason many are here grouped together and general remarks are made on biology and treatment. Damping-off and other root and foot rots are especially serious on ornamental bedding plants although it is commonly impossible to separate such diseases from stem and leaf rots of bedding plants therefore this group of problems is also described here. On other plants any stem rot not confined to the base or foot should be sought in the section on Stem and Leaf Rots (p. 252).

Among the other plants frequently attacked by general forms of root and foot rot are asparagus, glasshouse carnations, chrysanthemums, glasshouse cucumbers, cyclamen, delphiniums, gerberas, hyacinths, hydrangeas, leeks, lettuces, lilies, lilies of the valley, lupins, narcissi, peas and beans, pot plants, primulas, radishes, saintpaulias, strawberries, sweet peas, tomatoes, tulips, violas and zantedeschias. Descriptions of these are given below whereas the root and foot rots of certain other plants are rather more individual in terms of symptoms or treatment and are listed separately. Diseases predominantly of swollen storage organs such as carrots, parsnips, bulbs and corms are described in other sections (pp. 231 & 233) while related diseases affecting a wide range of host plants but with rather more readily recognised symptoms are *Sclerotinia* Disease (p. 247) and Violet Root Rot (p. 241). Damping-off of all types of seedlings is described on p. 243.

Symptoms. Although the primary effects are on the roots or stem base, the earliest signs of damage are often indicated by the leaves which may be smaller than usual, turn yellow and wilt, sometimes with dramatic suddenness. Flowering and fruiting may be reduced and when pulled up the root systems are seen to be feeble, blackened and/or decayed. The root decay may occur in discrete areas; on tomatoes for instance the tip may rot first while a tough core commonly remains after the outer tissues have disappeared. With less severe attacks dark lesions on the roots and stem base, with little actual decay, may be all that is visible.

Biology. The causes of root and foot rots are many and varied and may differ between plant species. All of the causal fungi are present in the soil as spores or other resting bodies or as mycelium and some are able to live saprophytically on dead plant remains. Many require small wounds through which to infect and are commonly more serious on plants growing under stress.

Treatment. Outdoors, affected plants should be removed and destroyed and correction of some underlying cause of stress is often the only way to minimise the likelihood of future attacks. In outdoor plant beds, improvement of drainage, nutrient status and pH, for instance, often indirectly cure root and foot rot problems. Such procedures are best combined with the introduction of cropping rotations of three or four years. Peas and beans are especially difficult to treat however and rotations of at least five years between crops may be necessary, although the digging in of quantities of brassica debris is sometimes claimed to help. In large gardens with extensive contamination the granular soil sterilant dazomet may be worth applying in accordance with the manufacturer's directions. In glasshouses, plants must be raised in sterilised compost in disinfected pots while persistent root rot problems on tomatoes and cucumbers can often be overcome by growing the plants in ready-prepared bags. Care must be taken to ensure that water supplies such as rain-water butts are cleaned out regularly. Valuable glasshouse plants may be induced to form new roots by packing moist peat around the stem base and applying top dressing; additions of nitrogen and phosphorus-containing fertilisers are especially effective with chrysanthemums.

DAMPING OFF Pl. 15

One of the commonest and most troublesome garden disease types, affecting the seedlings of a very wide range of plants but probably most serious on bedding plants, especially fast growing types such as alyssums, antirrhinums, callistephus, nemesias, penstemons, petunias, salvias, stocks and tagetes. Among many other plants commonly affected are brassicas of all types, cress, lettuces, tomatoes, peas and beans while very young seedlings of many trees are especially prone to the grey mould form of damping off.

Symptoms. These are exceedingly variable but all result in death of at least some of the seedlings in a box or bed. Young seedlings may die out in more or less circular patches, the larger affected plants sometimes having stem lesions at or about soil level. Seedlings may become unthrifty and have tough, shrivelled or wiry stems ('wire-stem'), usually after the first few leaves have formed. Sometimes roots may rot away completely or appear as a few discoloured stumps. On bedding plants, leaf spotting of various types may accompany the other effects while grey mould growth on the stem and leaves also commonly occurs.

Biology. The biology of the damping off organisms is as varied as the number of different types. The commonest causes of the dying out of seedlings in patches are the soil-borne fungi *Pythium* and *Rhizoctonia solani* which usually survive in the soil as spores or sclerotia respectively. The dark stem lesions are often caused by soil-inhabiting species of *Phytophthora* while the leaf spots on bedding plants are commonly formed by seed and/or soil-borne fungi and bacteria, particularly species of *Alternaria*, *Phyllosticta* and *Pseudomonas*. The grey mould symptoms which often accompany damping off are caused by *Botrytis cinerea* which is described more fully on p. 236.

Treatment. Damping off is not an easy problem to deal with in gardens, largely because none of the chemicals employed successfully for soil treatment in commercial practice is available for small scale use. Control is essentially synonymous with good hygiene therefore. Affected plants and contaminated compost must be disposed of and apparently healthy seedlings from a bed or box containing some diseased individuals must not be used as they may themselves be invisibly affected and thus spread the disease to healthy land. Seed boxes, whether or not they have contained diseased plants, should be disinfected routinely before use and then filled with sterilised compost. It is not safe to assume that all commercially prepared compost is sterile and small quantities for seed box use can be treated by cooking in an oven at about 150°C (gas regulo 2) for an hour or so. Care should also be taken that water supplies (such as rain-water butts) are cleaned out regularly as they may harbour pathogenic organisms. In glasshouses and cold frames avoid water-logging, high humidity or any other factors likely to place plants under stress as this will render them more susceptible to attack. Bedding plants such as alyssums, antirrhinums, carnations, cinerarias, lobelias and zinnias should be sprayed two or three times at seven to ten day intervals with thiram to prevent the spread of seed-borne diseases to healthy plants. It is advisable also to apply a single spray of benomyl or thiophanate-methyl to all bedding plants (but especially begonias and geraniums) immediately after pricking out to prevent infection by the grey mould fungus.

LAWN TURF ROTS

Because lawns are composed of grasses, the diseases to which they are subject are more akin to those affecting cereals and similar grass crops than they are to those on other garden plants. It is almost impossible to distinguish individual plants within turf and the root rot diseases considered here are essentially ones of the turf community. They are the commonest of a number of similar conditions. Dead patches of turf need not be due to root rotting problems of any sort, however, and very common alternatives are leatherjackets (p. 147), soil compaction, spillages of oil or petrol from lawnmowers, spillages of garden and household chemicals, of boiling water or of urine, usually by dogs or cats (p. 188); occasionally small boys also. If a disease seems the most probable cause, however, take steps to improve drainage; thoroughly fork the surface to admit air and do not apply top dressings, especially of nitrogenous fertilisers, after the beginning of September as these encourage soft, susceptible foliage. A few fungicides are effective but the often recommended mercury-containing products should be avoided. Benomyl or thiophanate-methyl should be applied immediately after mowing as eradicant and/or preventative treatments, in accordance with the manufacturers' instructions.

FAIRY RINGS

More or less circular rings of mushrooms and toadstools of several species are very common on lawns and rough grass. There are three main types: those which have no noticeable effect on the growth of the grass, those in which its growth is enhanced and those in which it is damaged. The associated basidiomycete fungi can be identified by reference to field guides, but in Britain the commonest of the damaging types is the fairy ring mushroom, *Marasmius oreades*. This produces a dryish buff cap, at first bell shaped but later flattened and up to 5 cm (2″) in diameter, sometimes with a wavy margin. The gills are thick, widely spaced, at first whitish but later turn buff. The stalk is slender and tough and the flesh off-white. The damage arises because mycelium on the inside of the ring exhausts the nutrients in the soil, dies and so produces an impervious layer which deprives the grass roots of moisture. A ring of enhanced growth of grass probably arises because of the liberation of nitrogenous compounds by fungal breakdown of organic material. The rate of radial growth of rings varies but can be 30 cm (12″) or more per year while extension may, under favourable conditions, continue for several hundred years. Treatment is difficult and highly poisonous mercurial compounds which are often recommended should be avoided. Remove a ring of turf for a radius of about 60 cm (24″) beyond the fungal ring; break up the soil and saturate it with a 1 : 50 solution of formalin (40% formaldehyde) at the rate of about 17 litres per square metre. If possible cover the treated area with plastic sheet for about two weeks to retain the gas. Remove the sheets, fork over the soil and re-seed after five weeks.

ONION WHITE ROT *Sclerotium cepivorum* Pl. 14

Very common and widespread on onions (especially salad onions), leeks and, less seriously, chives, garlic and shallots. It is the most serious disease affecting onions while they are still growing; neck rot (p. 238) is more important on stored bulb onions.

Symptoms. The leaves turn yellow and die back, and the plants later sometimes keel over as the roots rot, especially when seedlings are affected. White cottony fungal growth develops around the bulb and bears very small black bodies among the matted threads. The disease often appears as patches of diseased plants which may subsequently merge to affect considerable proportions of the row or bed.

Biology. The small black bodies are sclerotia that can survive in the soil for many years before germinating to produce mycelial threads and infect the roots. Once one plant is infected, spread to others can occur through contact between the roots or bulbs but the fungus is also able to grow through the soil to a limited extent: it may for instance spread along rows but not between them.

Treatment. Once soil is contaminated, it is virtually impossible to eradicate white rot disease although very careful removal of diseased onions and several spadesful of soil around them will prevent its further increase by minimising the numbers of new sclerotia that are added to the soil. Similarly, onions affected with white rot should never be composted because of the likelihood of spreading the disease further, and land already known to be contaminated should never be used for growing onions or related plants. The addition of calomel, benomyl or thiophanate-methyl dusts to the drill before sowing is a fairly satisfactory treatment for small numbers of plants and although white rot can now be controlled very effectively in commercial crops, the fungicide used, iprodione, is not yet available to gardeners.

POTATO BLACKLEG *Erwinia carotovora* var. *atroseptica* Pl. 15

Very common; often one of the earliest potato diseases to appear, especially in wet seasons. Both this bacterium and *E. carotovora* var. *carotovora* can also cause soft rots of potatoes.

Symptoms. These are generally most severe in wet seasons. The upper leaflets first curl inwards (and thus differ typically from the virus induced symptoms of secondary leaf roll where the lower leaves curl first and become stiff), and the colour fades to yellow-green. The stem base decays and becomes black and slimy but not all stems on a particular plant may show these black symptoms. In store, affected tubers rot completely and spread the bacteria to neighbouring healthy ones.

Biology. The disease is transmitted in diseased seed tubers and the bacteria do not remain viable in the soil from one season to the next but can survive in heaps of discarded potatoes. Affected plants may produce typical blackleg soft-rotted tubers, the organism penetrating through the stolon into the stem end and rotting the tuber tissues. Such plants may also produce tubers that appear quite healthy but in which the lenticels harbour the bacterium. These bacteria have been spread in the soil from the breakdown of the infected seed tubers. Tubers may also be infected through damage at the time of lifting and these may introduce serious rotting in neighbouring previously healthy tubers in store.

Treatment. Ensure that seed tuber stores are well-ventilated, and do not use as seed any tubers that have been in contact with soft-rotted material. Discard any tubers showing browning at the heel (stem) end and do not plant potatoes on waterlogged land. No resistant cultivars are known but 'King Edward' is less susceptible than many.

POTATO STEM CANKER and BLACK SCURF
Rhizoctonia solani

Very common and often serious. The causal fungus is also responsible for a wide range of root and other diseases on many host plants.

Symptoms. On tubers – harmless, hard black patches develop to which soil adheres and which cannot be washed off, although with gentle scraping (as with a finger nail) they pull away leaving the skin unaffected beneath. Sprouts from affected tubers develop sunken brown lesions which may cause complete girdling. If conditions before emergence are dry, the tips of the sprouts are often attacked and this leads to sprout proliferation, thinner stems and retarded emergence. Growing plants – rough, brown, cracked lesions on the underground parts of stems and stolons. The entire plant may be stunted, the leaves curled and sometimes coloured yellow or purple and clusters of small, knobbly tubers can develop at or immediately below ground level. Small, green aerial tubers can also form in the leaf axils. In moist conditions, white mould grows around the stem base above soil level, while in warm conditions on early cultivars, there may be some pitting of the tubers giving symptoms rather like wireworm damage (p. 163).

Biology. Several strains of *R. solani* exist and not all are able to infect all hosts. It is a common soil inhabitant, often existing saprophytically on plant debris or as the hard black sclerotia that form the scurf on tubers. Infection can thus arise from soil as well as from affected seed tubers.

Treatment. Very difficult. Rotation of potato crops should always be adopted and it is particularly important to avoid two successive crops on the same land. Although seed tuber disinfection is sometimes performed commercially it is scarcely practicable in gardens. The disease is often prevalent in spring in dry, cold land, particularly with high ridges, and may be reduced naturally with the onset of rain. Shallow planting is sometimes an effective control as this allows the plants to emerge and establish quickly and may reduce the chances of sprout infection. Similarly the knocking down of high ridges may help as attacks seem to cease once the shoot reaches soil level. Early lifting of the crop reduces the numbers of sclerotia on the tubers.

SCLEROTINIA DISEASE *Sclerotinia sclerotiorum* Pl. 15

Widespread; affects many vegetables and ornamentals and the host plant list given below is not exhaustive. It is generally most serious in northern areas and is common in the north of England and Scotland but frequent in all damp, cool regions.

Symptoms. A brown, more or less wet rot develops, often associated with masses of fluffy white mould commonly containing large, usually black but sometimes paler bodies. The symptoms occur especially at the stem base of beans, celery, chicory, cucumbers, Jerusalem artichokes, lettuces, peas, potatoes, tomatoes, campanulas, glasshouse chrysanthemums, convallarias, dahlias, delphiniums, gypsophilas, helianthus, lupins and sweet peas. The effects may occur occasionally on leaves and fruit as well as on stored bulbs, corms and tubers. They are very common and serious on stored carrot and parsnip roots, the symptoms often being restricted to the crown of the root. Growing plants may wilt suddenly, show yellowing of the basal leaves and topple over at the points of infection.

Biology. The large, usually black sclerotia lie dormant over winter in the soil and germinate in spring or summer to produce apothecia which emerge just above the soil surface. Ascospores from the apothecia infect leaves (the fungus usually establishing first on wounded or dying leaves unless the conditions are very moist, when healthy tissues may be attacked) and passes from there to the stem and to other leaves. Mycelium permeates the stem but usually does so in a restricted region within which more sclerotia are produced. It is possible that mycelium from germinated sclerotia may sometimes infect directly, without spore formation.

Treatment. Collect and destroy affected material to prevent sclerotia from contaminating the soil and do not grow susceptible plants on contaminated land for at least three years. Pay particular attention to the control of weeds, on which the disease might persist. Check stored roots regularly and remove any diseased. Late planting of potatoes sometimes helps to protect this crop as fewer dying leaves are then present at the time of spore release.

STRAWBERRY RED CORE *Phytophthora fragariae* **Pl. 15**
Also known as Lanarkshire disease. It was first found in Scotland in 1921 and remains commonest in the North although it now occurs also in southern England. It is a notifiable disease in Great Britain.
Symptoms. Most obvious in May or June. Patches of stunted plants appear with small and reddish central leaves and brown and stiff outer ones, the latter giving an overall brown appearance to the plants. When pulled up, the roots are dark brown or black and the outer root tissue is readily stripped off, revealing a red core; this symptom is diagnostic for the disease but is not usually visible during the summer months, when the symptoms may be confused with those of other strawberry root diseases.
Biology. Within the red tissues, resistant oospores form and these are released into the soil as the root decays. They can persist in the soil for at least twelve years but ultimately germinate, sometimes via a swimming swarm spore stage, to infect healthy roots in wet conditions. The disease is spread to uncontaminated land either by the planting of infected runners or in soil adhering to plants, roots or tools.
Treatment. It is virtually impossible to eradicate red core from contaminated land and anyone discovering strawberries believed to be affected with red core disease must, by law, inform officials of the Ministry of Agriculture.

TREE AND SHRUB ROTS
(Plate 15)

These rots are caused mainly by Basidiomycete fungi; mostly of the suborder Polyporinae which are known popularly as polypores. The basidiospores are produced in minute vertical tubes, usually in a bracket or hoof-like fructification with pores on the undersides through which the spores are liberated. These fructifications can be very large: 60 cm (24″) or more in diameter in some species. Some genera of polypores, such as *Polyporus*, produce a new fructification annually while in others, like *Fomes*, they are perennial and persist from year to year. Some related genera, however, such as *Stereum*, produce instead a flattened skin or plate-like fructification which is closely adpressed to the wood or bark. A few wood-rotting fungi are gill-bearing basidiomycetes of the order Agaricales and the most widespread of all, honey fungus (*Armillaria mellea*) is of this type, giving rise to annual clusters of toadstools. Many wood-rotting species are of world-wide distribution and most affect many host plants. Exceptions to Basidiomycete causes of rots are a few species of Ascomycetes while species of the Phycomycete genus *Phytophthora* are responsible for root death without any decay in the strict sense and for ink diseases.

A feature common to all wood-rotting fungi is the ability to degrade chemically either of the two main constituents of wood: cellulose, giving rise to a brown rot, or lignin, giving rise to a white rot. The distinction between saprophytes and parasites is not always easy among decay fungi however as the heart wood of trees is actually dead tissue while the sapwood is living. Exposure of the heartwood of trees may therefore permit saprophytic decay fungi to enter and cause structural weakness or other damage to still-living trees.

In this book, only two of the many different diseases, honey fungus and *Phytophthora* root death, are described in detail. This is largely because most tree rots are similar in respect of their biology and treatment. General advice is therefore given below.

General Treatment. Generalisations can be made concerning the prevention and treatment of decay in trees. A few species, such as honey fungus (see below) are truly parasitic and can enter through undamaged tissues. Most wood-rotting fungi, however, enter through wounds or dying tissue by the germination of air-borne basidiospores and every precaution should be taken to prevent or seal such entry sites. Remove dead or broken branches as close to the stem as possible with clean saw cuts, never leave jagged ends or stubs when pruning and treat all cuts and accidental wounds with a wound sealant containing fungicide. Once a tree is infected, the procedures are more difficult and specialised tree surgery may be necessary. Unless fungal fructifications are seen, it is often difficult to determine whether or not rot is present and even the presence of fructifications may not indicate the extent of rotting, although it usually may be considered an ominous sign. If fructifications are present on a branch, that branch should certainly be removed close to the trunk. If decay is seen to progress into the trunk, an attempt may be made to gouge it out before applying sealant but if the decay is obviously extensive, it is better to fell the tree as it is likely to be unstable and prone to windthrow. If in any doubt with trees in situations (such as gardens) where the fall may damage buildings, either fell or, especially with valuable or large trees, seek expert advice.

HONEY FUNGUS *Armillaria mellea* Pl. 15

An extremely serious pathogen of worldwide distribution recorded on almost all woody plants and several herbaceous species causing either death or decay. It is very common in gardens and is often found on sites close to old tree stumps but by no means invariably so, although a site history of broad-leaved trees is probably essential. It causes one of the most important garden plant diseases.

Symptoms. Toadstools can arise at any time between July and December but commonly disappear by October with the autumn frosts. The cap is up to 15 cm (6″) diameter, the stalk usually up to 15 cm (6″) high and they occur in clusters on stumps, roots, trunk bases and occasionally higher up on the stem. The toadstools are usually yellowish or tawny but are variable in colour and sometimes have a greenish, grey or pink tint. There are often darker specks or scales towards the centre of the cap and striations at the cap margin. The gills are whitish, becoming yellower with age and are sometimes spotted brown. The gills may merge into the top of stalk. The flesh is yellowish and the stalk similar in colour to the cap or paler, usually with a large, whitish yellow-bordered ring. The affected wood is initially stained, then a soft wet brown rot develops which eventually becomes fibrous, stringy and white, often mixed with flaky white material. The rot rarely develops for more than about 50 cm (20″) above ground level and sometimes is virtually confined to the roots. There may be dark zone-lines in the wood surrounding the most badly affected parts and often flat white sheets of fungal growth and sometimes masses of flat blackish-brown strands develop beneath the bark. Black, rounded bootlace-like strands can often be found among the soil around affected plants. Young trees are much more likely to be killed than older ones but root damage may render mature trees prone to windthrow or to death from other causes.

Despite these apparently distinct symptoms, the diagnosis of honey fungus attack is not always easy. The toadstools are only present in the autumn and do not always occur then, even on badly diseased trees. The bootlace strands are not always easy to detect in the soil and similar bodies may be formed by other fungi. If several woody plants are grown within a small area, honey fungus attack is often manifest by the gradual death of them in ones and twos over a period of years. The disease is unlikely however to kill many plants quickly in a small area or to kill trees and shrubs planted less than a year previously.

Biology. This fungus lives saprophytically in dead tree stumps and spreads from there through the soil as bootlace-like masses of aggregated mycelium termed rhizomorphs. The larger and closer the diseased stump, the more likely is honey fungus to infect neighbouring vigorous trees and although rhizomorph growth is the most important means of spread to healthy trees, infection by root contact can also occur. Basidiospores are produced on the gills of the toadstools and spread the fungus to infect new stumps. Several different strains of *A. mellea* are known but the biological importance of them is uncertain.

Treatment. This is extremely difficult, and honey fungus probably shares with clubroot more mythology than any other garden disease. There is considerable variation however in the susceptibility of plants to attack. On a site known to be infested, the following are among the common garden plants that should not be grown as they are all highly susceptible: apples, birches, cedars, cypresses and false cypresses, lilac, pines, privet, walnuts and willows. The following however are probably sufficiently resistant to make their planting on an infested site reasonably likely to succeed: ash, beech, box, clematis, Douglas fir, eleagnus, false acacia, hawthorn, holly, ivy, larch, laurel, lime, mahonia, silver firs, sumachs, tamarisk, tree of heaven and yew. Once infected, a tree or shrub cannot be cured of honey fungus and the only effective procedure to limit its spread to others is the prompt removal of the diseased individual, together with its entire root system and as much as possible of the surrounding soil. The removal of large stumps is very difficult but a number of commercial contractors offer the service. Chemical methods of stump destruction with paraffin and saltpetre or proprietary products are not effective. Once removed, no woody plant, even those listed above, should be planted on the same spot for at least a year to give the fungus time to die down. Sometimes the source of fungus for attacking plants in a particular area cannot be traced or may be on neighbouring land. In such cases, only resistant types should be grown while an attempt may be made to provide barriers to rhizomorph growth. Trenches or buried vertical sheeting may be effective but may need to penetrate to at least 60 cm (24″). Proprietary chemicals based on phenolic emulsions are sold for honey fungus control and could also be used to provide barriers if the soil is drenched with them in order to kill the rhizomorphs. Such materials may need re-applying annually however and cannot be relied upon at all times in all soil types. There seems scant evidence that they have any effect in curing already diseased plants.

PHYTOPHTHORA ROOT DEATH *Phytophthora* spp.

Very common, widespread and serious. This disease has begun to reach epidemic proportions in parts of England where it is one of the commonest causes of the death of ornamental trees and shrubs. The plants most severely affected include azaleas and rhododendrons, Lawson cypress, beech, heathers and heaths, apple, yew, limes, ornamental *Prunus* spp. and planes but many others can be attacked. In old coppiced woodland, sweet chestnut is frequently infected, the symptom being known as ink disease, while it is now thought that the condition known as 'the death' which affects fruit trees on heavy, waterlogged soils and following wet winters may have a similar cause. The fungus is solely a killer of roots and not a decay organism although other wood-rotting species often invade affected roots very rapidly.

Symptoms. Difficult to diagnose accurately. As with other root damage, the above-ground symptoms include small, yellowed and sparse foliage, partial dieback and, in severe cases, the total death of plants, sometimes only revealed when new growth fails to appear in the following season. The symptoms at the stem base are more diagnostic: the thicker parts of the roots close to the stem may be dead while the thinner younger parts are still alive but bearing scattered dead patches. Areas of dead bark may extend up the stem, either in strips or in more or less triangular patches, and if, as on cypresses, this dead patch reaches to the base of low-growing branches, a part of the tree dies. In the later stages diagnosis is difficult as the damaged tissues are commonly invaded by honey fungus (p. 249), symptoms of which mask the primary cause.

Biology. Several species of *Phytophthora* are responsible, especially *P. cambivora* and *P. cinnamomi*. Infection arises when swimming swarm-spores germinate from resistant resting spores present in the soil and penetrate the root tissues. Within the roots, mycelium and ultimately more spores form. Infection is favoured by warm, wet soils and probably also by any factor, such as farmyard manure or mulches, which increases soil water retention. Nursery sites where susceptible species are grown intensively are very prone to develop severe infestations.

Treatment. Some good chemical treatments are available but unfortunately not for garden use. The likelihood of attack can be minimised by only buying plants from reputable nurseries and avoiding any where debilitated or browned cypresses and other trees are evident. Never transplant from infested into clean land; avoid excessive watering, manuring or mulching of susceptible plants; do not allow hollows to form around stem bases – slope the soil away from trees and shrubs; do not plant into peaty or similar medium artificially introduced as pockets into heavy soils as these will rapidly become waterlogged; replace affected plants by more tolerant species – for example Leyland cypress (× *Cupressocyparis leylandii*) although less attractive, may be used instead of the susceptible Lawson cypress. In badly infested nurseries, a change to container production of plants is usually the only solution.

STEM AND LEAF ROTS (Herbaceous Plants)

(Plate 15)

These are caused by a wide range of fungi and bacteria and while most arise from infection by air-borne spores, some spread upwards after the tissues are invaded by soil-inhabiting organisms. The distinction between some stem diseases and root and foot rot conditions is however often blurred and in some instances the same organism may be responsible for both. Conditions such as crown rots of delphiniums, rhubarb or strawberries for instance could be classified as either stem or foot rots. Leaf rots often spread with extreme rapidity and some are commonly known as fire diseases or blights, although the latter term is often used indiscriminately for many unrelated plant diseases and some pests. Prevention is essential with such fast-spreading problems because cure or the arresting of development is very difficult. Many of the stem and leaf rots described here are caused by species of *Botrytis* against which systemic fungicides related to benomyl are often very effective although it is wise to try alternative chemicals first in some instances, to minimise the likelihood of tolerant strains of the pathogens developing.

CHRYSANTHEMUM STEM ROT *Botrytis cinerea*
Very common and widespread in glasshouses and especially troublesome on cuttings in cool, moist conditions or sometimes following slight frost damage. The infection arises from air-borne conidia and cuttings rot, become covered with grey mould growth, and die. The stems of mature plants keel over at the point of attack, which also bears grey mould, and the disease may spread to the buds and flowers and these in turn develop grey mould growth. General principles of hygiene for the prevention of grey mould are outlined on p. 237 while it may be possible to arrest an attack by removing badly diseased plants and spraying lightly affected and healthy stock three times at fortnightly intervals with benomyl.

HYDRANGEA STEM LEAF ROT *Botrytis cinerea*
This is the most important disease of hydrangeas and is common and widespread especially in cool moist conditions. It affects plants at all stages of growth. The grey mould growth arises from air-borne conidia and, on the leaves, it usually begins at the extremities, sometimes associated with hydathodes. On stems, infection is often centred around leaf scars but soon spreads and the stems keel over at the point of attack while the disease often spreads to cause a flower rot. General notes on the prevention of grey mould are given on p. 237 while a spray at three-week intervals with benomyl or thiophanate-methyl should check attacks in the early stages.

LETTUCE GREY MOULD *Botrytis cinerea* **Pl. 15**
Very common and widespread in glasshouses and on outdoor plants. Often the most serious disease of lettuces.
Symptoms. On seedlings: essentially a damping-off symptom, appearing as a brown leaf rot which spreads to the stem. The plants keel over and a mass of grey mould develops on affected parts. On older plants, as the

lettuces reach maturity, a leaf rot or more commonly a red-brown stem rot enables plants to be lifted clear of the ground by rupture of the almost non-existent stem tissues. If undisturbed, the entire plant wilts dramatically as natural severing of the stem occurs. In humid conditions, the rot may spread from the leaf margins to affect the head which becomes soft and slimy and often bears grey mould growth.

Biology. Rapid spread from plant to plant occurs by conidia produced on the grey mould whereas small black sclerotia produced on decaying tissues are possibly the means of survival in soil between crops, although the range of plants affected by grey mould is so large that there are probably always enough spores available to start new infections. The fungus is sometimes seed-borne, this being the cause of much of the damping-off symptoms.

Treatment. Prevent damage or stress to lettuce plants. Among common predisposing factors are downy mildew, soil-borne damping-off, chemical spray damage, waterlogging, mechanical damage to seedlings at transplanting, overcrowding, transplanting seedlings when too large, incorrect temperature control in glasshouses, inadequate ventilation or insufficient watering. It is nonetheless wise to spray lettuce plants routinely with benomyl or thiophanate-methyl at pricking out time and fortnightly thereafter. Simultaneous application of mancozeb to control downy mildew (p. 202) is also very desirable.

NARCISSUS SMOULDER *Sclerotinia narcissicola*

Common throughout Europe and generally most severe in cold, wet seasons, especially if such conditions occur early. In spring, shoots appear bearing grey mould growth and conidia produced on this mould spread the disease to other plants on which the lower parts of the leaves turn brown and later the upper regions become yellow and wilt. Eventually these plants become coated with grey mould growth. Black sclerotia may develop between the bulb scales and can be liberated into the soil where they persist and may infect plants in the following season, although not all the sclerotia commonly seen on narcissus bulbs indicate smoulder; many are produced by the grey mould fungus also. Bulbs affected with smoulder either fail to grow or give rise to diseased and distorted plants. Control is very difficult but the disease may be prevented by dipping bulbs for 15–30 minutes in suspensions of benomyl or thiophanate-methyl before planting or storage. This will protect against smoulder and certain bulb rots. Alternatively the papery scales bearing the sclerotia may be rubbed off before planting. This is usually adequate to prevent more than a few odd diseased plants from appearing.

ONION LEAF ROT *Sclerotinia squamosa*

This disease is common on onions and, to a lesser extent, on leeks and other alliums, especially in conditions of high humidity. It is frequent in the West of Britain and seems especially serious on soils with high nitrogen content. Small elliptical or circular white leaf flecks develop, often with water-soaked margins and congregated towards the leaf tips. The lesions later dry out and the leaf tips shrivel, collapse and hang down while in moist conditions a grey mould growth producing masses of conidia may grow over the damaged tissues. Attacks may sometimes be checked by spraying fortnightly with benomyl. Further outbreaks may be minimised in areas where the problem is prevalent by applying potash to the soil if it is deficient, and increasing the spacing between the plants.

This is not an easy disease to diagnose and among several factors having at least some symptoms in common are hail damage (p. 295), downy mildew (p. 202), copper deficiency (p. 290), grey mould (p. 232) or natural leaf senescence.

PAEONY GREY MOULD BLIGHT *Botrytis paeoniae* and *Botrytis cinerea* **Pl. 15**

Common in Britain; common and sometimes serious elsewhere in northern Europe. *B. paeoniae* is the most usual and serious cause and both fungi cause a comparable leaf and stem blight of lily of the valley, which may be similarly treated. Soft brown regions develop at the bases of the leaves, which wilt and fall over, and a dark brown rot subsequently develops in the bases of both stem and leaves while grey mould growth arises on the stem above soil level. The young buds blacken and wither, the flowers and leaves bear brown patches and grey mould develops on all damaged tissues. Affected plants should be cut down to ground level in autumn and the debris destroyed. Then scrape away the top soil around the plants and replace it with fresh soil. As a further protection, spray plants with benomyl or thiophanate-methyl as the leaves expand and then twice more at fortnightly intervals.

PELARGONIUM BLACK LEG *Pythium* sp.

Very common and widespread, particularly on cuttings but occasionally on mature plants also. A blackening of the stems spreads upwards from the base and the affected tissues shrivel and take on a characteristic pinched appearance while the leaves wilt and die. Although it is so often troublesome, black leg can be controlled by taking certain precautions. All pots and trays should be disinfected before use and compost sterilised carefully. Cuttings should be taken only from healthy plants and dipped in hormone rooting powder containing fungicide. Glasshouses should be kept dry and well-ventilated and the cuttings watered only with clean water, avoiding possibly contaminated sources such as rain butts.

POTATO and TOMATO BLIGHT *Phytophthora infestans* **Pl. 15**

Widespread; common and serious in wet seasons, less frequent in dry ones. Potato blight is one of the classic plant diseases and the succession of severe blight epidemics in the 1840s led directly to the Irish potato famine. It is also serious on outdoor and cool glasshouse tomatoes and is sometimes known as late blight to distinguish it from the much less serious early blight. **Symptoms.** POTATOES: dark brown-black blotches sometimes with paler margins develop on the leaves and are often concentrated at the leaf tips or edges. In damp conditions, white mould grows on the undersides of the blotches which increase in both size and number and may spread to the stems. In a humid atmosphere the entire foliage may be reduced rapidly to a collapsed, rotting mass and there is usually a rapid spread of the disease to neighbouring plants in these conditions. On tubers, brownish lesions on the surface extend gradually to envelop the whole tuber, giving a dry type of rot. Internally the affected tissue has a brownish-red speckled appearance. These tubers are often invaded by other fungi and bacteria and soft rotting may result in damp conditions. The fungus itself does not spread from tuber to tuber during storage.

TOMATOES: the foliage symptoms are similar to but less severe than those on potatoes. Dark streaks and spots develop on the stems and green fruit while more mature fruits decay rapidly with a usually dryish rot but may appear symptomless for several days after picking before the rot becomes visible. The fruit rot is usually accompanied by mould growth and the symptoms can be confused with other *Phytophthora* rots although these are more common on glasshouse plants. Also see blossom end rot (p. 287).

Biology. The fungus persists over winter in diseased potato tubers from the previous crop, either in the ground or more usually on dumps or in undetected seed tubers. When such tubers grow, either as seed in the ground or in large diseased heaps, they sometimes produce infected shoots. Spores may then be blown from them to infect a new crop. Tubers become infected by spores falling from the haulm onto the soil and being washed downwards by rain. Spores are produced and dispersed only in damp conditions and foggy weather in summer is therefore very favourable to the disease. Infection by blight spores is likely to take place when the temperature does not fall below 10°C (50°F) and the relative humidity does not fall below 75% during a period of 48 hours, this being known as a Beaumont period. The Ministry of Agriculture broadcasts warnings when Beaumont or the comparable Smith periods have occurred in the main potato growing regions and these indicate that commercial growers should apply protective sprays.

Treatment. There is little choice in terms of cultivar susceptibility to blight but 'Arran Comet', 'King Edward' and 'Ulster Chieftain' are particularly prone. Since rotten and unwanted potatoes often carry blighted tubers they should not be dumped but buried deeply away from land on which a new crop is to be grown. Seed tubers should be examined carefully and any showing symptoms destroyed while earthing up well may prevent spores produced on the foliage from reaching the tubers. Several chemicals are suitable for protective spraying but their application may not be generally worthwhile on potatoes in gardens. In damp seasons, however, particularly if blight is known to have been present in the vicinity in the same or the previous year, a spray programme is a wise precaution. Spray potatoes with mancozeb in the first week of July (earlier in the South-West of Britain and other mild areas) and repeat at about 14 day intervals depending on the wetness of season (which affects both symptom severity and the extent to which the chemical is washed off the foliage). Spray or dust outdoor tomatoes as a routine in all except the very driest seasons with mancozeb at ten-day intervals, beginning just after the first fruit set. Dust is often most effective applied in the early morning while dew is present but the fruit must be washed before eating.

SAINTPAULIA STEM and LEAF ROTS

Rots of saintpaulia stems and leaves are very common and widespread. Growth of grey mould (*Botrytis cinerea*) and an associated decay of stems and leaf stalks was formerly the commonest symptom but the bacterium *Erwinia chrysanthemi* has recently been serious in some areas. The symptoms of the latter are similar to those of *Phytophthora* foot rot with black lesions at the stem base and general debilitation but no mould growth. Unlike the fungal disease, the bacterial infection causes the leaves to detach from the rosette but the precise diagnosis of this still imperfectly understood condition is a matter for expert study. *B. cinerea* is readily controlled in the early stages by spraying with benomyl or thiophanate-methyl but there is no established control measure for *E. chrysanthemi*.

SWEET PEA WHITE MOULD *Ramularia deusta*

Common and widespread; especially important in the South and West of England and in Holland. It is easily confused with the very common powdery mildew (p. 204) but, unlike mildew, is favoured by dampness. A mealy white covering develops on the leaf surfaces and stems and sometimes water soaked spots appear which gradually turn red-brown at the leaf margins. The affected parts become shrunken and yellowed and the leaves may drop. To treat white mould, avoid damp, warm conditions in glasshouses and spray fortnightly with mancozeb, beginning at the first sign of symptoms. Grey mould (*Botrytis cinerea*) is sometimes the cause of a basal rot of sweet peas but is readily controlled by a spray with benomyl and improvement of the ventilation, if in glasshouses.

TOMATO GREY MOULD STEM ROT *Botrytis cinerea*

Common and widespread especially in cool glasshouses and when tomatoes are associated with other grey mould-prone plants, such as lettuce. Infection is normally from air-borne conidia through leaf scars or pruning cuts, which develop grey mould and rot. The symptoms may be associated with ghost spotting of the fruits (p. 272) and flower damage (p. 232) and the problem can often be avoided by adequate attention to ventilation, hygiene and other factors conducive to good plant growth. Do not leave leaf and shoot stubs when pruning and note the general comments made on grey mould biology and treatment on p. 236. Benomyl sprayed at fortnightly intervals should check any further spread of the disease.

TOMATO LEAF MOULD *Fulvia fulva* **Pl. 15**

Originally North American and now very common and widespread in glasshouses but rare on outdoor plants.

Symptoms. Sometimes appear as early as April but usually not until June or later. Patches, at first greyish but soon turning yellow, develop on the upper leaf surfaces and correspond with areas on the undersides covered with pale grey-brown mould growth. In moist, warm conditions the patches increase in size and number and darken to red-brown. Mould may then appear on the upper surface also and the leaves soon curl, wither and die but may not drop. Growth of the plant is checked, the fruit develops poorly and occasionally the flowers or fruit are themselves affected by mould.

Biology. The fungus probably survives over winter as conidia which initiate the first infections, usually on the lower leaves. More conidia are produced on the mould and spread easily by air movement and on hands and clothing. The disease is often restricted to the lower parts of plants as it is retarded by bright sunlight and is favoured by high humidity. Several races of the fungus occur and although many cultivars are resistant to some, very few are resistant to all.

Treatment. Disinfect glasshouses containing diseased plants by burning sulphur *before* the crop debris is removed (care should be taken with sulphur in non-wooden glasshouses and the manufacturer's instructions must be studied carefully). Maintain good ventilation throughout the growing season and take particular care to ensure that the lower layers of air do not stagnate. Do not allow high temperatures to coincide with high humidity; remove and destroy any lower leaves that show signs of disease and if leaf mould is a persistent problem, then apply protective sprays of benomyl or mancozeb at fortnightly intervals, but not within two days of picking the fruit.

TOMATO STEM and FRUIT ROT *Didymella lycopersici*

Common and widespread on glasshouse and, even more so, on outdoor tomatoes, but now less of a problem than formerly. It also occurs on aubergines (egg plants).

Symptoms. Sunken, brownish lesions with small black bodies usually appear on stems at soil level with yellowing of the lower leaves and sometimes the development of roots on the stems above ground. The stem may be girdled by the lesion and secondary lesions may form anywhere on the main stem or roots. On the fruit the calyx becomes blackened and a rot spreads from it to form a black, crusted surface (but also see blossom end rot (p. 287)).

Biology. The fungus persists on crop debris or in the soil, from which the first infections arise. It can be transmitted on seed from affected fruit but this is probably of little importance. The black bodies on the lesions and fruit are pycnidia, within which conidia are produced and spread the disease very rapidly to other plants by rain splash or on hands and tools.

Treatment. Never leave diseased plants over winter in the ground but remove and destroy them in autumn and wash and disinfect hands and implements that have been in contact with diseased material. Where plants are grown on soil believed to be contaminated, protect them by drenching the bottom 10 cm (4″) of stem and the soil around each plant with captan within three days of planting. Repeat this treatment after three weeks. Similarly, treat healthy plants after removing diseased individuals from a bed, disinfect glasshouses and boxes at the end of the season and do not dip seedlings in water before planting as any infection present spreads rapidly to all other plants in this way.

TULIP FIRE *Botrytis tulipae* Pl. 15

Common in all parts of northern Europe and sometimes devastating.

Symptoms. Distorted leaves or shoots appear soon after emergence from the soil but are usually present only on scattered plants in a bed. The shoots may be almost completely withered and in moist conditions are covered with grey mould growth bearing black bodies. Many small sunken yellowish leaf spots with surrounding dark green areas develop on neighbouring plants and there may be elongate dark brown patches bearing black bodies on the flower stalks. The flower buds may fail to open and be covered with mould while opened blooms may have small pale brown-white spots or blisters. On bulbs, small black bodies develop on the outer scales or on the remains of the flower stalk and the outermost fleshy scale, when exposed, may have depressed circular lesions, sometimes bearing black bodies. Occasionally the bulb may rot and have masses of black bodies around the outside.

Biology. Infection on newly planted tulip bulbs originates either from conidia on the bulbs, mycelium in the lesions on the outer scales (both usually derived from diseased parent bulbs) or from the black sclerotial bodies which can survive in the soil on the bulbs, and especially at the base of the old flower stalk, for about two years before germinating. Because of this short persistence, soil-borne infection is probably only important when tulips are grown continuously on the same land. The leaf and flower spotting is caused by conidia from the primary infections.

Treatment. Destroy affected tulips immediately as the spread to neighbouring plants can be very rapid. After removing the diseased individuals, spray the remaining healthy plants with benomyl. Carefully inspect bulbs for sclerotia and reject any affected and, as a precaution, all bulbs may be soaked before planting for 15–30 minutes in suspensions of benomyl or thiophanate-methyl, which will also give protection against certain other bulb diseases. Ideally tulips should not be grown on affected land for at least three years but in formal bedding this is impossible and in such cases, raking in quintozene dust at planting time may help, although this chemical is not normally available to gardeners.

SPOTS

(Plates 16–17)

This section is one of the largest in the book and it includes some of the commonest of all plant diseases. Thousands of species of fungi and many bacteria and viruses cause disfiguration, often of the leaves, on thousands of different host plants. This account includes only those that either lead to serious diseases or, although virtually harmless, cause symptoms that are so common or distinct that some comment upon them seems necessary, if only to allay concern. There are many instances where spots on leaves or other plant parts are only one outward expression of a disease in which some other effect is the more serious and descriptions of these will be found under other appropriate sections. Diseases, such as potato blight, in which leaves decay will be found described as leaf rots (p. 252) while leaf blistering is another special type of symptom also described separately (p. 222). Most of the lesions included in this section are characterised by death of the cells that comprise them and most arise from fungal or bacterial infection. Virus induced spots are described separately (p. 277) although a few spot diseases arising from non-pathological or unknown causes are included here. Although it is almost impossible to give any useful guidelines for deciding whether a spot symptom has a fungal, bacterial or viral origin, very small, usually black, dot-like bodies present on lesions are certain to be fungal reproductive structures. The most important spot-forming organisms are fungi of the genera *Alternaria*, *Ascochyta*, *Cercospora*, *Colletotrichum*, *Gloeosporium*, *Phyllosticta* and *Septoria*, which together account for over

150 different spotting conditions on cultivated plants in Britain alone, although not all are described here. It should also be appreciated that other very common causes of spotting are misdirected garden chemical sprays or other airborne pollutants which are considered in detail on p. 299. Any spotting that is markedly unidirectional in its distribution on plants, or that extends across several different species is likely to fall into this category. White flecks with a similar unidirectional distribution may be caused by environmental factors, such as hail damage (p. 295) and are very common on fleshy leaved plants, including onions, tulips and other bulbous species. Extreme caution moreover should be exercised in deciding that a plant is affected by any leaf disease in late summer and autumn when normal seasonal necrosis may give rise to many misleading appearances. It is also worth noting that gardeners are often misled because the leaves and stems of some plants, of which hydrangeas are probably among the best known examples, have spots of seemingly pathological origin as part of their normal colouration.

Disfigurements may take several forms, largely reflecting the extent to which the pathogen has penetrated the plant tissues before being arrested by some resistance mechanism, which usually takes the form of specialised and toughened cells. A spot differs from a blotch in its smaller size and commonly more regular shape. Angular spots or blotches reflect inability of the pathogen to invade the leaf veins, which thus form boundaries to the dead tissue, and concentric or target spots indicate some aspect of radial growth on the part of the causal organism. Scorch is the term used to describe a symptom that gives the impression of a leaf having been held close to a flame and the name anthracnose, literally charcoal-like, is often used to describe several diseases with black sunken lesions. Dead spots or patches of tissue in leaves often drop out to produce the symptom known as 'shot-hole'. Size or number of any of the above lesions need be no criterion for judging their effect on the plant; the very dramatic symptoms of horse chestnut leaf blotch or tar spot of maples for instance are associated with very little harm to the respective trees but the much smaller and relatively insignificant lesions of black currant leaf spot, for example, can indicate considerable potential damage to the host plant. Nonetheless, even small and biologically unimportant spots can be a matter of concern when ornamental species are disfigured.

When the cause is fungal or bacterial, spots usually indicate the point of entry of the pathogen to a diseased plant organ, although virus induced spots may be of two types: local lesions, which are entry points analagous to those of fungal or bacterial origin, and systemic spots, which arise when a plant carries widespread virus infection but the siting of the actual lesions is not necessarily related to the presence of virus in those particular cells.

Many spot diseases require no treatment and those that merely cause slight disfigurement on ornamental species scarcely justify the use of chemical control measures. Because of the wide variety of fungi involved in spot causation, it is difficult to make any general recommendations for fungicide usage, although on ornamental species it is probable that two or three sprays at fortnightly intervals with benomyl would give some control of the majority of spotting diseases. Bordeaux mixture is useful for some fungal spot diseases and is the only chemical likely to give any suppression of bacterial spots but as the fungicide itself causes spots on many plants, a general recommendation for its use would be unwise. For virus-induced necrotic spots, see the general comments on the treatment of virus diseases (p. 281).

ACER TAR SPOT *Rhytisma acerinum* **Pl. 16**

Very common and widespread on sycamore but many species of ornamental acer can also be affected. A very similar disease on willows is caused by the related fungus *R. salicinum.*

Symptoms. Quite unmistakable large black bituminous blotches with yellow halos form on the upper surfaces of leaves from mid-summer onwards, preceded by rarely noticed yellowish patches in spring.

Several other types of spot are also common and widespread on sycamores, field maples and, to a lesser extent, on other acers. They vary from red-brown lesions to large yellowish blotches and although there is still uncertainty over the identity of the causal fungi, none of these spots normally reach serious proportions and no control measures should be necessary.

Biology. After the leaves have fallen in autumn, reproductive structures develop within the black blotches and by spring mature ascospores eject from them to bring about fresh infections as the new season's leaves begin to emerge. Different strains of *Rhytisma* may exist, each only capable of infecting particular *Acer* spp. The disease normally has no effect on the tree's vigour although this is small consolation when a plant grown as an ornamental is so conspicuously disfigured.

Treatment. Tar spot is not easily controlled. As ornamental maples are often small trees, the collecting up and burning of affected fallen leaves is usually feasible and a spray with Bordeaux mixture during the summer has been claimed as an effective treatment. Outbreaks of tar spot are less severe in industrial areas where sulphur in the atmosphere is believed to limit fungal development.

ANTIRRHINUM LEAF SPOT *Phyllosticta antirrhini* **Pl. 16**

This is the commonest of several fungal spotting diseases on antirrhinum leaves and often becomes apparent suddenly during humid weather in spring. Dirty brown, round leaf spots appear, often with dark margins, and may fuse to form large blotches which can result in leaf death. Black dot-like pycnidia develop on the lesions and similar spots occur on the flower stalks, capsules and stems, the latter type of infection sometimes causing girdling and death of entire plants. The disease spreads from plant to plant by means of conidia liberated from the black pycnidia although the fungus, when present in dry plant debris among seeds, may also be a cause of seedling damping-off. Although seed treatment with fungicide can be used to control the damping-off symptoms, this is unlikely to be necessary in gardens although severe attacks on growing plants may be checked by one or two sprays with mancozeb.

BEAN ANTHRACNOSE *Colletotrichum lindemuthianum* **Pl. 16**

Widespread on dwarf and less severely on runner beans but usually only apparent in cool wet summers. Brown sunken stripes develop on the stems, reddening on the undersides of the leaf veins, sometimes followed by leaf withering and death, and reddish, rounded, brown-bordered spots on the pods. In damp conditions pink-brown slimy masses of conidia may form on the spots. The pod spots result in infection of the seed which may be detected as dark spots on light coloured seeds or indefinite pale marks on dark seeds. Such infected seeds result in infected seedlings. These are usually killed and conidia from them splash onto healthy plants. The disease is rarely severe enough to warrant treatment in Britain where many dwarf bean cultivars are resistant to some races of the fungus.

BEAN CHOCOLATE SPOT *Botrytis fabae*

Widespread and common on broad and field beans but varies greatly in intensity from year to year and may appear at any time from mid-winter onwards although most serious when late frosts precede wet mild weather in early summer.

Symptoms. Dark, chocolate brown, more or less rounded spots develop on the leaves (mainly the upper surfaces), on the stems (where the lesions are more elongate), and on the leaf stalks, pods, seed coats and flowers. The spots may merge and result in blackening and death of organs or entire plants and even slight attacks can result in reduced numbers of pods.

Other types of spot can also occur quite commonly on broad bean leaves and may be confused with chocolate spot. Sunken, ashen spots with a raised brown perimeter on leaves are caused by *Cercospora zonata*. Similar leaf lesions, but more usually with black pycnidia present and sometimes occurring also on the pods, are caused by *Ascochyta fabae*. Greyish blotches with veined, net-like margins and covered by a dark brown mould growth, with occasional leaf death, are the symptoms of net blotch caused by *Pleospora herbarum*. None are usually serious and treatments are not normally justified.

Biology. Since this disease is favoured by damp, shaded, overcrowded conditions, it is generally not nearly as common in gardens as in commercial field beans. Most infections originate from conidia over-wintering on plant debris but the seeds may also sometimes carry the disease. Plants infected in early spring seem much more likely to recover than plants infected later in the season..

Treatment. Apply potash fertilisers, improve drainage, increase spacing between plants and avoid sheltered sites. If all else fails, fortnightly sprays of benomyl may check outbreaks.

BEAN HALO BLIGHT *Pseudomonas phaseolicola* Pl. 16

Seed-borne bacterial diseases of dwarf and runner beans are quite common and widespread but there has been confusion in the past over the identity of the organisms responsible. It is now clear that in Britain *P. phaseolicola* is the most important.

Symptoms. Small water-soaked spots are sometimes visible on the cotyledons of newly emerged seedlings but are more likely on the first leaves. Leaf lesions gradually darken and dry and become surrounded by characteristic yellowish zones or halos. Later, inter-veinal yellowing appears on the leaves, which sometimes become entirely yellow, and lesions may also appear on the stems. Seedlings wither and die in severe attacks but less badly affected plants remain stunted. The pods may also become infected and develop greasy spots.

Biology. There are usually only a few infected seeds in any one batch but rain splash rapidly spreads bacteria from the resulting diseased plants to neighbouring healthy leaves, the bacteria gaining entry through stomata. Infected pods give rise to the infected seed. The search for resistance to this disease is complicated by the occurrence of two races of the pathogen. Although sources of resistance to both races are known, resistant cultivars are not yet available.

Treatment. Never soak bean seeds in water before planting as this will transfer the bacteria from contaminated to clean individuals. If it is necessary to pre-germinate seeds, place them for a time in damp peat which does not facilitate such transfer. One or two sprays with Bordeaux mixture will restrict the spread of the disease on growing plants but should not be applied after the first small pods are formed.

BLACKBERRY CANE SPOT and PURPLE BLOTCH

Septoria rubi and *Septocyta ramealis* **Pl. 16**

Both are occasional, widespread and very similar and also easily confused with raspberry cane and leaf spot (p. 258) which sometimes affects blackberries. Both cause grey-white elliptical spots with purple borders on the canes, each bearing black dot-like pycnidia. Cane spot also causes similar but circular spots on the leaves and such symptoms are sometimes severe on the cultivar 'Himalaya Giant'. No control is normally needed.

BOX LEAF SPOTS

Leaf lesions arising from various causes are very common and widespread. Pale brown spots with distinct purple margins are caused by *Phyllosticta* spp.; large yellow blotches, especially on the undersides of the leaves, are caused by *Hyponectria buxi* but there may well be others. Benomyl or Bordeaux mixture sprays are worth trying.

BRASSICA LEAF SPOTS

Leaf spotting is exceedingly common on brassica leaves and heads. A number of different types occur, some being associated with other, more serious symptoms. Fortunately the various types of spot are fairly distinct, the commonest confusion arising with virus spots and with white blister.

BRASSICA LIGHT LEAF SPOT

Cylindrosporium concentricum

Common, particularly so in northern Britain, on Brussels sprouts, cabbage, cauliflower and less commonly on other brassicas. Tiny, fluffy white lesions form, particularly on the under surfaces of older leaves, but are found also on other parts, including cauliflower curds. They occur in groups in characteristic ring formations, the individual rings occasionally fusing and the fluffiness being caused by masses of tiny white conidia which are squeezed out from beneath the leaf surface. Infection arises from fungus persisting in plant debris in the soil. Tiny black apothecia, in which ascospores are produced, can also occur but are rare. The disease may be troublesome in gardens where the two-year break between brassica crops which limits its impact is not always practicable.

BRASSICA RING SPOT *Mycosphaerella brassicicola* **Pl. 16**
Frequent throughout northern Europe but in Britain usually only serious in the South West in cool wet seasons. It is most frequent on Brussels sprouts, cabbages and cauliflowers but is found also on other brassicas and is commonest on intensively cropped and heavily manured land.
Symptoms. These are most usually seen on the older leaves. Rounded brown, sometimes faintly purple spots develop, often bearing more or less concentric target-like rings of abundant black dot-like bodies and often with a paler yellowish margin. The entire leaves may ultimately become yellow and shrivel. Lesions can also occur on other parts of the plants and on Brussels sprouts the buttons are often severely affected.
Biology. The tiny black bodies may be either pycnidia of unknown function or perithecia, within which ascospores develop, these spores, released from perithecia on plant debris in cool damp conditions being the main sources of disease. Transmission of the fungus in seeds produced in infected pods has been suggested but not proved definitely.
Treatment. Remove and burn all affected plant remains. No chemical treatment is suitable for gardens but 'Roscoff' types of cauliflower have some resistance.

BRASSICA WHITE SPOT *Pseudocercosporella capsellae*
Common and widespread on turnips and even more so on swedes but infrequent on other brassicas. Especially common in wetter areas in the West of Britain. Tiny more or less circular dirty white spots develop with a faint purple border on both leaf surfaces. These spots gradually enlarge and merge to result in yellowing and sometimes death of the leaves and defoliation of the plant. Conidia produced on fine mould growth over the surface of the spots bring about rapid disease spread and small resistant sclerotia survive over winter. Fortnightly sprays with Bordeaux mixture usually check outbreaks.

CELERY LEAF SPOT *Septoria apiicola* **Pl. 16**
Common throughout northern Europe and serious on celery, less so on celeriac.
Symptoms. Brown spots with either a lighter or darker border develop initially on the older leaves but they soon spread to other foliage and occasionally to the leaf stalks. The spots are sometimes very numerous and may fuse to form much larger blotches which cause leaf death. On and around the spots tiny black dots appear and in severe attacks the crowns may develop feebly as a result of the leaf damage.
Biology. The initial source of the disease is fungus persisting on the coats of seeds from affected plants, the seedlings which emerge from such seed in turn becoming infected. Tiny black pycnidia develop on them and produce conidia which are spread by rain splash onto healthy plants on which the leaf symptoms then develop. It is possible that diseased celery debris may also serve, for a limited period, as an initial source of the disease.
Treatment. Although attacks of the disease may be contained by one or two sprays with benomyl, eradication of the fungus from the seed is the only certain method of avoidance. Hot water treatment of the seed for 25 minutes at 50°C (122°F) gives good disease suppression but is difficult on a garden scale.

CHERRY LEAF SCORCH *Gnomonia erythrostoma*

A common and widespread problem; one of the most frequent cherry diseases.

Symptoms. Large yellow patches develop on the leaves early in the season and gradually enlarge and turn brown. The leaves eventually wither but remain hanging conspicuously on the trees throughout the following winter. Fruit may also be infected but this is rarely serious, although hard dark spots can develop within the flesh. Repeated and severe annual attacks can seriously weaken the trees.

Biology. From the leaf lesions mycelium grows into the leaf stalks and prevents development of the abscission layer by which the leaves should separate from the tree in autumn. During the winter ascospores develop within the dead leaves hanging on the branches and these are discharged in spring and are the sole means of infection. Wild cherries are often badly affected and can serve as disease sources when growing close to orchards and gardens.

Treatment. There are marked differences in susceptibility between cherry cultivars; 'Early Amber', 'Frogmore Bigarreau' and 'Waterloo' are badly affected while 'Napoleon' and 'Turk', among others, are highly resistant. Remove and burn all hanging dead leaves from trees in winter to eliminate the source of disease and, for further protection, spray the trees with mancozeb as the leaves are unfolding and preferably once again after petal drop.

CINERARIA LEAF SPOTS *Ascochyta cinerariae* and *Alternaria cinerariae*

These are very common and widespread seed-borne diseases, especially serious on bedding plants. More or less circular, gradually enlarging dark brown or black leaf spots are caused by *Ascochyta cinerariae.* The entire leaves may rot and shrivel and, in Britain at least, the same fungus also causes a rot. *Alternaria cinerariae* causes similar symptoms and, when the leaves are held up to the light, rot can sometimes be seen within the veins. Seedling damping-off caused by *Alternaria cinerariae* may result from using contaminated seed. It is not really feasible to eliminate such seed-borne infection but growing plants may be treated by removing affected leaves and spraying with Bordeaux mixture or mancozeb.

CUCUMBER ANTHRACNOSE *Colletotrichum lagenarium*

Common and important throughout northern Europe on cucumbers and less commonly on vegetable marrows and melons.

Symptoms. Very pale green, often transparent, spots develop on the leaves and later enlarge, become dry and red-brown in the centres. The spots may coalesce and the entire leaf may be killed and depressed, dry, powdery dark patches appear on the leaf stalks and stems. Similar sunken pale areas may develop on the fruits, which may eventually crack and die. When seedlings are attacked a damping-off symptom may result.

Biology. Masses of conidia are produced on the powdery patches in humid conditions. These adhere readily to hands and clothing and spread the disease to other plants and can also lead to fungal development on old woodwork in glasshouses and frames, on straw and on other plant debris and similar material.

Treatment. Provide adequate ventilation and routinely disinfect the glasshouse fabric, avoid wide fluctuations in temperature and remove all plant debris. At the first sign of symptoms destroy affected parts, spray the plants with a sulphur suspension and repeat at weekly intervals.

CURRANT LEAF SPOT *Pseudopeziza ribis* **Pl. 16**

Common and widespread on all types of currant and gooseberries.
Symptoms. Small irregular brownish spots develop from May onwards. They appear first on the older leaves, but often merge and the disease then spreads up the plant, the leaves falling progressively as it does so. Small sparkling droplets may appear on the spots in wet or damp conditions.
Biology. The tiny droplets are masses of conidia which spread the disease during the summer. During the winter apothecia develop on fallen leaves and from these ascospores are discharged in the spring and initiate new infections on the lower leaves. Severe attacks may result in a weakening of the bushes and a reduced crop in the following year.
Treatment. 'Baldwin' is probably the most susceptible black currant and the red currant cultivars 'Fertility' and 'Fays's Prolific' are also affected severely. Collect and burn affected leaves and spray the bushes with mancozeb, benomyl or thiophanate-methyl after flowering and repeat once or twice at fortnightly intervals, but no later than a month before the fruits are picked. Spray again immediately after the fruits have been picked.

DIANTHUS RING SPOT *Mycosphaerella dianthi* **Pl. 16**

Affects carnations and sweet williams but cross infection does not occur between the two. More or less circular greyish spots with very marked red-purple margins develop on the leaves, stems or rarely on the sepals. Individual spots may fuse and concentric rings of dark grey mould appear in other centres. Conidia, produced on this mould, rapidly spread the disease to other plants. The fungus over-winters as a perennial mycelium in the leaves. The chances of attack may be lessened in glasshouses by avoiding the development of high humidity. Outbreaks may sometimes be checked by spraying with Bordeaux mixture at three-week intervals during the summer.

HEBE LEAF SPOT *Septoria exotica*

Common. More or less circular brownish leaf spots form with distinct purple margins and bear dark brown dot-like pycnidia. There may also be serious dying back of the shoots. There are no established control measures but spraying at two- or three-week intervals with benomyl is likely to be effective.

HELLEBORUS LEAF SPOT *Coniothyrium hellebori* **Pl. 16**

Very common and widespread on most *Helleborus* spp.
Symptoms. Large, brown and/or black, blotches appear with concentric rings and may have minute black dots clustered towards the centre on the undersides. The leaves may turn prematurely yellow and die, when the symptoms spread to the rest of the plant, which suffers from the shortage of foliage. Lesions may also develop on the stem which in turn shrivels; the immature flower buds also shrink and wilt and the entire plant may topple

over on its weakened stem. In less severe cases, the flowers may be spoiled by black spots on the petals.

Biology. Ascospores, released from the dot-like perithecia, spread the disease but require constant moisture for the initial infection. Under appropriately damp conditions in autumn or spring an entire bed can be affected in a few days and no initial damage is needed for the infection to occur.

Treatment. Remove and destroy all infected foliage; spray at monthly intervals with Bordeaux mixture, beginning in October, and continue until the new growth ceases, except for the period when the flower buds are expanding. Avoid excess moisture on Christmas roses lifted in autumn for forcing.

HORSE CHESTNUT LEAF BLOTCH

Guignardia aesculi **Pl. 16**

Common throughout northern Europe; increasingly so in Britain on horse chestnut and other *Aesculus* spp. Irregular brown blotches with yellow halos appear on leaves from July onwards, although similar symptoms on leaf margins can arise from a variety of causes, including normal autumnal necrosis. Conidia are produced on the blotches and ascospores, which give rise to the first spring infections, originate on fallen leaves. There may be some premature leaf fall but usually there is little harm to the tree and no treatment is necessary.

IRIS LEAF SPOT *Mycosphaerella macrospora* **Pl. 17**

This disease has been known in England since the end of the last century and is common throughout northern Europe but varies considerably in its seriousness from season to season. It is worst in wet years and on wet sites and lime deficiency apparently aids disease development in some irises. It also affects freesias, hemerocallis and gladioli, among other iridaceous plants.

Symptoms. Tiny brown spots with yellowish margins develop on the leaves of rhizomatous irises in spring but are often not noticed until later. The spots enlarge to become elliptical with finally a grey mould in the centre and deep red-brown margins. On bulbous irises the symptoms arise earlier in the season, the spots lack borders and are ashen in colour. Parts of or entire leaves may die, occasionally early in the season, but more usually after flowering, with the result that the plants become gradually weakened.

Biology. Conidia produced on the spots spread the disease rapidly in the summer by rain splash or physical contact with other leaves. The fungus overwinters as mycelium or (in England) possibly as conidia and in Germany at least, perithecia are known to develop within the leaf tissues and survive the winter to produce ascospores in spring.

Treatment. There is some variation in cultivar susceptibility while among *Iris* species, *Iris sibirica* and *I. versicolor* are said to be highly resistant. Destroy all dead foliage in autumn and apply lime to the soil, although this must be done in moderation or the plants may become prone to attack by soft-rot organisms. Bordeaux mixture or sulphur sprays have been reasonably successful in the past; mancozeb more recently but the addition of a wetting agent is essential for fungicide adherence to the waxy foliage.

Begin the sprays with the first spring leaf growth and continue at about monthly intervals until the onset of cold weather in the autumn.

NARCISSUS LEAF SCORCH *Stagonospora curtisii* Pl. 17

This disease is common throughout northern Europe but was not recognised as serious until the later 1920s. It is commonest on narcissi but also affects *Amaryllis* spp., including *A. belladonna*, as well as sternbergias, crinums and galanthus.

Symptoms. The tips of young shoots take on a red-brown, typically scorched appearance soon after they emerge, to be followed, under damp conditions, by a gradual spreading of this symptom down the leaves and the appearance of brown spots. The leaves turn yellow, shrivel and die and similar symptoms develop on the spathes and leaf stalks while disfiguring brown blotches can occur on the flowers. Masses of tiny black dots appear on damaged areas.

Biology. Conidia produced in the dot-like pycnidia are dispersed by rain splash and bring about rapid spread of the disease onto healthy tissues and neighbouring plants. The fungus probably overwinters between the papery and fleshy leaf scales of the dormant bulb, from whence it infects new leaves as they emerge.

Treatment. The poeticus, polyanthus and poetaz groups of narcissi are most susceptible and should not be grown where the disease is prevalent. In gardens, prompt removal of scorched leaf tips will restrict the disease and, if this is not possible, a fortnightly spray with Bordeaux mixture or mancozeb may limit further spread but will not eradicate the primary infection. Bordeaux mixture may cause unsightly deposits if applied during flowering. Soaking the bulbs for two hours in 0.05% formalin before planting is also effective although care should be taken as any solution stronger than this is likely to be damaging if not lethal to the bulbs. Storage of the bulbs at low temperatures, especially if combined with late planting, sometimes increases the likelihood of damage.

ORCHID LEAF SPOTS

Spots are very common and widespread on many orchid genera and arise from a wide variety of causes. Commonest are small pale straw-coloured spots, of irregular shapes on the upper leaf surfaces. These rapidly enlarge, become sunken, brown-purple and show through to the undersides. The diseased areas shrivel and die but characteristically do not fall out. It is believed that local chilling is the cause but several other types of spot, usually brown and jointly known as 'orchid spot' are largely of unknown origin, although *Colletotrichum* spp. commonly occur on orchid leaves and may be at least partially responsible. Avoid draughts, dampness and, particularly, the exposure of leaves to dripping water. No other treatments are really effective.

PAEONY BLOTCH *Septoria paeoniae*

Common and widely distributed. Grey-brown spots with reddish margins and bearing black pycnidia develop on the leaves or stems. This disease is not usually serious and a spray with mancozeb should be effective in severe cases.

PEA LEAF and POD SPOT *Ascochyta pisi* and other fungi **Pl. 17**

Common throughout Europe and although known since the mid-nineteenth century only recently have all the causal fungi been identified.

Symptoms. The commonest symptoms are brown-yellow, often somewhat sunken spots which bear dark brown pycnidia and have darker perimeters. These arise on the leaves, flower stalks and pods. Less frequent are purple-brown spots sometimes with concentric markings on the leaves, pods and, in more elongate form, on the stems. The stem spots may also occur on very young seedlings which die as a result of the attack.

Biology. The symptoms are more severe in wet seasons. Diseased pods result in infected seeds which are the primary origin of the disease, although some carry-over of conidia in crop debris also occurs.

Treatment. Reject any seeds showing the sunken brown-purple lesions; burn plant debris after severe attacks and do not grow peas on the same land for as long as possible.

PEACH SHOT HOLE *Stigmina carpophila* and other causes

'Shot-hole' effects are common on the leaves of peaches and to a lesser extent on cherries, nectarines and almonds. The causes are often obscure and may be related to unsuitable soil conditions, such as waterlogging, although sometimes in Britain and probably more frequently elsewhere in Europe they are due to infection by *S. carpophila*. The symptoms are often confused with those of scab as the disease can also infect the twigs and fruit, on which scab-like lesions form. If there is no other obvious environmental cause for shot-holes, apply spray treatments as for apple scab (p. 228). Also see: plum and cherry bacterial canker (p. 218).

POTATO SILVER SCURF *Helminthosporium solani* **Pl. 17**

Common and widespread but merely a disfiguring skin blemish and only likely to be of consequence in gardens if the tubers are required for show purposes. The disease originates from fungus on the seed tubers and symptoms appear as brown or greyish patches, not usually obvious at lifting but extending in storage under humid conditions and developing a silvery sheen as air penetrates between the cell layers. A sooty appearance may develop as dark conidia are produced but the symptoms are entirely confined to the tubers, unlike the less serious black dot with which this disease is sometimes confused. Treatment is not worthwhile in gardens.

POTATO SKIN SPOT *Polyscytalum pustulans* **Pl. 17**

Common and widespread but usually only a disfiguring condition although it is one of the major causes of sprouting failure on seed stocks. It also causes wastage of tubers through the extra peeling necessary when cooking. The disease is worst in years when lifting conditions are wet and subsequent storage is cold.

Symptoms. Small brown-black pimples arise on the tubers or occasionally more penetrating brown lesions form, often in small groups in and around the eyes but sometimes virtually covering the entire organ. These tuber symptoms do not usually become evident until December–January. There may also be brownish discolouration of the surfaces of roots and stolons, sometimes with faint white mould growth on the upper part of the main root. Eyes and young sprouts may also be damaged and sprout tips may be killed although in itself this is not diagnostic.

Biology. Affected seed potatoes are the commonest sources of disease and superficial contamination develops on stem bases, stolons and roots, from where it spreads to new healthy tubers. Infection takes place through lenticels, skin or small wounds on growing tubers or on mature tubers before lifting but develops slowly until after harvest, when cold damp conditions are very favourable for further development. The lesions form when the tubers produce corky tissue to prevent penetration of the fungus. *P. pustulans* can also persist in soil on plant debris but in Britain at least, this is probably unimportant. Sprout infection may result in total tuber failure and a gappy crop.

Treatment. No fully resistant cultivars are known although 'Home Guard' is seldom affected in Britain and could be chosen where the disease is troublesome. 'King Edward' is very prone to eye infection and consequent tuber loss. Examine seed potatoes carefully, reject any showing appreciable amounts of disease and then sprout them before planting to reveal any with damaged or killed sprouts.

RASPBERRY CANE and LEAF SPOT

Elsinoë veneta **Pl. 17**

A common and widespread disease on raspberries but also affects blackberries although the similar but less serious blackberry cane spot or purple blotch diseases are more common on this plant. It is often a problem on loganberries.

Symptoms. Purple spots which later develop grey-white centres arise on the stems, leaves, flower stalks and, especially with loganberries, on the fruits which commonly develop one-sided. Leaves may drop when severely infected. On the canes, the lesions become elongated and the bark may split to form small cankers. Spots produced later in the summer and autumn are smaller and bear black dot-like bodies. The fruit yield is reduced and in severe attacks the canes may be distorted or killed.

Biology. Conidia from black fungal fruiting bodies infect young canes in May or June and more conidia form on the cane lesions to spread the disease to the leaves and fruit. The lesions on the fruiting canes develop from infections in the previous year.

Treatment. Do not grow susceptible cultivars such as 'Norfolk Giant' and 'Lloyd George' where this disease is a problem. Cut out and burn affected canes. Spray with benomyl at the time of bud burst and repeat fortnightly until the end of flowering.

RHODODENDRON LEAF SPOTS **Pl. 17**

Dark red-brown leaf blotches bearing black pycnidia are increasingly common, widespread and most serious on azaleas and often result in defoliation. The cause is *Septoria azaleae* and the disease is particularly severe on plants newly imported for forcing in glasshouses. The best preventative treatment is by spraying at fortnightly intervals from mid-summer onwards with Bordeaux mixture, although some azaleas are susceptible to damage and trial sprays should be made first on a few plants. Among other common leaf spots are rusty brown lesions caused by *Phyllosticta rhododendri*; large irregular brown blotches on several *Rhododendron* spp. caused by *Gloeosporium rhododendri. Pestalotiopsis guepini*, the cause of camellia leaf blotch also occurs in Britain on rhododendrons and is probably of increasing significance. However, most of these minor spots and blotches need not normally cause concern although the destruction of affected leaves and a spray with benomyl in the spring following an attack may be advisable.

ROSE BLACK SPOT *Diplocarpon rosae* Pl. 17

Extremely common and widespread on most rose cultivars as well as on wild roses.

Symptoms. Dark brown or black, occasionally coalescing blotches with irregular margins appear from late spring onwards on both leaf surfaces. The leaves frequently turn yellow and drop prematurely; repeated and severe attacks resulting in much weakened shoots and bushes.

Biology. Severe attacks can result in potentially dormant buds giving rise to feeble shoots in autumn which are then killed by frosts and so render the plant weak when growth should restart in spring. Conidia produced on the spots are released under moist conditions and are spread by rain splash or on hands, clothing and tools. Warm moist conditions favour further infection and the disease is worst in warm, wet seasons. In Europe most initial infections in spring are from conidia produced on over-wintering spots that develop on shoots and bud scales in the autumn, although some may originate from fallen leaves. Recently the ascospore producing stage of the fungus has been found for the first time in Europe on over-wintering leaves. This development is potentially serious as it gives scope for new races of the fungus to arise and so infect cultivars that have some resistance at present.

Treatment. Some cultivars are partially resistant but none is totally so. Susceptibility to powdery mildew and rust are also factors to be borne in mind in choosing black spot resistant cultivars while there may be marked variations between sites in terms of disease susceptibility. Generalisations can be misleading but certainly many of the older cultivars and proportionately more yellow than red or pink cultivars are susceptible to black spot. The following lists are not by any means exhaustive or to be relied upon in all areas but give a general indication of some of the most commonly grown cultivars:

Resistant large-flowered bush roses (Hybrid Teas): 'Alec's Red', 'Alexander', 'Blessings', 'Champs Elysées', 'Charlie's Aunt', 'Chicago Peace', 'Colour Wonder', 'Gail Borden', 'Honey Favourite', 'Jiminy Cricket', 'King's Ransom', 'Mme. Louis Laperrière', 'Michèle Meilland', 'My Choice', 'National Trust', 'Peace', 'Perfecta', 'Picture', 'Pink Favourite', 'Pink Peace', 'Prima Ballerina', 'Rose Gaujard', 'Shot Silk', 'Super Star', 'Sutter's Gold', 'Troika', 'Uncle Walter', 'Yellow Pages'.

Susceptible large-flowered bush roses (Hybrid Teas): 'Ballet', 'Belle Blonde', 'Blue Moon', 'Femina', 'Fragrant Cloud', 'Gay Gordons',

'Harry Wheatcroft', 'Lydia', 'McGredy's Yellow', 'Memoriam', 'Mrs Sam McGredy', 'Piccadilly', 'Wendy Cussons'.

Resistant cluster-flowered bush roses (Floribundas): 'Allgold', 'Arthur Bell', 'City of Belfast', 'City of Leeds', 'Dickson's Flame', 'Escapade', 'Golden Slippers', 'Jan Spek', 'Korresia', 'Manx Queen', 'Marlena', 'Michelle', 'Molly McGredy', 'Moon Maiden', 'Orange Silk', 'Queen Elizabeth', 'Sea Pearl', 'Southampton'.

Susceptible cluster-flowered bush roses (Floribundas): 'Anna Wheatcroft', 'Charleston', 'Copper Delight', 'Elizabeth of Glamis', 'Evelyn Fison', 'Iceberg', 'Korona', 'Orangeade', 'Orange Sensation', 'Pineapple Poll', 'Sarabande', 'Shepherd's Delight', 'Sir Lancelot', 'Tip Top', 'Zambra'.

If some susceptible cultivars must be grown then mixed planting with more resistant types sometimes decreases disease incidence while there are several cultural practices which may help to lessen black spot. Removing the first infected leaves and shoots early in the season may delay disease spread, although the collection of fallen leaves in autumn is probably of little value because most over-winter survival is on the shoots. Severe spring pruning of these shoots does therefore significantly reduce the potential infection while the improvement of drainage, avoidance of shading and of excess nitrate in fertilisers may also be beneficial. There are several possible chemical spray treatments, of which sulphur is traditionally effective, and in industrial areas with a high atmospheric sulphur content the disease is rarely serious whereas the general significance of black spot has undoubtedly increased with the passing of anti-air pollution legislation. Copper-containing materials should be avoided as they can cause disfiguring blotches. Proprietary mixtures available for rose disease control include bupirimate with triforine and carbendazium with maneb. Systemic fungicides such as benomyl apparently vary in their effectiveness. Many gardeners have found the very similar material thiophanate-methyl more reliable but all normally need applying at least fortnightly throughout the season.

SOOTY BLOTCH *Gloeodes pomigena* Pl. 17

Common and widespread on apples, pears and plums, especially in cold wet seasons and on shaded trees. On apples and plums it is often associated with fly speck disease. In Britain it is most prevalent in the South-West. The fruit bear dirty green-brown circular smoky blotches of fungal growth which can continue to spread in storage. In severe cases the fruit remain small and plums may shrivel after picking. Many cultivars are susceptible but it is particularly serious on pale coloured plums and gages. Routine scab control sprays (p. 230) should however prevent the disease from developing on apples. Also see: Sooty mould (p. 209).

STRAWBERRY LEAF BLOTCH *Gnomonia fragariae* Pl. 17

First recorded in Britain in 1941 and sometimes proves a serious problem in gardens although there is dispute over the identity of the causal fungus.
Symptoms. Black sunken patches form on the leaf stalks and stolons and

gradually enlarging brown and purple, yellow-bordered blotches arise on the leaves. A fruit rot may also be caused by the same fungus.

Biology. On the black areas on the leaf stalks and stolons, ascospores are formed but on the leaf spots and also on the fruit, only conidia develop. Abundant moisture and wet seasons favour the disease. This fungus has also been found on *Geum × borisii* and may possibly transfer from geums to strawberries.

Treatment. Do not plant strawberries in damp and shady places. The cultivars 'Cambridge Favourite' and 'Redgauntlet' are particularly prone to the fruit rotting condition and should be avoided where the disease is known to be prevalent. Remove and burn affected leaves and spray with mancozeb when growth begins in spring and again a fortnight later.

STRAWBERRY LEAF SCORCH *Diplocarpon earlianum*

Less of a problem than other strawberry leaf diseases but sometimes serious, especially in the north of Britain. Purplish spots form, similar to those of strawberry leaf spot (below) but unlike them, they do not develop a grey centre and eventually may turn dark brown. Sometimes the spots merge together to give larger scorched patches on the leaves, which usually turn yellow. Conidia develop in shiny black swellings on the spots. Burn off old foliage as described for leaf spot.

STRAWBERRY LEAF SPOT *Mycosphaerella fragariae* Pl. 17

Very common and widespread but rarely serious although it often causes concern to gardeners.

Symptoms. Appear as distinct, usually more or less circular deep reddish-purple leaf spots with a quickly developing grey centre. This centre frequently drops out and leaves a shot-hole. Rarely, spots may also cover the leaves and occasionally occur on leaf stalks and flower stalks also. A white mould and, later, tiny black dots may develop on the lesions. Rather similar symptoms, if associated with a hard rot of the fruit, may be caused by *Septogloeum fragariae*.

Biology. Conidia develop on the mould and spread the disease during the summer whereas the infrequently found black dots are ascospore-producing perithecia. Small hard black resistant sclerotia are often formed and these survive over winter and germinate in the spring to produce the conidia responsible for the first infections. Probably there are several fungal strains or races, not all of which are able to infect all cultivars.

Treatment. Burn off dead foliage at end of the season; if straw has been used between the plants this makes an ideal tinder. There are no effective chemical control measures for use in gardens.

TOMATO GHOST SPOT *Botrytis cinerea* Pl. 17

Common under conditions where very high moisture persists for short periods and therefore often seen in cool glasshouses towards the end of the growing season; it is frequently associated with other grey mould symptoms. Tiny pale rings with raised brown dots in the centres, form on the fruit. When dampness persists for long periods, grey mould fruit rot may set in. For treatment see the general notes on grey mould on p. 232 but note that benomyl and related chemicals are ineffective against ghost spot and only dichlofluanid should be used.

WALNUT LEAF BLOTCH *Gnomonia leptostyla* **Pl. 17**
Widespread; the commonest disease of walnuts. Tiny dark brown-black spots form and enlarge to become dirty yellow blotches on the surface of leaves with a corresponding greyish colouration beneath. Dark brown or black, often somewhat sunken lesions can also occur on young green nuts (which are thus impaired), and occasionally on the shoots. Premature defoliation may result. On the blotches, conidia develop and are spread by rain splash to other leaves and ascospores are formed in perithecia on the blotches (primarily those on fallen leaves) and these bring about the first new infections in spring about a fortnight after discharge. This disease is not easy to control, the oft-recommended procedures of collecting up infected leaves or spraying with Bordeaux mixture or mancozeb being fairly satisfactory on young plants but of little value to a gardener with a 15 m high tree. In the latter cases there is probably nothing that can be done.

YUCCA LEAF SPOT *Coniothyrium concentricum*
Very common and widespread. Large greyish spots form with a brown-purple border and concentric rings of tiny black pycnidia appear on the lesions. The causal fungus is one form of a species which (probably together with other fungi) gives rise to similar lesions on other more or less succulent plants, including agaves and dracaenas. Remove badly affected leaves and spray plants with Bordeaux mixture.

SLIME MOULDS

(Plate 18)

Slime moulds (Myxomycetes) are non-parasitic organisms, possibly related to fungi. They sometimes cause concern when found on lawns and garden plants. They are characterised by a mobile protoplasmic mass, the plasmodium, which may be likened to a giant amoeba that wanders freely among vegetation feeding on living bacteria, fungal spores and particles of dead organic matter before settling down to produce a spore-bearing body, the sporocarp.

All slime moulds are relatively harmless although some damage may result from the smothering of young plants, the blocking of stomata and the exclusion of light. No chemical control is necessary and washing them off with water is the easiest means of dispersal.

LICHENS

(Plate 18)

Very many species of lichen occur on all types of garden habitat, including lawns, but they are especially common on old walls, roofs and tree trunks. Although often attractive in such situations, they can be very unsightly when they grow on ornamental shrubs, as often happens on azaleas, heathers and rhododendrons, for example, especially on shaded sites and poor soil. They usually form either a grey-green crust-like or somewhat leafy covering to bark or scaly or woolly growths on twigs and branches. Lichens are biologically unique as they are dual organisms, comprising a fungus and an alga growing in close association. They are slow growing and this is why they are only likely to be seen on such plants as woody perennials and on lawns. Although enormous cloaks of lichens cover trees in the wetter, western parts of Britain, they are not generally believed to be harmful, although their development is probably greater on trees that are growing poorly, for various reasons. Lichens are very sensitive indicators of environmental pollution – generally speaking the more woolly or frondose the lichen species, the less polluted is the prevailing atmosphere. They can often be brushed off sturdy plants but tar oil winter washes may also be effective and are probably necessary on the inaccessible parts of trees.

ALGAE

(Plate 18)

Many algal species, especially those of green algae, such as *Pleurococcus*, form green coatings on plants growing in damp or shaded sites. They are very common but harmless on the north-facing bark of tree trunks and, unlike lichens, can grow in very polluted air. Among other garden habitats where algae occur frequently are on the glass panes of glasshouses and frames, from which they should be cleaned off regularly to prevent light transmission being impaired. They can also cause blockages in glasshouse watering systems, contribute to the blocking of garden ponds, cause paths to become slippery and form small jelly-like masses on neglected lawns. Usually physical removal is the most satisfactory treatment but if serious problems are caused a proprietary algicide should be applied in accordance with the manufacturer's directions.

HARMFUL FLOWERING PLANTS

(Plate 18)

Although only a few genera of flowering plants are definitely parasitic, several can be physically harmful in gardens. The latter are of much greater consequence than the former in Britain and northern Europe and in this category are clematis, honeysuckle and ivy. Parasitic or partially parasitic plants are represented by broomrapes, dodders, mistletoes and toothworts.

BROOMRAPES and TOOTHWORTS *Orobanche* spp. and *Lathraea* spp. **Pl. 18**

There are several species of these closely related plants which lack chlorophyll and are parasitic on the roots of wild and cultivated plant species. Many are widespread but only locally common in Britain and northern Europe. They produce erect, scaly, often brownish or purple shoots, bearing similarly coloured flowers. Toothworts are parasitic on trees and shrubs, especially elms, hazel, poplars and willows, and grow beneath them. Broomrapes occur on a wide variety of plants, including potatoes and tomatoes in some parts of Europe, but none are likely to cause much damage and are primarily of interest as curiosities.

CLEMATIS *Clematis vitalba*

Common, especially on alkaline soils in the southern parts of northern Europe. It is closely related to the large flowered, mainly Asiatic garden species and scrambles over hedgerows, shrubs and sometimes quite large trees, forming a blanket of vegetation. The shoots are covered from July onwards with greenish white flowers and from late summer with large, conspicuous hairy silver seed heads, commonly known as 'old man's beard'. Despite its very attractive appearance and valuable cover for wild-life, clematis can smother young plants, largely by the exclusion of light from them, and some cutting back may be essential.

DODDERS *Cuscuta* spp. **Pl. 18**

There are two native species, *C. europaea* and *C. epithymum*. Only the latter is of importance in Britain although the former can also be troublesome in parts of Europe. They are widely distributed in southern Britain and Europe south of central Scandinavia and are infrequent in Scotland. Both species are parasitic; the seeds germinate on the ground but leafless, reddish shoots twine counter-clockwise around the host plants and soon become wholly aerial. The shoot derives nutrients from the plant by inserting feeding structures into the stem and bears clusters of pinkish-white flowers. They may form a completely matted blanket over shrubs and herbaceous plants. Dodders are commonest on gorse and heather but are sometimes found on other plants and can cause stunting, but only rarely death. The only treatment is the total destruction of the infested plant or branches, preferably before the dodder seed is formed and shed.

HONEYSUCKLE *Lonicera periclymenum* **Pl. 18**

Common throughout Europe except the extreme North; the same species as garden honeysuckle. Grows on moist soil types and is often frequent on well-shaded sites, but it only flowers in good light and growth is generally more vigorous in the open. It commonly scrambles around the bases of trees but is most damaging when the shoots twine around young trees and strangle them. It is essential therefore to keep young trees free of honey-suckle shoots and to cut back and untwine any already established. Once trees have developed sturdy trunks, damage is very unlikely to occur and honeysuckle may be allowed more or less free rein.

IVY *Hedera helix* **Pl. 18**

Very common throughout Britain and northern Europe, either trailing along the ground, over walls or climbing to 30 m up tree trunks. The flowers and black berries form only when a shoot can climb no further. Many hedgerow trees, especially old elms and ash, almost invariably sup-port some ivy growth. It is generally only harmful on already unthrifty trees which may be partly constricted by large ivy stems around the trunk or may have their top growth suppressed by a mass of flowering shoots in the crown. The latter development can also render trees unstable and liable to windthrow. Ivy should only be removed if absolutely necessary because of the abundant cover that it gives to wildlife and then by severing twice close to the ground and removing a length of stem.

MISTLETOES *Viscum album* and other species **Pl. 18**
These members of the family Loranthaceae are very serious on trees in some parts of the world but there is only one species, *V. album*, in Britain and it occurs roughly from Yorkshire southwards. It is common elsewhere in Europe south of southern Scandinavia, growing on a wide range of deciduous trees and especially common on apples, limes, hybrid black poplars and sycamore. It is semi-parasitic; it has yellow-green leaves for photosynthesis but obtains minerals and water from the conducting tissues of the host tree, with which it is intimately connected by a special organ which replaces a conventional root. Seeds produced in the sticky white berries are transferred by birds which lodge them in the bark. It generally causes only slight damage in Britain by weakening trees and even this is often offset by the value of the mistletoe itself. Elsewhere in northern Europe, forms, probably of the same species, infest conifers and can cause considerable damage, especially to firs. *Loranthus europaeus*, a non-British species with short, dark green leaves and yellow berries, sometimes damages oaks in parts of Europe. Where they are seriously disfiguring small ornamentals, mistletoes can be controlled by pruning off the affected branches, although such treatment usually results in considerable mutilation of the tree. In gardens mistletoes are better tolerated, or possibly even actively encouraged. Attempts to infest trees artificially with mistletoe usually fail for no apparent reason.

ROOT NODULES

(Plate 18)

Small nodular swellings occur on the roots of many plants. They may be symptoms of pest or disease attack, such as crown gall (p. 224), root knot eelworm (p. 88) or clubroot (p. 223), and occasionally are of unknown origin. On leguminous plants they are formed by bacteria of the genus *Rhizobium* and are essential in maintaining not only the health of the plants concerned, but also the general soil fertility. *Rhizobium* bacteria are able to fix atmospheric nitrogen, that is, to convert it to an organically combined form which is available for plant growth. In this they play an essential role in the garden and for this reason it is wise, in rotations, to follow leguminous crops, such as peas and beans, with those, such as brassicas, that derive particular benefit from the increased soil nitrogen.

MYCORRHIZA

(Plate 18)

Mycorrhiza occur regularly on many trees and other woody plants and sometimes cause unwarranted concern to gardeners when root symptoms are seen or toadstools appear. Repeated branching of fine roots and thickening of the root tips, sometimes with sheathing whitish growths, is commonly visible on close examination of the young root systems of beech, birch, cedars, chestnut, firs, oaks, pines, poplars, spruces and other trees. Many of the toadstools which emerge from the soil under trees in autumn or spring are the fructifications of the soil-inhabiting fungi, the enveloping mycelial threads of which give rise to the root symptoms. The fungal mycelium forms an intimate contact with the root tissues and mycorrhiza are often mistaken for root hairs, whose function they virtually usurp in acting as a medium for the transfer of nutrient materials from soil to roots. In return, the mycorrhizal fungi take certain nutrients from the roots. Plants that are always naturally infected with mycorrhiza have been shown experimentally to be quite capable of sustained healthy growth when the fungus has been removed and why in nature mycorrhiza should be so essential therefore is unknown. Nonetheless on many infertile soils, they have been deliberately introduced to aid plant growth.

VIRUSES AND VIRUS-LIKE ORGANISMS

(Plates 19–20)

Viruses and other sub-microscopic organisms are important and widespread plant pathogens. The symptoms they cause have long been known to be transmissible by grafting from diseased to healthy plants but although such 'graft-transmissible agents' were proved many years ago to be smaller than bacteria, not until the advent of the electron microscope could they be 'seen'. Viruses have been described as absolute parasites but structurally they are simple, comprising a nucleic acid and one or more proteins. They possess the characteristic of usually occurring more or less systemically in diseased plants and are not confined to the parts in which symptoms appear. This results in the transmission of virus from generation to generation of vegetatively propagated plants and is the reason why such plants, which include potatoes, carnations, chrysanthemums and bulbous ornamentals, are so commonly subject to serious virus problems. A further important feature of viruses is the ability of many to exist in host plants as latent infections; although present in the tissues, no symptoms result, but they can be induced to appear when the virus is transmitted by grafting to a different cultivar or variety. Related to this phenomenon is the fact that only now that many plants can be artificially freed of virus (see below) may it be seen that those normally and naturally carrying latent infection are of considerably reduced thriftiness and that their full growth potential is far from being realised. For instance, the flowers of the finest garden pelargoniums seem miserable now that virus-free plants can be raised and compared with them. Latent virus infection is not, of course, the only reason that plants may be unthrifty!

Recently a number of so called 'virus-like' organisms have been recognised, of which mycoplasmas, first shown in 1967 to be the causes of a number of what were previously thought to be virus-induced symptoms, are the best known. Mycoplasmas may be thought of as similar to bacteria, although lacking a cell wall, but it is as yet impossible to differentiate between different types of mycoplasma. There remain a large number of diseases, characterised by symptoms typical of viral or mycoplasmal infection and transmissible by grafting, but in which no organism has yet been recognised.

The naming of viruses and the diseases they cause can be confusing. The description of a virus by a Latin name comparable with those given to other organisms is not recommended and most viruses have been named after the host plant in which they were first found and the symptoms that they caused on it. Thus names like cucumber mosaic virus or passionfruit woodiness virus were self explanatory and the diseases that they caused were known as cucumber mosaic and passionfruit woodiness respectively. Indeed in many instances the name of the disease was given before the causal virus was found. However, it soon became apparent that most viruses affect more than one host plant and may cause quite differing symptoms in them. Thus among the symptoms caused by cucumber mosaic virus are mild stunting of dahlias and, indeed one form of woodiness in passion-fruits. With a number of viruses, such as arabis mosaic virus, the original host plant subsequently turned out to be much less significant in terms of disease symptoms than others identified later. In an attempt to minimise gardeners' confusion therefore, relatively few viruses are mentioned here individually; the exceptions are those very widespread or important ones whose names have found their way into fairly general use in gardening.

Most plants, except possibly conifers, are known to be, or are probably, the hosts for at least one virus. Mycoplasmas, in as far as they have been identified, infect a wide range of ornamental and fruit plants but are not known to cause any symptoms in vegetables, apart from potatoes and tomatoes.

Symptoms. A wide range of symptom types occurs, including many similar to those of diseases induced by fungi and bacteria. They include cankers, dwarfing and stunting, leaf fall, rosetting, wilting and witches' brooms and similar proliferations. A few symptom types, most notably rotting, are however never induced by viruses although tissues may be damaged by virus attack so that they are pre-disposed to them. A further range of symptoms, typical of and, in several instances, peculiar to virus attack are illustrated in Plates 19–20 and the principal types are listed below. It should be remembered that only part (commonly, with trees, a very small part) of the plant may display the effects and that symptoms may disappear entirely especially during hot weather. Cool, dull days are generally best for observing the effects but it can be difficult to diagnose virus-induced leaf symptoms in autumn when normal seasonal colour changes and necrosis make identification uncertain. Although many other factors can induce symptoms in certain plants similar to those caused by viruses, the commonest confusion probably arises with environmental effects, such as late frost (p. 292) or drought (p. 291), and with mineral deficiency symptoms (p. 283). In general, however, such effects usually appear on all plants in a particular crop while viruses normally leave at least a few healthy individuals or, with large plants, a few healthy branches. The following are the most common and important virus-induced symptoms on garden plants although it should be remembered that many of them will also be accompanied by a general unthriftiness. Under each category a list is given of the plants on which the particular symptom is most likely to be seen, together, in certain instances with some notes on the disease and/or its causal organism.

Leaf symptoms

YELLOWING: this is the loss to some extent of the normal green colour of the leaves. It may affect the entire leaf, leaf edges or leaf veins and, when localised in patches, yellowing is known as *variegation* and takes the four main forms listed below. Overall virus yellowing is commonly seen on: beans, celery, cherries and other *Prunus* spp., irises, lettuces, onions, parsnips, peas, plums, potatoes, spinach, strawberries and tomatoes.

MOSAICS: yellowed areas of varying size, although usually angular in form through restriction by the leaf veins. On monocotyledonous plants with parallel-veined leaves, mosaics take the form of *streaking* while, when bands of either dark or light coloured cells occur along the main veins, the effect is known as *vein banding*. Related to the latter symptom is that of *vein clearing*, in which the veins become clear and translucent rather than yellowed. Mosaics occur commonly on: abutilons (where the effects of abutilon mosaic virus are deliberately perpetuated for their aesthetic appeal), apples, beans, brassicas (typically as vein clearing and vein banding caused by cauliflower mosaic virus), celery, cherries, cucurbits (where the effects are caused frequently by the most widespread and common of all garden plant viruses, cucumber mosaic virus, an organism with an enormous host range), dahlias (usually vein banding effects caused by dahlia mosaic virus), gooseberries (vein banding only), horse radish, onions (typical streak effects), pears, plums, raspberries and blackberries (very common indeed and caused by a number of different viruses), roses and tomatoes.

MOTTLES: yellowed areas of more rounded or diffuse shape, commonly distributed in the same way as mosaics. Sometimes intermediate symptoms occur between the two. Small, irregular, mottles may be known as dots, flecks, spots or similar descriptive terms. Mottle effects are seen commonly on: apples, beans, carrots (where they are accompanied by the red colouration typical of carrot motley dwarf disease), celery, cherries, cucurbits (the result of cucumber mosaic virus infection), dianthus carnation mottle virus is the commonest cause), freesias and gladioli (both affected by bean yellow mosaic virus which spreads from peas and beans), hyacinths, hydrangeas, lettuces, parsnips, peas, pears, plums, potatoes, strawberries and tomatoes.

RING SPOTS: rings of yellow or pale green tissue with normal green centres, or concentric rings of light and dark tissue; common on apples, brassicas, celery, cherries, dianthus, hydrangeas (hydrangea ringspot virus is extremely common and readily spread by handling), pears, pelargoniums (the inappropriately named pelargonium leaf curl virus is the very common cause of this symptom which however, does little harm), and plums.

LINE PATTERNS: irregular single or multiple yellow or pale green lines and bands, taking many forms, one of the most characteristic resembling the outline of an oak leaf and known as *oak leaf pattern*. Line patterns, sometimes accompanying ring spots, occur commonly on apples, celery, cherries, pears, plums and roses.

Flower symptoms

FLOWER-BREAKING: a very characteristic symptom and the first virus-induced effect ever to be described in plants. Dark-flowered plants show either darker or, more usually, white or yellowish streaks and patches on the petals. No comparable effects occur on plants with white or yellow flowers. The symptom is seen most typically on: gladioli, irises, sweet peas, tulips (caused by the very common tulip breaking virus), and wallflowers (the effects being caused by turnip mosaic virus which aphids can spread to vegetable brassicas where it can cause considerable damage).

GREEN FLOWERS: a greater or lesser degree of green colour to the petals, usually with other flower malformations such as dwarfing or *phyllody* (the development of leafy outgrowths). The condition is almost invariably mycoplasma-induced and is seen most often on blackberries, chrysanthemums, hydrangeas and strawberries (on which the so-called green petal disease can cause serious fruit loss).

General symptoms

MALFORMATIONS: may take many forms, the commonest known descriptively as *crinkling* (very common on strawberry leaves); *enations* (green outgrowths from the leaves, seen most typically as a result of pea enation mosaic virus infection of peas); *fern-leaf* effects (characteristic indentations of the leaves, typical of tobacco mosaic virus infection of tomatoes); *uneven fruit ripening* (also common on tomatoes but occurring additionally on red-fruited plums affected by sharka disease, a notifiable condition); *leaf-rolling* (very common on beans and also on potatoes affected by potato leaf roll virus); *spraing* effects (the development of dark, more or less crescentic marks in the tuber flesh) are caused by two different viruses in potatoes; *distorted fruit* can occur with a number of virus problems but is probably most common as stony pit on pears and as chat fruit and related conditions on apples.

NECROSIS: the death of selected tissues resulting in patches in the form of spots, ring-spots or other shapes is common on many plants but perhaps most frequent as the cabbage black ringspot symptom of turnip mosaic virus on brassicas.

EPINASTY: the more rapid growth of the upper surface of the leaf or its stalk, resulting in pronounced down-bending, is frequent with several virus problems.

GRASSINESS: the proliferation of leafy shoots is an effect rather akin to witches' brooms (p. 227) and is perhaps seen most commonly on narcissi. It is probably mycoplasma-induced.

Biology. The intra-cellular biology and behaviour of viruses is complex and will not be considered here. Of very considerable importance to gardeners however is the means by which viruses are transmitted, for the recognition of this may aid control measures. Transmission may be by vectors or by other means. Among aerial vectors, beetles, mites, thrips, weevils, whiteflies and other arthropods transmit a few viruses but by far the most important agents in temperate regions are aphids, of which the potato-peach aphid, *Myzus persicae*, probably outweighs all others in its significance. Although the relationship between viruses and aphids is complex, the facet of greatest significance to the gardener is probably the length of the retention time – the period for which a virus remains infective within or on an aphid – as this dictates whether insect control measures are likely to be of much importance in controlling the disease (see below). Among soil-borne virus vectors, eelworms are the most important, although a few viruses are transmitted by soil fungi with swimming swarm spores. Mycoplasmas seem to be almost invariably transmitted by leafhoppers. Although generalisations over the relationship between symptom type and means of transmission can be misleading, it is true that many mosaic and mottle type effects are commonly caused by aphid-transmitted viruses while ring-spots are commonly induced by those that are soil-borne. While aphid-transmitted viruses are often of importance because of their very rapid spread among crop plants, soil-borne viruses are significant because soil, once contaminated, is very difficult to free of the infestation, which thus persists from crop to crop.

Non-vector transmission may be for example via pollen or seeds or even by physical contact, sometimes by the slightest touch. Many viruses have no known means of natural transmission and in some, such as certain fruit tree viruses, this seems to be extremely slow with very little plant to plant spread.

Treatment. There are no viricidal chemicals comparable with insecticides and fungicides although a few substances may suppress certain symptoms. Some measures can be taken to minimise the effects of viruses however. The first requirement, where possible, is to ensure that planting stock is virus free. Such stocks have been available for a few crops for some time – certified potato 'seed' for instance, raised in Scotland or other northern areas where aphid vectors are few. With seed-transmitted viruses, such as lettuce mosaic virus, contamination-free seed should of course be used if available but it should be noted that the designation 'virus tested' or 'mosaic tested' applied to seed is for practical purposes meaningless and a very high proportion of the seed may still carry virus. Only if the percentage of contaminated seed present is quoted and less than 0.01% or so should any reliability be placed on the description. (The term 'virus-tested' is however also applied to planting stock of some fruits, such as raspberries, and in these particular instances does imply that the material is of the highest quality).

More recently, methods have become available by which viruses are not merely avoided but can actually be removed from plant material. This is usually achieved by heat treatment of the diseased plants and from the plants initially treated, virus-free stocks can be propagated. The most conspicuous success in this field has been with the EMLA rootstock and scions of apples, pears, plums and cherries developed in Britain at the East Malling and Long Ashton Research Stations and the certified raspberry stocks from the Scottish Horticultural Research Institute (now the Scottish Crop Research Institute). These should always be selected when new orchards or soft fruit plantings are being made.

An alternative method of raising virus-free stock is by meristem culture; the initiating of plants in the laboratory by culturing a few cells from the meristem (the fastest growing tissue of the plant) where the plant's growth may just exceed the rate at which the virus can spread into the cells. A continually extending range of virus-free stocks of plants, particularly of ornamentals, is becoming available, initially for professional growers but commonly available to gardeners on enquiry at the most reputable suppliers. Even if such stocks are not available, the buying of carefully selected plants from reputable suppliers will go far towards ensuring good quality planting material. Once planted, virus-free fruit stocks, apart possibly from raspberries, usually remain so as with a few exceptions, the natural means of spread of fruit tree viruses, although unknown, seems very slow and the plants are not re-infected.

The moral, therefore, when a virus problem is causing severe damage to fruit trees or bushes, or vegetatively propagated perennials such as chrysanthemums, dahlias, carnations, strawberries, or bulbs and corms, is to dig up and burn the affected individuals and replace them with certified planting stock.

Even when vegetable and ornamental plants are freed of viruses, which include those readily and rapidly transmitted by aphids, reinfection of stock is commonly not as fast as might be expected and they can be used for five or six years at least. The importance of rogueing of plant stocks for any showing virus symptoms cannot be over-stressed. With many virus-induced diseases, the prompt removal and destruction by burning of such plants is the only means of protecting further healthy plants from becoming diseased.

Viruses transmitted by insects (and these include most of the mosaic and mottle-type symptoms, especially on non-perennials), can commonly be controlled by the application of insecticides to eliminate the vector. This is not invariably so, however, for aphids transmit many viruses in what is termed a non-persistent manner; the virus remains viable on the aphid for a very short period only, often a matter of hours, and control of the insect does not therefore reduce significantly the amount of virus available for infection of further plants. Nonetheless, routine aphid control will go a long way towards keeping many virus problems in check and it is a practice that every good gardener should observe. Control of the vectors of soil-borne viruses (which commonly give rise to ring-spot symptoms) is exceedingly difficult, but where a crop has been infected by a soil-borne virus fresh stock should be planted on a different site, away from contaminated land. In some circumstances, such as non-availability of alternative land, the use of the granular sterilant chemical dazomet, in accordance with the manufacturer's instructions, may be worthwhile.

In relatively few instances are cultivars of plants available with resistance to virus-induced diseases; notable exceptions being the tomatoes recently introduced as resistant to tobacco mosaic virus and such potato cultivars as 'Pentland Crown' (unaffected by leaf roll virus), 'Desirée', 'Pentland Crown', 'Pentland Ivory', 'Ulster Chieftain' and 'Ulster Prince' (unaffected by potato virus Y), and 'Arran Pilot', 'Home Guard', 'Record' and 'Ulster Chieftain' (unaffected by tobacco rattle virus).

Weed control is as important for eradicating potential virus hosts as it is for other reasons. In particular, the presence of weeds botanically related to the crop among which they grow is undesirable. The prompt removal and destruction of old plants remaining at the end of the season is also very important in reducing the population of viruses available to infect new stock, although among some vegetables, such as brassicas, it may of course be very difficult to avoid having crops of different ages in the garden at the same time.

Disorders

A healthy growing plant is in harmony not only with the biological environment but also with its physical components. These can at times operate to the plant's detriment however and in many instances, their effects produce distinct and recognisable symptoms. These symptoms, produced without the intervention of pest or pathogen, are termed disorders. For convenience, in this book, disorders are divided into those that arise purely from nutrient deficiency and those that arise from non-nutritional causes.

MINERAL NUTRIENT DEFICIENCIES
(Plates 21–22)

It is common knowledge that all garden plants require chemical nutrients from the soil and that, from time to time, supplementation of the natural supply is necessary in the form of fertilisers; either 'organic' (composts, farmyard manure, dried blood, bone meal and so on) or 'artificial' (sulphate of ammonia and super-phosphate for example). The soil chemical elements essential to plants are nitrogen, phosphorus and potassium (all required in large amounts) and calcium, magnesium and sulphur (required in lesser amounts), these six being known as major nutrients. Additionally plants require smaller amounts of the minor or trace elements, iron, manganese, boron, copper, molybdenum, zinc and sometimes, sodium and chlorine. A deficiency in any of these elements gives rise to specific symptoms and in this section an attempt is made, not to give general guidance on fertiliser practice, but to indicate the principal symptoms caused by the various deficiencies.

In general, deficiencies of nitrogen, and to a lesser extent of phosphorus and potassium, are readily recognised by gardeners as overall unthrifty growth. Certain of the other deficiency symptoms are however sometimes difficult to distinguish from each other, or from other quite different causes, and reference should be made to Plates 21–22 to give supporting information to the written descriptions. It is also very important to note whether symptoms appear first on the youngest or the oldest leaves as this can give a valuable clue to the element concerned. As with most leaf symptoms however, attempts to diagnose mineral deficiencies should not be made in the autumn when normal seasonal necrosis produces confusing effects.

There is chemical interaction between the elements in the soil and an excess of one element can give rise to deficiency symptoms of another. In such instances the second element may be present in adequate amounts but be chemically unavailable to the plants. Such an effect is known as induced deficiency and although the same phenomenon can also arise under certain physical conditions, such as waterlogging, the most important predisposing factor is incorrect soil pH. All the trace elements except molybdenum are more or less unavailable to plants in alkaline soils, and even a pH of 7 (i.e. neutrality) can result in symptoms of nutrient deficiency. In gardens, soil alkalinity is probably the commonest cause of trace element deficiency symptoms. In addition to confusion with each other, the foliar symptoms of the various nutrient deficiencies are most commonly confused with those of virus-induced diseases or with environmental effects, such as air-borne pollutants, drought, frost or wind. Deficiency symptoms have been fairly intensively studied on fruit and vegetable crops but little on ornamentals, although they may be expected to show the same general features.

Deficiencies of sulphur are virtually unknown in British soils while chlorine, sodium and zinc deficiencies are also uncommon and restricted to very few crops. These four elements are therefore not considered here in detail. Excessive amounts of some mineral elements, may have damaging toxic effects on plants and these are referred to on p. 301.

MAJOR NUTRIENTS

NITROGEN Pl. 21

Nitrogen can be, and commonly is deficient in almost any type of soil (although those of low organic matter content are most prone) and it is much influenced by the way in which the land has been cropped. In gardens, when little fertiliser is used, and especially when peas and beans are not grown and brassicas repeatedly are, nitrogen deficiency symptoms may be expected. Sometimes soils, such as peats containing ample organic matter which is insufficiently decomposed, can also become deficient in nitrogen. Many different types of plant are affected but brassicas are particularly prone and the symptoms are generally readily recognisable.

Symptoms. The leaves are reduced in size, pale coloured and sometimes, as on brassicas, with yellow, red or purplish tints. The symptoms appear first on the older leaves and then spread upwards. All growth is restricted and weak, and flowering and fruiting may sometimes be reduced and delayed. Potatoes produce few tubers; apples tend to be smaller and red (not always undesirably so) and the many large, leafy vegetables yield little usable produce.

Physiology. Nitrogen is essential for many aspects of plant growth and is a major constituent of protein, of protoplasm and other plant components and is incorporated into a wide range of organic chemical compounds. Many nitrogenous materials are highly mobile and readily transported to young from old leaves, which explains why the deficiency symptoms therefore appear there first. Atmospheric nitrogen gas is 'fixed' or converted to forms usable by plants by the nodule bacteria on the roots of leguminous crops (see p. 276).

Treatment. Apply top dressings of nitrogen-containing fertilisers, such as ammonium sulphate, at or before planting and periodically thereafter in accordance with manufacturer's directions. Adequate nitrogen is commonly supplied with phosphorus and potassium in balanced NPK fertilisers but it should be remembered that nitrogen, unlike phosphorus and potassium, is readily leached from the soil and fresh applications must be made for each crop. In gardens however the regular application of compost provides a steady supply of nitrogen that is not as readily leached as that in 'artificial' fertilisers and many gardeners find they are able to satisfy all the soil's needs in this way.

PHOSPHORUS **Pl. 21**

This is most usually deficient in acid soils, from which it is readily leached, and also in those in areas of high rainfall. Deficiencies occur additionally in many clay soils and in the poor soils of chalk downs. Phosphorus deficiency effects are generally different from those of nitrogen although there may be confusion between the two on brassicas. A wide variety of other plants may also commonly be affected.

Symptoms. As with nitrogen deficiency, all growth is restricted and weak and flowering and fruiting are reduced and delayed. The leaves are reduced in size and, beginning with the oldest, may drop prematurely. Unlike nitrogen deficiency, it rarely induces yellow or red colours in leaves, which instead become dull blue-green with dull purple tints. The latter symptoms can also however arise from a number of other causes, including various types of root damage. Currants typically show dull bronzing with brown-purple spots and although a few plants, such as potatoes, may have scorching at the leaf margins, this is not a general response.

Physiology. Like nitrogen, phosphorus is involved in many aspects of plant growth, including the chemistry of fats, proteins and carbohydrates, and it is particularly important in the ripening of fruits and the ripening and germination of seeds. Because phosphorus is closely associated with the functioning of nitrogen in the plant, it is surprising that there are not more similarities between the deficiency symptoms they each induce.

Treatment. Fertilisers containing phosphorus should be applied according to manufacturer's directions and this is done most readily in combination with nitrogen and potassium in balanced NPK fertilisers. Phosphorus alone is most readily available as super-phosphate, which should be placed as close to the seeds or plants as possible; in commercial practice it is commonly applied with the seed. The reasons for this are complex but germinating seeds and very young plants seem to require a particularly high phosphorus concentration.

POTASSIUM **Pl. 21**

Potassium is commonly deficient in light sandy soils and also on chalky and peaty soils low in clay content. Where potassium demanding crops, such as very leafy vegetables, potatoes, tomatoes, beans and many fruits, are grown intensively, deficiencies can occur even on clay soils and these crops most commonly show symptoms.

Symptoms. Variable, but most typical is browning or scorching of the tips and margins of the leaves, often accompanied by brown spotting on the undersides. These effects appear first on the older leaves and the affected leaf edges are often curled. Somewhat similar symptoms of marginal scorching can occur as a result of exposure to drying winds, drought or airborne pollutants, including salt spray. If these seem improbable causes, potassium deficiency should be strongly suspected, although sometimes deficiencies of phosphorus or calcium can also bring about similar effects.

Additional symptoms may include a blue-green leaf colouration, some inter-veinal yellowing or spotting, general plant stunting and dying back of shoots. On tomatoes, potassium deficiency may be a cause of blotchy ripening; the fruit appear normal while still green (cf. tobacco mosaic virus p. 280) but unripened areas persist as it reddens.

Physiology. This is very imperfectly understood but potassium is known to be highly mobile in plant tissues and accumulates particularly in young leaves and at growing points. It is believed that most of the element is present in the cell sap rather than the cell walls. Among possible roles suggested for potassium are those of controlling water loss from plants and in part of the photosynthetic process.

Treatment. Where potassium alone is deficient, apply sulphate of potash before sowing and rake in thoroughly. Where nitrogen and/or phosphorus are also deficient, NPK fertilisers containing appropriate proportions of the three elements should be applied in accordance with manufacturer's instructions.

CALCIUM **Pl. 22**

Calcium deficiency symptoms occur most commonly in plants growing on acid peats (i.e. not fen peats) and in acid soils originating from rocks of low calcium content, such as many granitic types and silica sandstones. They occur also on light, free-draining and easily leached sandy soils; less usually so on poorly draining clays, but rarely on alkaline soils derived from limestone or chalk. Although external leaf symptoms of calcium deficiency are rarely seen, a number of disorders arise from inadequate calcium levels in fruits, roots and also in the heart leaves of leafy vegetables. Plants commonly affected by clearly recognisable and distinct symptoms are apples, Brussels sprouts, cabbages, carrots, celery, chicory, lettuces, peppers, potatoes and tomatoes. It is probably extremely rare for there to be an actual soil calcium deficiency, the effects almost always being induced by an imbalance of calcium with other elements (see below) or a restriction on the availability of calcium to the plant because of some interfering environmental factor. Many plants, commonly termed calcicoles, require the particular iron-calcium relationship that occurs in calcium-rich soils while conversely those known as calcifuges require a different relationship between these elements and do not thrive under such conditions. Consideration of these falls outside the scope of this book however and horticultural and gardening texts should be consulted.

Symptoms. GENERAL: when foliar symptoms occur they are most common at young leaf or shoot tips which may be curled inwards or ragged, scorched and killed. APPLE: fruit, the commonest symptom is bitter pit – dark spots or pits on the surface with brownish spots beneath and also scattered throughout the flesh. Bitter pit is most frequent on young, vigorously growing trees and other symptoms on apples include glassiness (translucency of the tissues), lenticel spotting and low temperature breakdown (the death of fruit tissues when stored under too cold conditions). BRUSSELS SPROUTS (and sometimes cabbages): internal browning; a very common browning and death of the tips of some of the internal leaves of the buttons or head. CARROTS: cavity spot; elongate transverse spots on the roots which crack open to reveal small craters, is sometimes thought to be due to calcium deficiency but the condition is imperfectly understood and bacteria have also been claimed to be associated with it. CELERY AND CHICORY: black heart; usually only seen on fen soils, the central leaves of the crown becoming blackened and stunted. LETTUCES: tip burn; marginal leaf scorching is common in lettuce and calcium deficiency may be one cause; attack by bacteria, grey mould or other fungi may be others. POTATOES: the commonest symptoms are the production of 'leggy shoots' with rolled leaves and many very small tubers. TOMATOES (and to some extent peppers): blossom end rot; a more or less rounded dark brown gradually shrinking and toughening area of skin at the blossom end of the fruit, often induced during periods of water shortage. Calcium deficiency can also be a contributory cause towards splitting in tomatoes.

Physiology. Calcium is relatively immobile in tissues, not moving readily from old to young leaves, which can therefore be 'starved' of the element and display the deficiency symptoms. It is a vital component of plant cell walls and is also essential for the correct functioning of growing points and for several aspects of root growth. Within plants, it is generally in greatest concentration in the older leaves with less in young leaves and fruit. There is a complex interrelationship between calcium availability and that of other elements. For various reasons excess potassium, and to a lesser extent magnesium and ammonium-nitrogen, in the soil decrease the availability of calcium to plants. Other factors limiting calcium availability include water stress and high humidity. Boron deficiency can also lead to calcium deficiency symptoms, probably because boron is needed for the transport of calcium within plant tissues.

Treatment. This is not easy because of the interrelationship with other factors. In acid soils, apply lime to raise the pH to about 6.5, although this will not help on sites where calcium is not deficient, merely unavailable to the plants. It is important to appreciate that the effects of liming are not quick to appear. In gardens the best plan is to arrange for a pH test to be conducted professionally (or even by using one of the kits sold for garden use) and then apply lime in accordance with the recommendations issued for different soil types by the Ministry of Agriculture. It is important however not to apply lime to areas where calcifuge plants or soft fruit are to be grown and, except for brassicas on clubroot-infested soil, a pH of about 6.5 is probably sufficiently high for most vegetables. The time of application of lime is not very critical but hydrated lime should not be applied immediately before planting as it can be harmful to plants. Calcium deficiency is also minimised by reducing applications of potash and ammonium, while symptoms such as bitter pit in apples or blossom end rot in tomatoes can sometimes be cured by spraying at fortnightly intervals with solutions of calcium nitrate or calcium chloride containing approximately 2 g per litre.

MAGNESIUM **Pl. 22**

Commonly deficient on light, acid, sandy soils and others where calcium deficiency also occurs. Magnesium is readily leached and so the effects are worst in wet seasons and also after excessive applications of potassium fertilisers. Symptoms are commonly seen on many plants but are particularly noticeable on apples, tomatoes, some brassicas, annual bedding plants, lettuce and potatoes.

Symptoms. Symptoms vary greatly between plant types but are most common late in the season. In general the most characteristic symptom is that of yellowing between the leaf veins, giving a marbled effect, the veins and areas immediately adjacent remaining green. Red-pigmented plants, such as beetroot, may turn purplish instead of yellow and similar colours can arise on normal green plants as the symptoms progress. The symptoms always arise first on the older leaves (cf. iron deficiency below) and sometimes, especially on peas and beans, the marbling may be confined to the central parts of the leaf, the margins remaining relatively normal. On apples severe premature defoliation can result.
Physiology. Magnesium is a constituent of the green colouring matter chlorophyll and also has several other metabolic functions in plants. It is very mobile in plant tissues and this explains why deficiency symptoms arise first in the older leaves, the magnesium having been transported to the young tissues during periods of shortage.
Treatment. Because magnesium does not usually affect yield (except perhaps on apples), treatments are usually applied only to improve appearance. As calcium is also commonly deficient with magnesium, the use of magnesian limestone when liming should correct the problem.

MINOR NUTRIENTS

IRON Pl. 21

Actual deficiency of iron in soils is uncommon and the presence of iron compounds generally gives the familiar red and brown colouration to many soils. It is often rendered unavailable to plants however, especially on alkaline sites. Deficiency symptoms are thus most commonly seen on soils overlying chalk or limestone while high organic matter content tends to increase its availability to plants and lessen the severity of the symptoms. Many plants can be affected by iron deficiency but in gardens symptoms are most likely to be seen on azaleas and rhododendrons, camellias, ceanothus, chaenomeles, hydrangeas, roses and some fruit trees and soft fruits especially raspberries and strawberries. There may be wide variations in susceptibility between cultivars of some plants.
Symptoms. Familiar as 'lime-induced chlorosis' : bleaching or yellowing, usually of the youngest leaves but not affecting the veins, which stand out as conspicuously dark green. Plants may become generally unthrifty and in severe conditions fail to flower or fruit and may die.
Physiology. Iron is associated with several functions in plants but most importantly with the formation of chlorophyll, and plants therefore become pale when it is absent. It is relatively immobile in plants and the bleaching symptoms can sometimes arise because of an increase in this immobility. Although the presence of abundant calcium in the soil induces iron deficiency symptoms, the mechanism of this process is not fully understood. High concentrations of a number of other elements, notably phosphorus, can also bring about iron deficiency.
Treatment. Mere application of inorganic iron compounds to soil on which deficiency symptoms occur rarely improves matters as the added iron will itself become unavailable. To eliminate the causes, liming must

be severely restricted, although of course on naturally alkaline soils the lime content cannot readily be reduced. Superphosphate fertilisers should be used sparingly on iron deficient plants or on those susceptible to such deficiency. The most satisfactory treatment is to apply iron in a form in which it is available to plants; such compounds are on sale to gardeners and are known as chelates or sequestrenes. In these compounds, the iron is bound to organic molecules which largely prevent its reaction with other soil chemicals and thus its unavailability. Sequestrenes should be applied to the soil or sometimes as foliar sprays in accordance with manufacturer's directions.

MANGANESE **Pl. 22**

This element is deficient on a wide range of soil types but mainly on poorly draining sands, highly organic soils, such as fen peats and marshy land, and other wet areas of low acidity. A wide range of plants is affected, including beetroot, brassicas, parsnips, peas and beans, potatoes, spinach and several types of fruit trees and bushes.

Symptoms. Variable but there is commonly some inter-veinal yellowing which usually appears first on the older leaves. Patches of dead tissue may appear among the yellowed areas and on some plants, such as potatoes, there may be a general paleness to the younger foliage and also an upward rolling of the leaves, although this alone can arise from a variety of other causes. Peas, and to a lesser extent beans, develop a symptom known as marsh spot – more or less circular brown areas seen within the seed when the two cotyledons are pulled apart.

Physiology. This is imperfectly understood but one role is associated with the formation of chlorophyll. Manganese deficiency may be induced by an excess of soil iron and vice versa, although deficiencies of both elements do frequently occur together.

Treatment. Affected plants can be cured by spraying with a solution of manganese sulphate at the rate of 1.5 g per litre per 2 square metres. It is difficult to correct soil manganese deficiency permanently but over-liming of susceptible soils, such as those listed above, should be avoided.

BORON **Pl. 22**

Boron is sometimes deficient in soils derived from parent rocks, such as granites, which are low in boron content, or in freely-draining sands from which it is readily leached. More commonly, boron is present but unavailable either because it occurs in minerals, such as tourmaline, which plants are unable to utilise or because the soils have a high lime content. Deficiency symptoms commonly arise therefore after liming or in dry summers following wet winters or springs. Adequate boron supplies occur in soils derived from marine sediments and when the soil is enriched with the remains of boron-containing plants. The importance of boron is linked with the availability of calcium (see p. 286) and deficiency symptoms of the two elements are sometimes similar. Plants in which boron deficiency symptoms are most marked include apples, beetroot, cauliflowers and other brassicas, celery, lettuce and sweet corn.

Symptoms. GENERAL: as with calcium deficiency, the symptoms commonly appear as distortion, blackening or death of young growing points of leaves and shoots while leaves flag and become yellow and scorched. Root growth may be seriously retarded. APPLE AND PEAR: there may be some dying back of shoots in spring giving a tufted or rosette appearance but this can also arise from other causes. The leaves are narrowed and thickened and may have smooth margins while cracking and corky patches may develop on the surfaces and within the fruit (corky pit) (but also see viruses p. 277, and scab p. 228). BEETROOT, SWEDES AND TURNIPS: rough patches form on the skin surface and watersoaked brown or sometimes black patches and rings develop within the heart of the root tissues (a symptom known in some areas as 'raan'). The growing point of the shoot is shrivelled or otherwise distorted. Frequently there is a corky development on the surface of shoots, leaf stalks and other areas. CAULIFLOWER: water-soaked and later brown patches develop on the curd and some leaves may be stunted and brittle. When cut lengthwise, brownish patches and hollows are seen within the curd and pith and the curd taste is bitter. The pith of Brussels sprout and cabbage stems may similarly be brown and hollowed. CELERY: general unthriftiness with yellowing of the leaves and brown corky mottling and cracking of the leaf stalks, usually on the inner side. LETTUCE: indistinguishable from the symptoms of calcium deficiency (p. 286). SWEETCORN: cobs usually fail to develop, the growing point dies and transparent or whitish stripes appear on the leaves. Similar leaf symptoms are however also caused by frit fly (see p. 148).

Physiology. Imperfectly understood but boron is relatively immobile in plant tissues and performs many functions, including roles in the regulation of water uptake and of the germination of pollen; it may be concerned in some way with hormone control systems and probably with the movement of calcium, this explaining the close inter-relationship between symptoms caused by deficiencies of the two elements.

Treatment. Soil deficiencies can be corrected by raking in borax at the rate of 3 g per square metre at planting time but although the effects are rapid, the chemical will not persist long in the soil and repeated applications may be necessary from year to year.

COPPER

Deficiencies can occur on highly organic soils, such as peats, and are relatively unusual on mineral soils. Heathland and chalky soils in Dorset, Wiltshire and S. Devon often give rise to deficiency symptoms. A wide range of plants may be affected but onions, peas and beans, tomatoes and some fruit are most likely to show symptoms, which arise first on the younger leaves. The foliage may turn blue-green and later yellow and be partly wilted. On fruit trees, the shoot tips may die back but all symptoms are particularly difficult to diagnose and in serious suspected cases expert opinion should be sought. Although much has been suggested, there is little evidence for the precise role of copper in plant nutrition but deficiency effects in gardens can be corrected by spraying growing plants with 5 litres of 0.05% copper oxychloride solution per 10 square metres.

MOLYBDENUM **Pl. 22**

Rarely deficient in soils but sometimes rendered unavailable to plants on acid sites. Many annual plant species can be affected but in Britain the

symptoms are only likely to be seen on broccoli and cauliflowers.
Symptoms. There is yellowish mottling of the leaves and suppression of growth and/or death of the leaf blade, giving rise in cauliflower to the 'whip-tail' effect. In many other plants the growing tips distort and die but this symptom is far from diagnostic.
Physiology. Molybdenum is needed in plants for the reduction of nitrate to ammonium, and also for nitrogen fixation by the root nodule bacteria of leguminous plants (see p. 276).
Treatment. On acid sites, increase pH by lime application or water affected plant beds after seedling emergence with a solution of ammonium or sodium molybdate at the rate of 2.5 g per half litre per square metre.

NON-NUTRITIONAL DISORDERS

(Plates 23–24)

This section includes the many physical factors of the environment, other than nutrients, that can affect plants adversely. Many are climatic such as wind or frost; others are man-made, such as pollutants or mechanical injuries, and some arise from combinations of these factors. Greatest emphasis is given in this account to those agencies which are, like pollutants and frost, very commonly harmful to plants. Other factors, such as soil moisture, the regulation of which falls more under the heading of general plant husbandry, are considered only in as far as they can give rise to well defined symptoms of disorder. For convenience, two special categories are also included here: one covers the genetic disturbances that arise through some inherent aberration in the plants while the other is described as disturbed growth phenomena and includes those problems that arise through particular combinations of factors which are commonly manifest as unseasonal growth patterns.

Particular mention must also be made of glasshouse and, more especially, of house plants since these are grown in an artificial environment, free from the likelihood of lightning, precipitation or wind injury but still affected by the temperature, moisture, light and atmospheric purity of their surroundings. Although it is often possible to pinpoint the causes of poor growth or abnormal symptoms on house plants, they frequently arise through combinations of factors. The most common cause is waterlogging but fluctuating temperatures, shortage of water, too much or too little light, incorrect nutrient status of the growing medium and any of a range of household chemicals from gas to hair lacquer can give rise to particular effects. It must also be stressed that house plants embrace a very wide range of plant types (far more than can be described in detail in this book), each with its own environmental requirements. Reference should be made therefore to specialist books which describe in detail the growing needs of each type.

CLIMATIC EFFECTS

DROUGHT — Pl. 23

Water is necessary for the growth of all plants, both as an essential chemical in its own right and also as the solvent within which other nutrients are dissolved. Its shortage in the soil or sometimes in the air can result in conspicuous damage or ultimately death and plants with large, smooth leaves, such as many vegetables, are particularly prone to damage from such shortage. Shortage of soil water may result from insufficient rainfall or poor water retention by the soil while a dry atmosphere can be caused by low humidity, wind or high temperature. This then causes dessication in the plant because it loses through its leaves more water than it is able to replace from its roots. Hence wilting occurs. The related phenomenon of physiological drought arises when there is plenty of water in the soil but the plant is unable to extract and transport it sufficiently fast to prevent damage occurring to the above-ground parts. Such conditions can arise when strong or warm drying winds are prevalent or when the soil is frozen.

Symptoms. SOIL DROUGHT: a general dullness of the leaves followed by wilting is the first and most obvious symptom. As water shortage continues, leaves and roots become toughened and leaves gradually turn brownish. In severe conditions they may drop and plants run to seed and/or die. A common symptom on tomatoes and capsicums is blossom end rot, a problem caused by an imbalance of calcium within the plant, which is very often brought about by water shortage; a dark-coloured sunken area arises at the blossom end of the fruit. DRY AIR: in many respects the symptoms are similar to those induced by soil drought but the browning or scorching of the leaves is the prevalent symptom (see also under wind damage p. 296). Other common effects resulting from a dry atmosphere are the dry set conditions, especially frequent on tomatoes, in which the fruit fails to develop beyond a few millimetres in diameter, and also the shedding of flowers and buds which occurs on many house and glasshouse plants.

Treatment. Maintain adequate but not excessive watering of plants at all times. Take particular care at the time of flowering and when the fruit are forming and pay special attention to tomatoes or other plants in growing bags as the compost can easily dry out unseen. Mulches should be used on sites, such as those with light or shallow well-drained soils, where drying out of the land is likely to occur. Dry air and its effects cannot be avoided outdoors but in glasshouses spray plants such as tomatoes, cucumbers and vines at flowering time with water in morning or evening to aid pollination.

FROST — Pl. 23

Several phenomena associated with low temperatures can cause damage to garden plants and each results in a particular type of injury. By far the most important is frost, although its symptoms and effects are complex and can be considered very briefly. Other related and damaging phenomena are winter-cold, glazed frost, snow and hail.

Symptoms. Damage due to frost is usually self-evident and plants not normally harmed by the severities usually experienced in particular areas during the winter are said to be hardy under such conditions. The above-ground parts of non-hardy types rapidly blacken, wilt and shrivel on exposure to the first autumn air frost. Especially early autumn frosts can cause blackening or dying back of still-growing shoots of hardy species but this is relatively unusual. Of much greater importance is damage caused to hardy and non-hardy plants alike by late spring frosts. Even in southern England, frosts are not infrequently experienced in May and they damage young growing leaves and especially flowers of a wide range of plants while if such frosts occur immediately before bud burst the buds may be killed. Leaves may be merely scorched at the edges or killed but do not usually drop. Shoots may be scorched at the tips or die back to the old wood and flowers are usually killed outright. Repeated spring frost damage to some trees can render them permanently dwarfed, with an appearance reminiscent of browsing damage, while sometimes, although relatively unusually, stem and branch cankers or splitting can arise. An enormous range of plants is prone to spring frost damage but of outstanding importance among hardy trees and shrubs are blossoms of both top and soft fruit, and shoots, leaves or flowers of beech, camellias, ceanothus, eucalyptus, larches, magnolias, skimmias, sumac, viburnums, and walnuts. Severe virus infections very commonly render plants more liable to be injured or killed by frost.

A rather different type of frost injury is frost lift or frost heaving; the forcible ejection of plants from frozen soil. This commonly occurs with small or seedling plants, few of which are likely to be in the open ground during the winter, but may be a problem in nurseries where young woody plants are being raised. It can also sometimes be a problem, especially on highly organic soils, with over-wintered vegetable crops which can suffer severe damage through the roots being broken.

Prolonged exposure of potato tubers, particularly during storage, to temperatures slightly above freezing commonly gives rise to chilling injury which appears as small diffuse, blackish patches in the flesh. The causes of all such discolourations of tuber flesh are not easy to determine however and viruses (p. 277) are another possibility.

Biology. The meteorology of frost causation is complex and beyond the scope of this book. The mechanism of frost hardiness in plants is also complex but depends on the amount of water that can be drawn from the protoplasm of the plant's cells. Frost damage occurs largely through the formation of ice crystals in the plant's tissues; this can only happen if water can be drawn from the cells to be frozen. In hardy plants very little such water can be drawn out during certain times of the year. There is no relationship between winter and spring hardiness however; a plant with little 'available' water in winter may be physiologically very different in spring and so quite liable to be damaged at that time.

Prevention. A number of measures can be taken to minimise freezing injury to plants. Species hardy for local conditions should always be chosen; nurserymen or experienced local gardeners can advise on the selection. Certain sites are especially prone to frosts; often only experience will indicate where frost-hollows (which may be as large as a valley or small as part of a garden) occur. Such areas should naturally be avoided for more sensitive plants. Notoriously frosty areas in England include the Breckland of East Anglia, the Cheshire plain and the Vale of Evesham. Many methods of physical protection outdoors can be employed, including cold-frames, earthing-up or covering with straw or hessian; note however that plastic covered cloches offer little protection and indeed can become colder inside than out. Large heaters may be used to protect blossom in extensive and valuable orchards but few gardeners would be likely to undertake such precautions. Shelter belts of hardy species are of limited value; they will protect plants from wind or air frosts when cold air is transported over land but not from radiation or ground frosts (such as most spring frosts) when freezing occurs because of the rapid loss of heat from the soil. Relatively few plants possess resistance to freezing injury but indirect benefit is achieved when, for instance, later flowering types can be used to avoid spring frost damage; a number of fruit trees and bushes are now being selectively bred for this purpose.

HIGH TEMPERATURE **Pl. 24**

Can induce a variety of disorders in a wide range of plants. The two most common conditions are both known as sun scald. One form arises when hot sun strikes the bark of thin barked trees, such as beech, cherries, maples or poplars and results in its death either in patches or down the entire south or south-west face of the trunk. The other form of sun scald occurs when fruit are similarly struck by hot sun; apples, gooseberries, grapes, pears and tomatoes are most commonly affected. On tomatoes also, a condition known as greenback is common; the fruit develop a hard green or sometimes yellow area on the side where it is struck by high sunlight. Occasionally leaves, especially of glasshouse or house plants, can be scorched in a similar way and if flower bulbs are exposed to hot sun after lifting they may be damaged and fail to flower as a result. Most commonly the scorch symptoms result in papery, pale brownish patches on the affected parts. The problem can be minimised on glasshouse plants by adequate ventilation and particularly by summer shading. Greenback incidence on tomatoes can also be lessened by not over-stripping the foliage and thus exposing the fruit to too much sunlight. Additionally cultivars bred with greenback resistance may be chosen; those derived from 'Moneymaker' and most F_1 hybrids have this attribute.

A second type of high temperature injury is caused to the stem bases of plants by hot soil. On woody plants the symptom is usually known as heat canker and commonly heals satisfactorily. On other plants, especially on root vegetables, the effect can be very damaging and is usually termed strangles.

LIGHT **Pl. 24**

Adequate light is essential for the satisfactory growth of all green plants and its absence, through shading, is the main reason for the death of the lower and inner branches of trees and shrubs and for the yellowing and subsequent general debilitation of sun-loving plants when overhung or overgrown by larger species. There are also occasions when the effects of high light have been thought damaging. In most of these instances, such as greenback development in tomatoes, the damage is probably caused by the high temperatures associated with the high light level. The development of green chlorophyll in potato tubers (which are stem, not root tissues and so potentially photosynthetic), so rendering them inedible is however an almost exclusively light-induced effect. Potato tubers should always be stored in the dark therefore. A curious and unique effect associated with high light intensity (and a certain measure of warmth) occurs when cold water is splashed onto the leaves of saintpaulias and other gesneriaceous plants. This results in ringspot and line pattern symptoms indistinguishable from those induced on many plants by viruses. The problem is remedied by watering such plants only from below and avoiding their exposure to direct sunlight.

LIGHTNING Pl. 24

Although lightning strikes can damage low growing plants, gardeners are only likely to see the effects on trees. Isolated trees are more prone to damage than are groups and it is sometimes thought that certain species, such as beech, are damaged less frequently. Symptoms are normally either complete shattering of the trunk or a long jagged scar down one side. Trees need not be killed by a lightning strike nor need they fall, although in a garden they should normally be removed as the damage is usually extensive and predisposes them to attack by decay organisms. Although some sites are more prone than others to lightning strikes, only in the most exceptional situations, such as very valuable trees close to buildings, does the risk justify the fitting of lightning conductors.

PRECIPITATION

Hail. Injury caused by hail is usual in most years; soft fleshy plants are particularly prone and symptoms are commonly seen on the leaves of onions, tulips and similar plants as small white flecks. More severe hail storms can cause serious damage to fruit and to young shoots and twigs, on which the bark may be pitted or torn. Damage can be differentiated from that arising from other causes by its presence on one side only of affected plants. On larger woody stems and on fruit, even small hailstone wounds can provide entry sites for decay organisms.

Rain and glazed frost. Although rain normally causes only temporary damage through beating down flowers, it is a very important agent in the dispersal of spores of parasitic fungi; many fruit diseases for example can be minimised by supporting the produce well clear of the soil and out of reach of rain splash and contaminated earth. Glazed frosts, the result of periods of freezing rain, are relatively uncommon in Britain but when they do occur can be very damaging because of the considerable weight that layers of ice can impart to both herbaceous and woody plants. This weight can be sufficient to break branches and may even uproot large shrubs and trees.

Snow. A covering of snow for long periods of the winter is normal in many parts of northern Europe and is an important factor in protecting plants from winter cold. Heavy falls of snow can cause damage similar to that of glazed frost.

WATERLOGGING

Although drought injury occurs commonly on both outdoor and house plants, damage through waterlogging is relatively infrequent outdoors. It is probably the commonest cause of the decline of house plants however and although its effects arise in a number of ways, the most important are through the limiting of oxygen supplies to the roots and the inability of carbon dioxide to diffuse away. The commonest symptom is the yellowing of leaves, sometimes with the development of dry angular blotches and a general growth stunting, but the secondary effect of encouraging the development of root rotting organisms is often more serious. The treatment for house plants is usually simple; check carefully the water requirements for each type of plant – they differ widely but many do not flourish when standing permanently in dishes of water. Outdoors, take appropriate measures to lighten heavy soils and improve drainage. Actual installing of drainage systems is scarcely practicable in most gardens but thorough and deep digging in autumn and working in organic matter will help.

WIND Pl. 24

Wind may induce damage in a number of indirect ways, such as by the transport of pollutants and by its influence on temperature and humidity. These are described under the appropriate headings but wind may also have a more direct or purely mechanical effect on plants. Wind damage of this type is naturally most common on exposed sites, such as high land and the sea coast, and, not surprisingly, large and/or tender plants are those most affected. The wind effects of most importance to gardeners are:

WINDTHROW: the uprooting of plants, especially trees, by gales. Gardeners will probably consider this beyond their control although it is possible to predict those situations in which it is most likely to occur. Tall trees with large crowns (or, as often happens with elms for example, crowns overgrown with ivy), standing on shallow soils and with defective or small root systems are very prone to windthrow. Trees that have always grown isolated from others will generally be inherently more stable than those either in plantations or from around which neighbouring trees have been removed.

WINDROCK: very commonly occurs on young trees, shrubs and herbaceous plants with a large top in relation to the root system. Plants are moved to and fro in the ground but are not uprooted. The consequent effect can be that the stem base is chafed and pathogenic organisms invade. If rainwater fills the soil hollow produced at the stem base and then freezes, further serious damage or death can occur. Any plant rocked by strong wind should always be firmed in again promptly.

WINDBREAK: the snapping off of tree trunks or branches or stems of other plants at some distance from the ground commonly occurs after winter gales and if branches are broken off in this way from garden trees, the broken stub should subsequently be sawn off close to the trunk and the cuts treated with a wound sealant containing fungicide. No particular types of tree are especially prone to windbreak although it is very common on beech affected by beech bark disease.

WIND-SCORCHING and WIND-PRUNING: on very exposed sites trees often appear permanently leaning over, as if blown by the wind. This effect is due to the death of buds on the windward side of the trees by the direct drying effect of the wind. The buds are killed by induced localised drought. On other exposed sites, scorching or wind-blast damage caused by similar dry and/or cold wind effects can affect foliage and thus tree growth. It is considered the major factor limiting the growth of forests at high altitude in Britain. On the sea coast it is commonly accompanied by the damaging effect of windborne salt spray. The symptom may appear as an overall browning of the foliage on the side of the plant facing the wind, while on individual leaves the margins may be very markedly more browned than the centres. Sensitive plants can be protected by shelter belts of resistant tree species such as beech, Monterey cypress, Austrian pine or sycamore. Even in relatively sheltered gardens and orchards cold wind is probably the commonest cause (apart from pesticides) of russetting on apples and other fruit (but also see scab p. 228, viruses p. 277, and boron deficiency p. 289).

It is scarcely practicable or necessary to attempt to control this in gardens and commercially russetting is only a problem because it affects the appearance and thus the marketability of the produce.

NON-CLIMATIC EFFECTS

DISTURBED GROWTH PHENOMENA Pl. 23

Several forms of disturbed plant growth can give rise to concern and perplexity in gardens. They are quite different in their causes and effects but are conveniently grouped together although galls, which are a special form of disturbed growth, are considered in detail on p. 222.

Blindness. Arises when growth stops through absence or malfunction of the growing point. Among vegetables it can be particularly troublesome in broccoli, cauliflowers and other brassicas while tulips and other bulbous plants are the ornamentals most commonly affected. The causes of blindness may be varied and damage arising from pest or pathogen attack, nutrient deficiency, waterlogging or dryness are common causes. The exposure of bulbs to high temperatures after lifting or during storage is another frequent cause.

Bolting. The premature flowering and seeding of vegetable plants, which often causes frustration to gardeners when crops are lost in this way before maturity. Vegetables that are very prone to bolting include beetroot, brassicas, celery, lettuce, onions and spinach but the factors controlling it are very complex and vary from crop to crop and even between cultivars of the same crop. In general however, in order to flower, such plants require exposure to cold temperatures at a certain critical stage of their growth and for certain lengths of time. Once they have been exposed in this way, nothing, not even prolonged periods of high temperature, can prevent flowering. There is no real way to prevent bolting although some cultivars have been selected for resistance to it and may be so indicated in seed catalogues. In general however, early cultivars will bolt much more readily because they are more likely to experience the appropriate cold temperatures. Bolting will be less of a problem in a season following a mild and early spring and more serious after a late and cold one. Brassicas for spring planting, if raised under glass, will be more prone to bolting than plants raised outdoors if low temperatures occur in late spring as they will be further advanced and will have already reached the critical growth stage. It must be added, however, that day-length also influences the onset of flowering and can interact with, or modify, the temperature-induced response.

A rather different type of bolting is that commonly arising during periods of dry weather when plants are under stress. A natural response of most plants under such conditions is to flower and produce seed but the likelihood of this can be lessened by giving them additional water at such times. Conversely, ornamental plants that fail to flower often do so because they are too well looked after, i.e. not placed under sufficient stress, and the withholding of water from them can often induce flower formation.

Oedema. Sometimes known as dropsy or intumescence; a rough and warty condition in which small outgrowths develop on the undersides of the leaves and on the stems of a wide range of plants, including begonias, brassicas, cacti, camellias, capsicums, pelargoniums, peperomias, solanums, tomatoes and vines. It occurs most commonly in glasshouses as a result of overwatering and too high humidity or other factors leading to an excess of water in the plant. This water excess induces extra growth of discrete patches of cells and so the formation of the warts. Oedema can be prevented by a reduction in watering and improved ventilation.

Splitting. Very common on many plants but especially so on cabbages, carrots, celery, cherries, onions, parsnips, plums, potatoes, swedes and tomatoes and is most usually brought about when rapid growth is induced by the onset of wet conditions following a long dry spell. Related symptoms include the development of hollow fruit on apples. The only way that these conditions can be minimised is by improvement of the water retention of the soil by incorporation of organic matter, and by regular and careful watering (if permitted) during periods of drought, although cultivars of some plants have been bred with resistance to splitting and may be so indicated in seed catalogues.

Woody shoot malformations. A number of sometimes bizarre shoot malformations on woody plants may cause concern although none is harmful. Flattened stems, sometimes known as fasciation, occur occasionally on a wide variety of trees. Deeply ridged bark on young shoots, also known as winged cork, is common on field maples and on elms, especially as hedgerow plants. Spiral growth is also fairly common on many trees and shrubs and some species when so affected are deliberately propagated as 'contorta' cultivars. A symptom superficially like spiralling also occurs when stems are entwined with honeysuckle (p. 275). Bursting into life of dormant buds occurs in the form of lammas shoot production on oaks and other trees late in the season, and also as epicormic shoot growth, particularly frequent on larches affected by canker and/or dieback.

GENETIC DISTURBANCES Pl. 23

A few types of plant malformation are genetic in origin; they are natural in the sense that they are produced under the plant's normal genetic control but may only appear under certain environmental conditions, following a particular breeding history or a particular genetic mutation. Among examples commonly seen in gardens are the hard swellings on swede and occasionally turnip roots, often mistaken for clubroot and known as hybridisation nodules; very pale coloured or albino seedlings that only survive until the food reserve in the seed is exhausted – lacking chlorophyll they are unable to produce their own nutrient; and silvering in tomatoes which appears as silver-green patches on leaves and stem with sterility of trusses on affected plants.

MECHANICAL INJURIES Pl. 23

Most of the damage in this category could be described as originating from maltreatment as it is usually induced by avoidable actions by unthinking or uncaring persons. The question of subsequent treatment or reparation usually only arises with trees and shrubs and although it is inappropriate to consider in detail all features of the incorrect husbandry of such plants, the following commonly cause trouble in gardens.

Covering of bases of established plant stems. Compacted soil, asphalt or worse, concrete (such as that laid for paths) will upset the water-air balance in which a plant and its root system have become established and may well give rise to asphyxiation and death of the tissues. Symptoms usually appear as a wholesale dying back of the plant and although removal of the asphyxiating surface, if done sufficiently early, may result in recovery, it frequently does not.

Incorrect planting. Constriction of roots can result in the development of a very shallow root system and consequent instability while roots badly arranged in the planting hole can subsequently encircle the stem base and cause a girdling dieback. Soil should be sloped away from newly planted trees to prevent rainwater from collecting and either giving rise to injury when it freezes or predisposing the stem base to attack by decay organisms.

Pruning damage. Incorrect pruning can be very harmful, especially if branch stumps are left unprotected; these will die and provide entry points for decay organisms. Inadequate pruning can result in a mass of twigs which leads to general unthriftiness and provides conditions in which many pathogenic organisms can flourish. Pruning should be performed carefully, at the appropriate season for each plant and large wounds should be dressed with a sealant containing fungicide.

Wounding. From any cause, ranging from penknives to over-tight support wires, can injure trees, and shrubs. Any agency, such as lawnmowers or gates, that physically strikes plants is likely to remove bark and/or other tissues and so enable decay organisms to enter. Support wires, stem ties or fencing nails can cause damage which results in a gradual dieback. Any constricting agencies should be removed and stem wounds should be cut clean and treated with a wound sealant. Such wounds may be mistaken for cankers but unlike them do not usually display any annual extension of damage. Careless handling of fruit and vegetable produce, especially at harvest time, will almost always lead to injuries and subsequent losses through decay if they are later stored.

POLLUTANTS

Pl. 24

Many chemical substances can damage plants. While it is commonly impossible even for experts to determine the specific causes of chemical damage solely on the basis of symptoms, it is useful for gardeners to be able to distinguish such damage from other non-chemical causes. Although it is also usually impossible to avoid the effects of air-borne pollutants, resistant plants may sometimes be selected. Many chemicals harmful to plants are commonly used in the home and garden however and knowledge of their effects may not only explain otherwise puzzling damage but may enable its recurrence to be prevented. It is convenient therefore to divide pollutant chemicals into those that are air-borne or widespread and those that are more localised but because of the frequent similarity of symptoms caused by widely different chemicals, a considerable measure of commonsense is necessary in considering possible causes. On exposed coastal gardens, subject to seawater spray but far from towns for instance, marginal scorching of leaves is more likely to be caused by airborne salt or cold wind than by fluorides produced in a chemical factory.

Widespread pollutants

The commonest of the widespread pollutants in Britain and northern Europe are probably carbon monoxide, sulphur dioxide, nitrogen oxides, chlorides (including common salt, sodium chloride), fluorides, ethylene, various hydro-carbons, ammonia, ozone, aldehydes, arsine, phosphine, pesticides and herbicides (especially those containing copper, polysulphides or insecticidal oils or emulsions), various heavy metal salts and dusts such as smoke and cement. Many of these materials can be produced by a wide range of industrial processes and a general indication of their presence (especially that of sulphur dioxide) can be gained by an examination of the type of lichen growing in the area (see p. 273). Automobile exhausts are another common source of several pollutants. Airborne pesticides and herbicides commonly arrive in gardens as drift from agricultural spraying but their effects are described more fully under localised pollutants (p. 301). As a widespread pollutant, common salt is usually only a problem when it is blown by wind as seaspray onto coastal plants but it can have a more local importance in gardens (below). Sulphur in the atmosphere can actually have a beneficial effect through its fungicidal action on certain plant diseases, such as the well known instance of its suppression of blackspot of roses in industrial areas.

Symptoms and Physiology. Symptoms are commonly divided into chronic, where tissue is injured but not killed, usually by exposure to low levels of pollutants for long periods, and acute, where tissues are killed, often by a brief exposure to a high level of pollutant; pesticide damage for instance usually falls into the latter category. Despite the wide variation in symptom types, the commonest are necrotic or bleached flecks or stipples on leaves, especially on the upper surfaces and between the veins, or broad bands of marginal necrosis or scorching. Premature leaf fall is common. These symptoms, induced by pollutants, can sometimes occur uniformly over plants, but wherever any type of leaf injury is markedly unidirectional in its disposition (especially on the side facing the prevailing wind) and/or extends over several species, an airborne pollutant should be immediately suspected. Young plants are generally more susceptible than older ones and evergreen more so than deciduous types while damage is greatest close to the source of the pollution and usually in spring. The mechanism of the injury is as varied as the chemicals causing it.

Prevention. Real prevention depends on removing the source of the pollutants but with widespread materials this is impossible and the use of plants resistant to damage either for their own sake or as wind-breaks is the best that the gardener can hope to achieve. There is considerable argument over the relative susceptibilities of plants to different chemical pollutants but the following list includes some generally thought to have well-defined responses to chronic pollution injury and may be useful in badly polluted areas. Few plants are likely to resist acute injury. Unlikely to develop pollution damage: apples, aquilegias, cabbages and Brussels sprouts, ericas, gladioli, hornbeams, laburnums, lilacs, limes, marguerites, planes, privets, prunus, roses, sycamores and sugar maples, thujas, and tsugas. Likely to develop pollution damage: asters, barberries, beans, beech, beetroot, begonias, birches, cauliflowers, chrysanthemums, cinerarias, crocus, dahlias, dianthi, firs, freesias, gooseberries, hyacinths, irises, larches, lettuces, lupins, narcissi, nerines, some types of oak, onions, passifloras, petunias, many types of pine, potatoes, primulas, salvias, scillas, spruces and tobacco. In addition, the following trees and shrubs are usually resistant to salt-spray damage and may be useful in coastal gardens: Monterey cypress, escallonias, hebes, holm oaks, hydrangeas, olearias, Austrian and Monterey pines and tamarisks.

Localised pollutants

Although the effects of these are commonly similar to those of widespread pollutants, the symptoms are often more uniformly distributed on vegetation. Among the agencies commonly causing such damage in gardens are tar, hot water, paint (quite common in newly painted glasshouses), zinc (damage can occur on strawberries for example if a cage of new galvanised wire is erected over them), creosote (near to fences), oil and petrol (very often spillages from lawn mowers cause bare patches on lawns), urine (especially on lawns), fertilisers used in excess, salt used on roads or garden paths in winter (a common cause of injury to or death of roadside trees and hedges or plants in borders adjoining paths), or gas (from leaking mains; sections of hedges sometimes die when a leak from an underground main kills part of the root system).

FUNGICIDES AND INSECTICIDES. Although most agricultural and garden pesticides are intended for application onto growing plants, damage can ensue if they are used on plants for which they were not intended, at too high a concentration, under inappropriate climatic conditions or too frequently. Most pesticides are therefore potentially phytotoxic or damaging to plants. Damage in gardens from such pesticides may be due to spray drift from nearby agricultural land but frequently misuse of pesticides by gardeners themselves can cause damage. Rules that should be observed when using pesticides are described on p. 18 and the necessity of adhering to them cannot be overstressed. Symptoms of pesticide damage are generally very similar to those of other airborne pollutants (see p. 299).

HERBICIDES. Herbicides (weed-killers) differ from insecticides and fungicides in that they are intended to kill plants. Problems arise in gardens when weed-killers are inadvertently blown or sprayed onto crop plants or are misused in some way. Where the effects are not fatal to the plants, the symptoms are similar to those of other airborne pollutants, although one group of herbicides produces quite different effects and may cause damage much more insidiously. These are the hormone herbicides which are absorbed into plant tissues and cause abnormal growth; leaves may become narrowed (sometimes extremely so), straplike and thickened; stems twisted, callused and contorted and fruits set poorly and become irregularly shaped. Such herbicides may occur in gardens as spray drift (from farms or from within the garden itself if they are being used on lawns), or as residue in inadequately washed watering cans. A very common additional source of damage is from contaminated straw, derived from cereal crops on which the herbicides have been sprayed. The symptoms then develop on plants on which a straw mulch has been used or if farmyard manure containing such contaminated straw has been applied to the soil. Tomatoes and cucumbers are especially sensitive to this type of damage. In such circumstances all soil contaminated with the straw should be removed to at least a spade's depth and if the problem persists in glasshouses it may be worthwhile growing the next one or two crops in containers to give the chemical time to disperse from the ground.

Bibliography

Books

The following selected list of books provides a basis for further reading on various specialised aspects of the recognition, biology and treatment of pests, diseases and disorders. Several of the older works are now out of print and/or out of date, especially with respect to control measures, but they are virtually the only sources of more detailed information and may therefore still be worth consulting through public libraries.

General

The natural history of the garden by M. Chinery, 1977, Collins.

A field guide to the insects of Britain and northern Europe by M. Chinery, 1976, Collins.

Beneficial insects and mites by B. D. Moreton, 1970, MAFF Bulletin 20, H.M.S.O.

Horticultural pests. Detection and control by G. Fox Wilson (3rd edition revised by P. Becker, 1960), Crosby Lockwood.

The pests of protected cultivation by N. W. Hussey, W. H. Read and J. J. Hesling, 1969, Edward Arnold.

The pocket encyclopaedia of plant galls in colour by A. Darlington, 1968, Blandford Press.

Pathology of trees and shrubs with special reference to Britain by T. R. Peace, 1962, Clarendon Press.

Decay of timber and its prevention by K. St. G. Cartwright and W. P. K. Findley, 2nd edition, 1958, H.M.S.O.

Collins guide to mushrooms and toadstools by M. Lange and F. B. Hora, 2nd edition, 1965, Collins.

Introduction to fungi by J. Webster, 2nd edition, 1980, Cambridge University Press.

A textbook of plant virus diseases by K. M. Smith, 3rd edition, 1972, Longman.

Plant viruses by K. M. Smith, 1977, Chapman and Hall.

The diagnosis of mineral deficiencies in plants by visual symptoms by T. Wallace, 3rd edition, 1961, H.M.S.O.

Fruits and vegetables

The pests of fruits and hops by A. M. Massee, 3rd edition, 1954, Crosby Lockwood.

Pests and diseases of fruit and vegetables in the garden by A. M. Toms and M. H. Dahl, 1976, Blandford Press.

Diseases of fruit and hops by H. Wormald, 3rd edition, 1955, Crosby Lockwood.
Diseases of vegetables by L. Ogilvie, 5th edition, 1961, MAFF Bulletin 123, H.M.S.O.

Ornamentals

Pests of ornamental plants by P. Becker, 1974, MAFF Bulletin 97, H.M.S.O.
Garden pests and diseases of flowers and shrubs by M. H. Dahl and T. B. Thygesen, 1974, Blandford Press.
Pests, diseases and nutritional disorders of chrysanthemums by N. E. A. Scopes, 2nd edition, 1975, National Chrysanthemum Society.
Fungal diseases of turf grasses by J. D. Smith, 2nd edition, 1965, Sports Turf Research Institute.
Diseases of bulbs by W. C. Moore, 2nd edition, 1979 revised by A. A. Brunt, D. Price and A. R. Reeves, MAFF Book HPD1, H.M.S.O.

Ministry of Agriculture and Agricultural Research Council publications

The Ministry of Agriculture produces a comprehensive series of Bulletins and Advisory Leaflets. They are intended for use by farmers and commercial horticulturists but contain much information that is of interest to keen gardeners. Some of the relevant Bulletins are noted in the book list above and a full list of current publications can usually be consulted at Government Bookshops or may be obtained direct from MAFF Publications, Lion House, Willowburn Estate, Alnwick, Northumberland, NE66 2PF.

Several of the research institutes supported by the Agricultural Research Council, especially East Malling Research Station, the Glasshouse Crops Research Institute and the National Vegetable Research Station also produce occasional booklets and leaflets that contain useful information for gardeners.

Forestry Commission publications

The Forestry Commission is mainly concerned with commercial forestry but useful information may be found in the Leaflets, Forest Records and Bulletins that it produces. A list of current publications can usually be consulted at Government Bookshops or may be obtained direct from Forestry Commission Publications, Forest Research Station, Alice Holt Lodge, Wrecclesham, Farnham, Surrey, GU10 4LH.

Magazines and Journals

Frequent comment and occasional articles on pests, diseases and disorders appear in the following publications and some of them also run advisory services to answer queries from readers.

Amateur Gardening (weekly)
Garden News (weekly)

Popular Gardening (weekly)
The Garden (monthly Journal of the Royal Horticultural Society)
Gardening from Which? (irregular)
Gardening World (monthly)
Greenhouse (monthly)
Flora (monthly)
Practical Gardening (monthly)
Garden Answers (monthly)

Promotional literature of commercial firms

The major firms engaged in marketing chemicals for pest and disease control and for the treatment of disorders in garden plants produce various leaflets, booklets and wall-charts on these subjects. They are up-dated frequently so are useful sources of information. 'Be your own garden doctor' and 'Be your own vegetable doctor' by D. G. Hessayon are useful illustrated summaries that include both chemical and non-chemical recommendations for treatment.

The British Agrochemicals Association, Alembic House, 93 Albert Embankment, London, SE1 7TU publishes an annual 'Directory of garden chemicals' and all BAA member companies listed in this directory will supply charts, booklets or other information.

Societies

Many national and local societies exist to promote general and specialised interest in horticulture and most of these are involved to some extent with problems posed by pests, diseases and disorders. The Royal Horticultural Society, Vincent Square, Westminster, London, SW1P 2PE, is the major national society with interests in all aspects of horticulture. Membership is open to anyone and members are entitled to many facilities, including a free advisory service on the diagnosis and treatment of pests, diseases and disorders that is provided by professional scientists working in the Entomology and Plant Pathology Departments at the R.H.S. Garden, Wisley. Much useful information is also provided by articles published in the Society's monthly journal 'The Garden' and in various booklets, of which the following are especially relevant.

Fruit pests, diseases and disorders Wisley Handbook 27 (1980)
Vegetable pests, diseases and disorders Wisley Handbook 28 (1979)
The fruit garden displayed (revised 1981)
The vegetable garden displayed (revised 1981)
Garden pests and diseases (in the *RHS Encyclopaedia of practical gardening*, 1980)

Other national societies with specialised interests are too numerous to list here but a list, with addresses, is published annually in the R.H.S. gardener's diary.

Glossary

Aeciospore. A type of spore produced by a rust fungus (see p. 191).

Alternate host. Either of the two unlike host-plants of a pest or pathogen that requires both to complete its full life-cycle.

Alternative hosts. Host-plants other than the main host on which an organism (bacterium, fungus, insect, mite etc.) can develop. Weeds and wild plants are often alternative hosts of certain pests and diseases.

Antennae. Paired sensory structures on the heads of insects and other invertebrates. They are often long, thread-like and conspicuous (as in cockroaches, grasshoppers and aphids) but may be small and relatively inconspicuous in many groups of insects.

Ascospore. A spore produced by sexual reproduction in a fungus of the class Ascomycetes.

Basidiospore. A spore produced by sexual reproduction in a fungus of the class Basidiomycetes.

Biological control. Methods developed to control pests by using predators and parasites that feed on them. This may involve introducing and establishing species from other parts of the world. Use of *Phytoseiulus* against glasshouse red spider mites (p. 173) and of *Encarsia* against glasshouse whitefly (p. 102) are examples of the small-scale application of this technique in gardens but many large-scale schemes have been operated overseas to control pests and weeds.

Certified stock. Plant material guaranteed to be of a defined quality, especially of freedom from virus infections.

Chlamydospore. A type of asexually produced fungal spore that is resistant to desiccation or other adverse environmental conditions.

Conidium (pl. conidia). An asexually produced fungal spore.

Cultivar. A variant of a plant species that has arisen (either accidentally or deliberately) in cultivation and is perpetuated by propagation for some desirable horticultural feature (e.g. 'Cox's Orange Pippin' apple). The term 'variety' has a more restricted botanical meaning (see p. 308).

Cocoon. A silken case constructed by an insect larva (e.g. caterpillar) to protect the pupal stage.

Galls. Unusual growths of plant tissues produced as a specific response to attack by various groups of gall-inducing organisms, especially root-knot eelworms (p. 88), gall wasps (p. 158), gall midges (p. 152) and gall mites (p. 177). Galls may develop on roots, stems, buds, leaves, flowers or other parts of plants and they often have a distinctive and elaborate structure.

Honeydew. A sweet excretion produced by aphids, scale insects, mealybugs and other insects that feed on plant sap. It contains sugars derived from sap when the insects feed and it makes infested plants sticky and encourages the growth of sooty moulds (see p. 209).

Host or **host-plant.** A plant on which a pathogen or pest develops. Most pathogens and pests are restricted to a few host-plants on which they can develop successfully.

Host range. The complete range of host-plants on which a pathogen or pest can develop.

Hypha (pl. hyphae). The basic thread-like structure of most fungi.

Immune. Free from infection or infestation; having qualities that prevent the development of a disease or pest.

Infection. The entry of a parasitic organism into a host. A plant may be infected but is not said to be diseased if no visible and damaging symptoms develop.

Infestation. Establishment of pest populations on plants or inside plant tissues.

Larva (pl. larvae). An immature insect. Usually applied to insects that develop through the sequence: egg – larva – pupa – adult (e.g. caterpillars of butterflies, moths and sawflies or maggots of flies). The larva is usually the main feeding stage and is therefore the cause of most damage to plants.

Latent infection. An infection that does not produce obvious symptoms.

Lenticel. One of many pores in the bark of woody plants through which gaseous exchange takes place.

Life-cycle. The succession of stages through which an organism develops, usually between one period of reproductive activity and the next (e.g. egg – larva – pupa – adult in insects or spore – mycelium – fruiting body in fungi).

Mandibles. Horny jaw-like mouth-parts of insects; used to bite and to chew food.

Mould. A vague term applied fairly indiscriminately to the visible mycelial or spore mass of microfungi.

Mouth-parts. The structures that surround the mouth in insects and mites. They are adapted for various functions, especially for biting and chewing solid food or for piercing plant tissues to extract sap.

Mycelium. A mass of fungal hyphae.

Necrotic. Dead and usually dark coloured plant tissues.

Notifiable (pest or disease). Required by law to be reported to officials of the Ministry of Agriculture.

Nymph. The immature stage of those insects that develop directly from nymph to adult without an intermediate pupal stage (e.g. aphids, capsid bugs and related groups).

Oospore. A spore produced by sexual reproduction in a phycomycete fungus of the sub-class Oomycetes.

Ovipositor. The special structure that many female insects have to facilitate egg-laying. This may be relatively simple if eggs are just deposited on plants but in some groups (e.g. sawflies) it consists of a pair of saw-like blades that are used to cut slits in plant tissue before eggs are inserted.

Parasite. An organism living on or in another organism from which it obtains its food and to which it gives no benefit in return.

Parthenogenesis. A type of asexual reproduction in which unfertilised eggs develop normally to produce adults. It occurs quite commonly in aphids, gall wasps and other groups of insects.

Pathogen. A parasitic organism (e.g. fungus, bacterium, virus) that causes disease.

Perithecium (pl. perithecia). A small flask-like body within which ascospores are produced in some fungi of the class Ascomycetes.

Persistent (of a pesticide). Persisting on plants or in soil for weeks or months after application, during which time it retains some of its pesticidal activity.

Phytotoxic (of a chemical). Injurious to plants. Many pesticides are phytotoxic to some plants and information about the main hazards is usually given on labels and in manufacturer's instructions.

Predator. An animal that feeds by preying on other animals. The larvae of some insects (e.g. coccinellid beetles, syrphid flies) prey on pests and are therefore beneficial.

Pupa. The non-feeding stage in the metamorphosis of insects that develop through the sequence: egg – larva – pupa – adult. This appears to be a quiescent stage but intense biochemical activity within the pupa reorganises the tissues of the larva to produce the adult, often in only a few days or weeks.

Puparium. A special type of pupa formed during the development of many flies. The general shape is of a cylinder with rounded ends and the fully formed puparium is usually glossy brown or black.

Pycnidium (pl. pycnidia). A small, usually flask-like body, within which conidia are produced in some fungi of the class Deuteromycetes.

Pycniospore. A type of spore produced by a rust fungus (see p. 191).

Pyrethroids. Insecticides based either on natural pyrethrum or on the recently developed synthetic pyrethroids (bioresmethrin, resmethrin and permethrin). These are all very safe to use as they are virtually non-toxic to mammals, do not damage plants and persist for only a few days (except for permethrin, which remains active up to three weeks after application).

Race (of a pathogen or pest). A population or strain of a species that can only attack some of the host-plants that are susceptible to the whole species, e.g. races of stem eelworm (see p. 84).

Repellents. Chemicals that are used to repel pests from plants, usually by their unpleasant taste or smell. They are mostly used against birds and mammals.

Resistant (plant). Able to withstand attack by a pest or disease. Many plants are naturally resistant to certain pests and diseases and others have been made resistant through artificial selection and plant breeding.

— (pest). Able to withstand exposure to certain pesticides. Some pests have become highly resistant to pesticides, usually because frequent or continuous treatment of large populations with chemicals selects individuals that have inheritable characters conferring some degree of resistance.

— (spore or sclerotium). Able to survive a period of adverse environmental conditions, such as winter.

Resting (of a spore or sclerotium). Able to become dormant to survive a period of adverse environmental conditions.

Rogueing. The removal and destruction of diseased or infested plants.

Rotation. The alternation, season by season, of different crop plants on a particular area of land to limit the build-up of pests and diseases.

Saprophyte. An organism that feeds on dead organic material.

Sclerotium (pl. sclerotia). A firm, more or less rounded mass of hyphae, often functioning as a resting body (q.v.).

Shot-hole. A symptom of disease in which discrete more or less circular areas of leaf tissues dry and drop out, or a symptom of attack by certain wood-boring beetles on tree trunks and branches (see p. 162).

Siphunculi. Paired tubes near the end of the abdomen of aphids. Shape, size and colour varies appreciably between species. They are the openings of glands that produce waxes and other chemicals that may protect aphids against some predators.

Sooty moulds. Black soot-like growths of fungi that develop on leaves and other parts of plants infested by sap-feeding insects, such as aphids, mealybugs and scale insects. The insects produce a sugary excretion (honeydew) which contaminates plant surfaces and encourages the growth of the sooty moulds (see p. 209).

Spore. A microscopic reproductive structure produced by fungi, bacteria, non-flowering plants (e.g. ferns), and protozoons.

Stag's head. The antler-like appearance of a tree when the upper branches die and are bare of foliage.

Stoma (pl. stomata). A pore in the outer tissues of plants, especially the leaves, through which gaseous exchange takes place.

Swarm spore. A type of spore produced by certain fungi of the class Phycomycetes (and some other organisms) which has limited powers of movement in water films in soil or plant surfaces.

Systemic. Generally distributed within an organism. Used to describe the nature of infection by certain diseases or the mode of action of certain pesticides.

Teliospore. A type of spore produced by a rust fungus (see p. 191).

Tolerant. Able to tolerate attack by a pathogen or pest or action by a chemical. Plants and their cultivars often show different degrees of tolerance.

Urediniospore. A type of spore produced by a rust fungus (see p. 191).

Variety. This term is often used in the same sense as cultivar (q.v.) but should really be restricted to its correct botanical meaning which indicates a variant that has arisen in a plant species growing in the wild and therefore not subjected to selection through cultivation (e.g. *Pinus nigra* var. *maritima*). Many such plant varieties have been taken into cultivation.

Vector. An organism that transports and transmits a pathogen. The most important vectors of plant diseases are aphids and eelworms that transmit viruses but some other pests may also be vectors of certain diseases.

Virulent (of a pathogen). Spreading rapidly and causing serious disease.

Viviparous. Giving birth to live young.

Zone lines. Narrow dark brown or black lines in decayed wood; generally caused by fungi.

General Index

Index of Scientific Names